NATIONAL SAFETY COUNCIL
INJURY FACTS®
2016 EDITION

ALL INJURIES

OCCUPATIONAL

MOTOR VEHICLE

HOME AND COMMUNITY

STATE DATA

INTERNATIONAL

Francis U. and Mary F. Ritz Library
Dutchess Community College
Poughkeepsie, NY

FORMERLY
ACCIDENT FACTS®

PDF See page ii for information on
your free downloadable book

The National Safety Council, chartered by an act of Congress, is a nongovernmental, not-for-profit, public service organization. The mission of the National Safety Council is to save lives by preventing injuries and deaths at work, in homes and communities, and on the roads through leadership, research, education, and advocacy.

Injury Facts®, the Council's annual statistical report on unintentional injuries and their characteristics and costs, was prepared by:

Research and Safety Management Solutions Group:
Kenneth P. Kolosh, Manager, Statistics Department
Kevin T. Fearn, Sr. Statistical Associate
Kathleen T. Porretta, Technical Editor

Questions or comments about the content of *Injury Facts* should be directed to the Research and Safety Management Solutions Group, National Safety Council, 1121 Spring Lake Drive, Itasca, IL, 60143, by phone at (630) 775-2322, fax at (630) 285-0242, or email *rssdept@nsc.org*.

For price and ordering information, visit *www.nsc.org* or write:

Customer Service
National Safety Council, 1121 Spring Lake Drive, Itasca, IL, 60143, call (800) 621-7619, or fax (630) 285-0797.

Acknowledgments
The information presented in *Injury Facts* was made possible by the cooperation of many organizations and individuals, including state vital and health statistics authorities, state traffic authorities, state workers' compensation authorities, trade associations, Bureau of the Census, Bureau of Labor Statistics, Consumer Product Safety Commission, Federal Highway Administration, Federal Railroad Administration, International Labour Organization, National Center for Health Statistics, National Fire Protection Association, National Highway Traffic Safety Administration, National Transportation Safety Board, National Weather Service, Mine Safety and Health Administration, and the World Health Organization. Specific contributions are acknowledged in footnotes and source notes throughout the book.

Visit the National Safety Council website:
nsc.org
nsc.org/learn/safety-knowledge/Pages/injury-facts.aspx

Copyright ©2016 National Safety Council
All rights reserved.
The copyrighting of *Injury Facts*® is not intended to prevent use of the material for injury prevention purposes. The information may be used (except where copyright is held by another organization), with credit to the National Safety Council – the only restriction being that the original meaning shall be preserved.
Suggested citation: National Safety Council. (2016). *Injury Facts*®, *2016 Edition*. Itasca, IL: Author.
Library of Congress Catalog Card Number: 99-74142
Printed in U.S.A. ISBN 978-0-87912-339-0   NSC Press Product No. 02331-0000

Access your free downloadable copy of Injury Facts:
nsc.org/getif2016

Table of Contents

Unintentional injuries are now ranked as the fourth leading cause of death behind heart disease, cancer, and chronic lower respiratory disease, after overtaking strokes in 2013. The number of unintentional deaths in the United States is at an all-time high while the population death rate is little changed from the 1980's. With headlines like this it is tempting to overgeneralize and conclude that safety is simply getting worse. However, as is so often the case the truth is far more complicated than it first appears.

In many ways the safety landscape is becoming more complex. In the past, safety was dominated by a single issue that disproportionally impacted a single demographic group. This one issue was motor-vehicle safety and the demographic was young drivers. A little over three decades ago, over half of all unintentional deaths in the United States were a result of motor-vehicle crashes. The next leading cause of death, falls, accounted for only about 12%. As illustrated in the top graph of the facing page, in 1981 motor vehicle was overwhelmingly the leading cause of unintentional death among young adults and was also the leading cause of unintentional death for most other ages. Given this safety landscape there was little doubt that improving motor-vehicle safety was the top priority.

Today's safety landscape tells a very different story. Now, three leading causes of unintentional death dominate and collectively impact nearly every phase of life. The three leading causes of death (motor vehicle, poisoning, and falls) now account for nearly 80% of all unintentional deaths in the United States. Over the last decade these three leading causes of death have displayed a distinctive pattern with each cause of death dominating a specific age group. As shown on the bottom of the facing page, motor-vehicle deaths dominate from the mid-teens through early 20's. From the mid-20's through early 60's poisoning deaths dominate. Finally, as people approach their 70's fall deaths start to dramatically increase. No longer is there one clear dominating safety priority, but three almost equal priorities.

Comparing the 1981 and 2013 graphs on the facing page provides several additional insights. First, although the number of overall unintentional deaths has increased since 1981, incredible progress has been achieved regarding motor-vehicle safety, particularly regarding young driver safety. In 1981 motor-vehicle deaths peaked at age 18 with 2,190 deaths. Now, in 2013, deaths peak at age 21 with 894 deaths and overall motor-vehicle deaths have dropped by more than 30%. Unfortunately, the comparison also highlights the fact that we face challenges today regarding poisoning and falls that were not issues in 1981. However, what is also clear is that if we focus on these issues as we have with motor-vehicle safety, great improvements are possible. *Injury Facts®* will continue to highlight the changing safety trends so that the most critical issues are identified and prioritized for improvement.

The latest data show a continuation of the recent negative trend with an increase of over 4% in unintentional-injury deaths in 2014 compared to the revised 2013 total. Unintentional-injury deaths were estimated to total 130,557 in 2013 and 127,792 in 2012.

The resident population of the United States was 318,857,000 in 2014, an increase of less than 1% from 2013. The unintentional death rate in 2014 was 42.7 per 100,000 population – an increase of over 3% from 2013 and 25% greater than the lowest rate on record, which was 34.0 in 1992.

A more complete summary of the situation in 2014 and recent trends is given on page 2.

Changes in the 2016 edition

For the second year, a downloadable electronic version of *Injury Facts®* is being made available FREE with each hard copy book! Please see page ii for additional information on how to download your copy today.

Look for new data on…
- Expanded cost estimates including government and employer costs
- Contractor workplace fatalities
- Cost of consumer product injuries
- Falls
- Home fires

And updated or expanded data on…
- General mortality
- Occupational injury and illness incidence rates by industry
- Occupational injury and illness profile data by industry sector
- Forklift injury trends
- Workers' compensation claims and costs
- Disasters
- Distracted driving
- Young drivers
- Comparing safety of transportation mode
- Traffic safety issues – alcohol, occupant protection, speeding, and others
- Consumer product-related injuries
- Unintentional deaths by states

We also continue to receive questions regarding a change made three years ago. Editions of *Injury Facts®* prior to 2011 included estimates of disabling injuries. Starting with the 2011 edition, the National Safety Council (NSC) transitioned to the concept of "medically consulted injury" in place of "disabling injury." This new definition was adopted from the National Health Interview Survey, a household survey conducted by the National Center for Health Statistics (NCHS). A refinement of the medically consulted injury estimate was also made this year to better account for intentional injuries. This refinement makes comparison of medically consulted injuries to previous years inappropriate. A medically consulted injury is defined by NCHS as an injury serious enough that a medical professional was consulted. Moving *Injury Facts*® estimates from disabling injuries to medically consulted injuries provides several advantages. First and foremost, a medically consulted injury is a more inclusive definition that allows for more comprehensive estimates of the true burden of unintentional injuries. Second, medically consulted injury estimates are updated each year by NCHS, allowing NSC to provide the most timely and accurate data possible. Finally, the previous definition of disabling injury was often misinterpreted as

a workers' compensation injury. Using the term medically consulted injuries should help eliminate this confusion. For more information on medically consulted injuries, please see the technical appendix.

For more information on *Injury Facts*® and other products, visit NSC's web site (nsc.org), call Customer Service at 800-621-7619, or contact your local council.

Your comments and suggestions on how to improve *Injury Facts*® are welcome. Contact information is given on page ii.

Age distribution of top three leading causes of unintentional death, United States, 1981

Age distribution of top three leading causes of unintentional death, United States, 2013

All Injuries

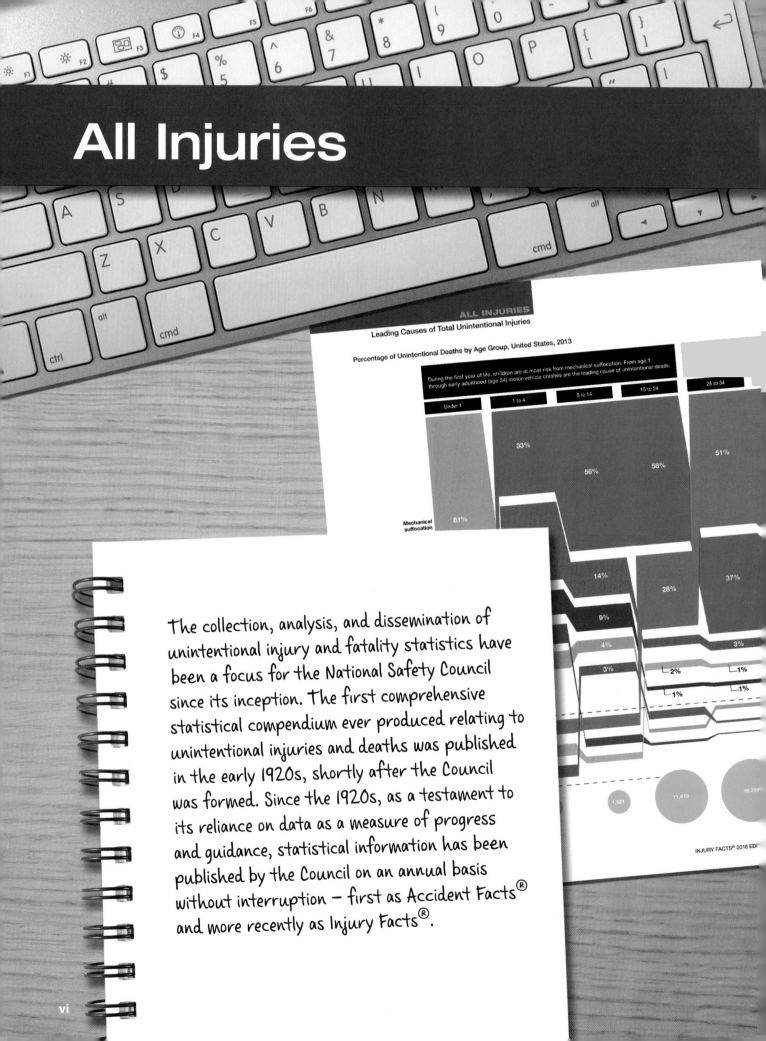

ALL INJURIES

Leading Causes of Total Unintentional Injuries

Percentage of Unintentional Deaths by Age Group, United States, 2013

During the first year of life, children are at most risk from mechanical suffocation. From age 1 through early adulthood (age 24) motor-vehicle crashes are the leading cause of unintentional death.

The collection, analysis, and dissemination of unintentional injury and fatality statistics have been a focus for the National Safety Council since its inception. The first comprehensive statistical compendium ever produced relating to unintentional injuries and deaths was published in the early 1920s, shortly after the Council was formed. Since the 1920s, as a testament to its reliance on data as a measure of progress and guidance, statistical information has been published by the Council on an annual basis without interruption — first as Accident Facts® and more recently as Injury Facts®.

National Safety Council

Unintentional-injury-related deaths were up 4.2% in 2014, compared to the revised 2013 estimate. Unintentional-injury-related deaths totaled 136,053 in 2014 and 130,557 in 2013. The 2014 estimate is 57% greater than the 1992 total of 86,777 (the lowest annual total since 1924).

The death rate in 2014 was 42.7 per 100,000 population – 26% greater than the lowest rate on record, which was 34.0 in 1992. The 2014 death rate increased 3.4% from the 2013 revised rate.

Comparing 2014 to 2013, work deaths and motor-vehicle deaths remained stable while home and public deaths both increased. The population death rate for motor vehicle decreased, remained stable for work, and increased for the public as well as home classes.

The motor-vehicle death total changed less than 0.5% in 2014. The 2014 mileage death rate of 1.16 per 100,000,000 vehicle miles was down 2% from the revised 2013 rate of 1.18. The 2014 rate was down 6% from the revised 2012 rate of 1.23.

Unintentional injuries continued to be the fourth leading cause of death, exceeded only by heart disease, cancer, and chronic lower respiratory diseases. In 2013 unintentional injuries overtook strokes to become the fourth leading cause of death.

Nonfatal injuries also affect millions of Americans. In 2014, 39 million people – about 1 out of 8 – sought medical attention.

The economic impact of these fatal and nonfatal unintentional injuries amounted to $853.4 billion in 2014. This is equivalent to about $2,700 per capita, or about $6,900 per household. These are costs that every individual and household pays whether directly out of pocket, through higher prices for goods and services, or through higher taxes. Please note that the cost estimate model was extensively updated for the 2014 estimates and are not comparable to previous estimates.

Between 1912 and 2014, unintentional-injury-related deaths per 100,000 population were reduced nearly 50% (after adjusting for the classification change in 1948) from 82.5 to 42.7. The reduction in the overall rate during a period when the nation's population tripled has resulted in 6,300,000 fewer people being killed due to unintentional injuries than there would have been if the rate had not been reduced.

All unintentional injuries, 2014

Class	Deaths	Change from 2013	Deaths per 100,000 people	Medically consulted injuries[a]
All classes[b]	136,053	4.2%	42.7	39,100,000
Motor vehicle	35,398	<0.5%	11.1	4,100,000
Public nonwork	33,564			*3,900,000*
Work	1,634			*200,000*
Home	200			*(c)*
Work	4,008	-<0.5%	1.3	4,700,000
Non-motor vehicle	2,374			*4,500,000*
Motor vehicle	1,634			*200,000*
Home	69,500	6%	21.8	20,200,000
Non-motor vehicle	69,300			*20,200,000*
Motor vehicle	200			*(c)*
Public	29,100	7%	9.1	10,300,000

Source: National Safety Council estimates (rounded) based on data from the National Center for Health Statistics (NCHS), state departments of health, and state traffic authorities, except for the work figures, which are from the Bureau of Labor Statistics, Census of Fatal Occupational Injuries (CFOI). The National Safety Council adopted the CFOI count for work-related unintentional injuries beginning with 1992 data. See the Glossary for definitions and the Technical Appendix for estimating procedures. Beginning with 1999 data, deaths are classified according to the 10th revision of the International Classification of Diseases. Caution should be used in comparing data classified under the two systems.

[a]The totals shown are approximations based on the National Safety Council's analysis of National Health Interview Survey results that is conducted by NCHS. The totals are the best estimates for the current year. They should not, however, be compared with totals shown in previous editions of this book to indicate year-to-year changes or trends. See the Glossary for definitions and the Technical Appendix for estimating procedures.

[b]Deaths and injuries above for the four separate classes add to more than the "All classes" figures due to rounding and because some deaths and injuries are included in more than one class. For example, 1,634 work deaths involved motor vehicles and are in both the work and motor vehicle totals, and 200 motor vehicle deaths occurred on home premises and are in both home and motor vehicle. The total of such duplication amounted to about 1,834 deaths and 200,000 injuries in 2014.

[c]Less than 10,000.

All Injury-Related Deaths, 2014

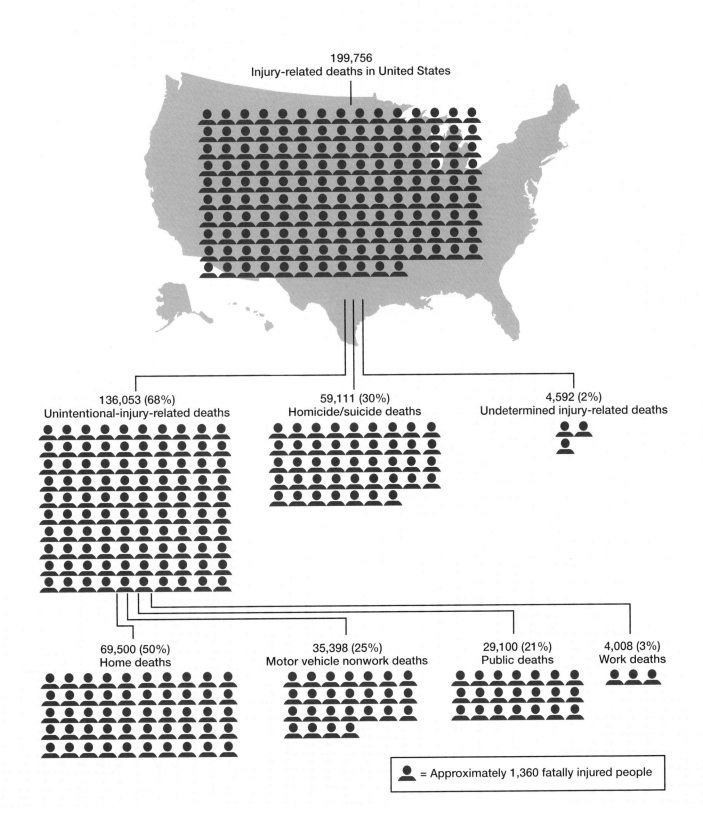

4,000,000
Injury deaths worldwide

199,756
Injury-related deaths in United States

136,053 (68%)
Unintentional-injury-related deaths

59,111 (30%)
Homicide/suicide deaths

4,592 (2%)
Undetermined injury-related deaths

69,500 (50%)
Home deaths

35,398 (25%)
Motor vehicle nonwork deaths

29,100 (21%)
Public deaths

4,008 (3%)
Work deaths

= Approximately 1,360 fatally injured people

Unintentional-injury-related deaths by class, United States, 2014

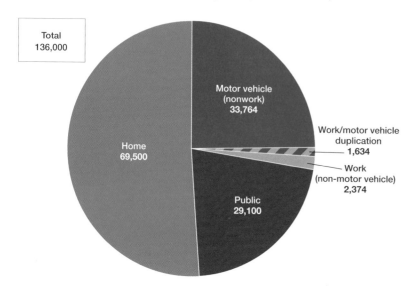

Total
136,000

Motor vehicle
(nonwork)
33,764

Work/motor vehicle
duplication
1,634

Work
(non-motor vehicle)
2,374

Home
69,500

Public
29,100

Unintentional medically consulted injuries[a] by class, United States, 2014

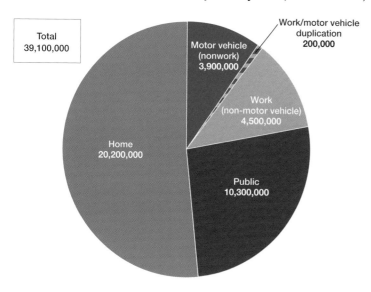

Total
39,100,000

Work/motor vehicle
duplication
200,000

Motor vehicle
(nonwork)
3,900,000

Work
(non-motor vehicle)
4,500,000

Home
20,200,000

Public
10,300,000

[a]Medically consulted injury estimate method was updated for the 2014 estimate and is not comparable with previous estimates.

While you make a 10-minute safety speech, three people in the United States will be killed and about 744 will suffer an injury severe enough to require a consultation with a medical professional.[a] Costs will amount to $16,240,000. On average,

16 unintentional-injury-related deaths and about 4,460 medically consulted injuries occur every hour during the year.

Deaths and medically consulted injuries by class occurred in the nation at the following rates in 2014:

Deaths and medically consulted injuries by class, 2014

Class	Severity	One every ...	Number per ...			2014 total
			Hour	Day	Week	
All	Deaths	4 minutes	16	373	2,620	136,053
	Injuries[a]	1 second	4,460	107,100	751,900	39,100,000
Motor vehicle	Deaths	15 minutes	4	97	680	35,398
	Injuries	8 seconds	470	11,200	78,800	4,100,000
Work	Deaths	131 minutes	<1	11	80	4,008
	Injuries	7 seconds	540	12,900	90,400	4,700,000
Workers off the job	Deaths	9 minutes	7	159	1,120	58,000
	Injuries	2 seconds	1,640	39,500	276,900	14,400,000
Home	Deaths	8 minutes	8	190	1,340	69,500
	Injuries	2 second	2,310	55,300	388,500	20,200,000
Public non-motor vehicle	Deaths	18 minutes	3	80	560	29,100
	Injuries	3 seconds	1,180	28,200	198,100	10,300,000

Source: National Safety Council estimates.

[a]Starting with the 2011 edition of Injury Facts, the National Safety Council adopted the definition of "medically consulted injuries" to replace "disabling injuries." For a full description of medically consulted injuries, please see the Technical Appendix. Please note that for this 2016 edition, the estimates have been refined to better exclude intentional injuries and are not comparable to previous editions.

Deaths every hour...

An unintentional-injury-related death occurs every four minutes.

Four minutes

Leading Causes of Total Unintentional Injuries

Percentage of Unintentional Deaths by Age Group, United States, 2013

During the first year of life, children are at most risk from mechanical suffocation. From age 1 through early adulthood (age 24) motor-vehicle crashes are the leading cause of unintentional death.

	Under 1	1 to 4	5 to 14	15 to 24	25 to 34

Top five causes of unintentional death by percentage of deaths within each age group

Mechanical suffocation

| | | 33% | 56% | 58% | 51% |

| | 81% | 30% | 14% | | |

| | | 10% | 9% | 28% | 37% |

Motor-vehicle — 6% | 7% | | | 3%

Suffocation by ingestion, inhalation — 4% | 6% | 4% | 2% | 1%

Drowning — 2% | | 3% | 1% | 1%

Fires, flames, smoke — 2% | | | |

Causes outside the top five that appear in the top five of other ages

Falls

Poisoning

Firearms

Total unintentional deaths by age group

1,156 | 1,316 | 1,521 | 11,619 | 16,209

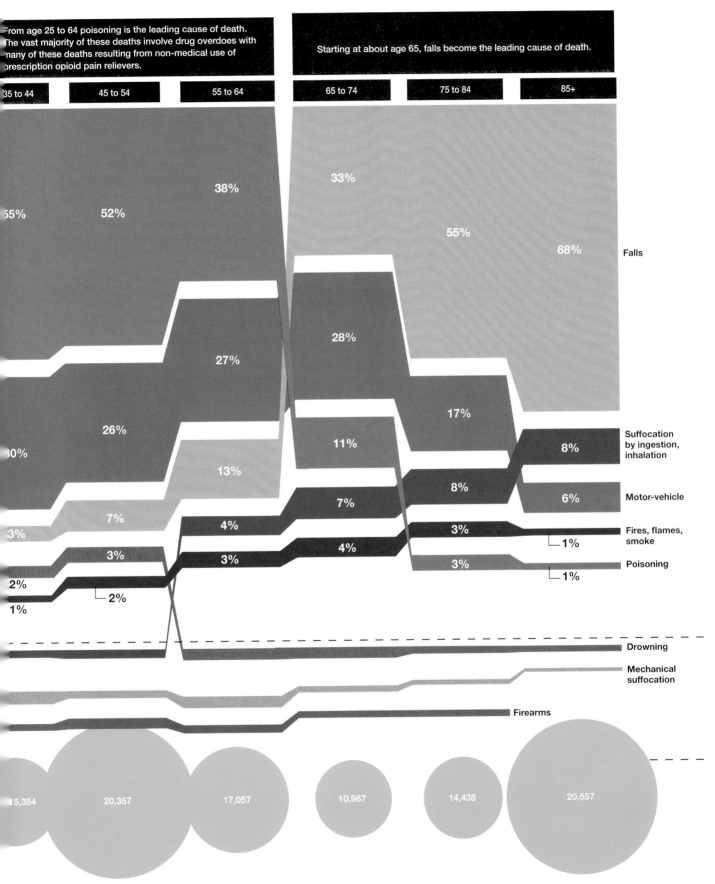

From age 25 to 64 poisoning is the leading cause of death. The vast majority of these deaths involve drug overdoes with many of these deaths resulting from non-medical use of prescription opioid pain relievers.

Starting at about age 65, falls become the leading cause of death.

| 35 to 44 | 45 to 54 | 55 to 64 | 65 to 74 | 75 to 84 | 85+ |

55% | 52% | 38% | 33% | 55% | 68% | Falls

30% | 26% | 27% | 28% | 17% |

| 13% | 11% | | 8% | Suffocation by ingestion, inhalation

3% | 7% | 4% | 7% | 8% | 6% | Motor-vehicle

2% | 3% | 3% | 4% | 3% | 1% | Fires, flames, smoke

1% | 2% | | 4% | 3% | 1% | Poisoning

Drowning

Mechanical suffocation

Firearms

5,354 | 20,357 | 17,057 | 10,967 | 14,438 | 20,557

Major revisions were made to the National Safety Council cost model for this edition that take advantage of data sources not previously available. Because of the changes made to the cost model, cost estimates provided in this edition are not comparable to previously published estimates.

The total cost of unintentional injuries in 2014, $853.4 billion, includes estimates of economic costs of fatal and nonfatal unintentional injuries together with employers' uninsured costs, vehicle damage costs, and fire losses. Wage and productivity losses, medical expenses, administrative expenses, and employers' uninsured costs are included in all four classes of injuries. Cost components unique to each class are identified below.

Motor-vehicle crash costs include property damage from motor-vehicle incidents. Work costs include the value of property damage in on-the-job motor-vehicle incidents and

fires. Home and public costs include estimated fire losses, but do not include other property damage costs.

Besides the estimated $853.4 billion in economic losses from unintentional injuries in 2014, lost quality of life from those injuries is valued at an additional $3,345.5 billion, making the comprehensive cost $4,198.9 billion in 2014.

As mentioned above, several cost benchmarks were updated for this edition of *Injury Facts*, making costs estimates not comparable to previous years. In addition, the method for estimating the number of medically attended injuries by class was also revised to use the latest National Health Interview Survey data. Estimated property damage costs in motor-vehicle crashes were re-benchmarked using data from the National Highway Traffic Safety Administration. Finally, the value of a statistical life was updated for this edition, affecting the comprehensive cost mentioned in the paragraph above.

Certain costs of unintentional injuries by class, 2014 ($ billions)

Cost	Total[a]	Motor vehicle	Work	Home	Public non-motor vehicle
Total	$853.4	$379.4	$140.0	$241.9	$120.6
Wage and productivity losses	432.2	169.2	45.7	152.1	71.9
Medical expenses	173.0	44.8	31.7	66.4	35.5
Administrative expenses[b]	143.7	92.4	44.7	13.3	8.5
Motor vehicle damage	69.8	69.8	3.5	(c)	(c)
Employers' uninsured costs	23.0	3.2	11.5	5.9	3.1
Fire loss	11.7	(c)	2.9	7.2	1.6

Source: National Safety Council estimates. See the Technical Appendix. Cost-estimating procedures were revised extensively for the 1993, 2005-2006 editions, and again for this current 2016 edition of Injury Facts®. In general, cost estimates are not comparable from year to year. As additional data or new benchmarks become available, they are used from that point forward. Previously estimated figures are not revised.
[a]Duplication between work and motor vehicle, which amounted to $28.5 billion, was eliminated from the total.
[b]Home and public insurance administration costs may include costs of administering medical treatment claims for some motor vehicle injuries filed through health insurance plans.
[c]Not included, see comments above.

Costs of unintentional injuries by class, 2014

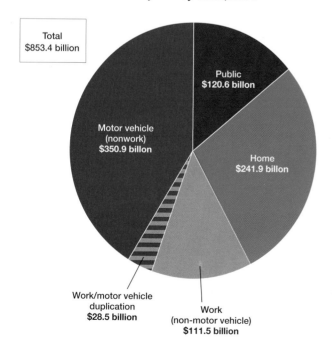

Total $853.4 billion

Motor vehicle (nonwork) $350.9 billon

Public $120.6 billon

Home $241.9 billon

Work/motor vehicle duplication $28.5 billion

Work (non-motor vehicle) $111.5 billion

Comprehensive Cost of Unintentional Injuries by Source of Payment

The two tables below provide estimates of the unintentional-injury-related costs that are paid by employers and government. These cost estimates reflect comprehensive costs including lost quality of life estimates. Employers and governments incur lost quality of life costs in part through higher wages paid to workers in high risk jobs. Because government agencies are also employers the two tables are not mutually exclusive and should not be added together.

Comprehensive Cost of Unintentional Injuries Paid by Employers, 2014 ($ billions)

Cost category	Total	Motor vehicle (nonwork)	Work/motor vehicle duplication	Work (non-motor vehicle)	Home	Public
Total employer costs	**$631.78**	**$31.41**	**$72.74**	**$480.06**	**$30.74**	**$16.83**
Productivity and wage loss	$43.11	$8.52	$2.50	$15.47	$10.91	$5.70
Medical expenses (including employee health insurance)	$61.27	$8.87	$2.48	$29.20	$13.28	$7.45
Administrative expense (insurance administrative and legal)	$67.23	$11.52	$21.21	$33.29	$0.64	$0.57
Motor-vehicle damage	$4.19	$0.00	$4.19	$0.00	$0.00	$0.00
Employer uninsured costs	$23.06	$2.50	$0.69	$10.85	$5.90	$3.12
Fire loss	$2.86	$0.00	$0.00	$2.86	$0.00	$0.00
Wage risk premiums (higher wages paid for risky jobs)	$430.07	$0.00	$41.68	$388.39	$0.00	$0.00
Public services (police, etc)	$0.00	$0.00	$0.00	$0.00	$0.00	$0.00

Comprehensive Cost of Unintentional Injuries Paid by Government, 2014 ($ billions)

Cost category	Total	Motor vehicle (nonwork)	Work/motor vehicle duplication	Work (non-motor vehicle)	Home	Public
Total government costs	**$172.96**	**$26.32**	**$9.36**	**$44.49**	**$58.48**	**$34.31**
Productivity and wage loss	$31.10	$8.93	$0.80	$4.95	$10.54	$5.88
Medical expenses (including employee health insurance)	$85.21	$12.64	$0.19	$2.32	$44.89	$25.17
Administrative expense (insurance administrative and legal)	$11.81	$2.48	$2.58	$2.65	$2.16	$1.94
Motor-vehicle damage	$0.89	$0.35	$0.54	$0.00	$0.00	$0.00
Employer uninsured costs	$2.67	$0.37	$0.08	$0.86	$0.88	$0.47
Fire loss	$3.71	$0.00	$0.00	$2.86	$0.00	$0.86
Wage risk premiums (higher wages paid for risky jobs)	$35.93	$0.00	$5.07	$30.86	$0.00	$0.00
Public services (police, etc)	$1.64	$1.54	$0.10	$0.00	$0.00	$0.00

Source: National Safety Council estimates. See the Technical Appendix.

Major revisions were made to the National Safety Council cost model for this edition that take advantage of data sources not previously available. Because of the changes made to the cost model, cost estimates provided in this edition are not comparable to previously published estimates.

Wage and productivity losses

A person's contribution to the wealth of the nation usually is measured in terms of wages and household production. The total of wages and fringe benefits, together with an estimate of the replacement-cost value of household services, provides an estimate of this lost productivity. Also included is travel delay for motor-vehicle incidents.

Medical expenses

Doctor fees; hospital charges; the cost of medicines; future medical costs; and ambulance, helicopter, and other emergency medical services are included.

Administrative expenses

Includes the administrative cost of public and private insurance, as well as police and legal costs. Private insurance administrative costs are the difference between premiums paid to insurance companies and claims paid out by them. It is their cost of doing business and a part of the cost total. Claims paid by insurance companies are not identified separately, as every claim is compensation for losses such as wages, medical expenses, property damage, etc.

Motor vehicle damage

Includes the value of damage to vehicles from motor-vehicle crashes. The cost of normal wear and tear to vehicles is not included.

Employers' uninsured costs

This is an estimate of the uninsured costs incurred by employers, representing the dollar value of time lost by uninjured workers. It includes time spent investigating and reporting injuries, administering first aid, hiring and training replacement workers, and the extra cost of overtime for uninjured workers.

Fire loss

Includes losses from both structure fires and nonstructure fires, such as vehicles, outside storage, crops, and timber.

Work – motor vehicle duplication

The cost of motor-vehicle crashes that involve people in the course of their work is included in both classes, but the duplication is eliminated from the total. The duplication in 2014 amounted to $28.5 billion and consists of $6.7 billion in wage and productivity losses, $2.4 billion in medical expenses, $15.2 billion in administrative expenses, $3.5 billion in vehicle damage, and $0.7 billion in employers' uninsured costs.

Costs of unintentional injuries by component[a], 2014

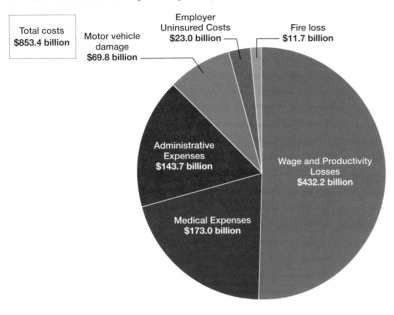

Total costs $853.4 billion

Motor vehicle damage $69.8 billion

Employer Uninsured Costs $23.0 billion

Fire loss $11.7 billion

Administrative Expenses $143.7 billion

Wage and Productivity Losses $432.2 billion

Medical Expenses $173.0 billion

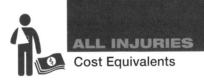

The costs of unintentional injuries are immense — billions of dollars. Because figures this large can be difficult to comprehend, it is sometimes useful to reduce the numbers to a more understandable scale by relating them to quantities encountered in daily life. The table below shows how the costs of unintentional injuries compare to common quantities such as taxes, corporate profits, or stock dividends.

Cost equivalents, 2014

The cost of...	Is equivalent to...
...All injuries ($853.4 billion)	...62 cents of every dollar paid in federal personal income taxes, **or** ...52 cents of every dollar spent on food in the United States.
...Motor vehicle crashes ($379.4 billion)	...purchasing 440 gallons of gasoline for each registered vehicle in the United States, **or** ...more than $1,800 per licensed driver.
...Work injuries ($140.0 billion)	...15 cents of every dollar of corporate dividends to stockholders, **or** ...6 cents of every dollar of pre-tax corporate profits, **or** ...exceeds the combined profits reported by the 6 largest Fortune 500 companies.
...Home injuries ($241.9 billion)	...a $377,800 rebate on each new single-family home built, **or** ...54 cents of every dollar of property taxes paid.
...Public injuries ($120.6 billion)	...a $13.3 million grant to each public library in the United States, **or** ...a $90,800 bonus for each police officer and firefighter.

Source: National Safety Council estimates.
[a]Major revisions were made to the National Safety Council cost model for this edition that take advantage of data sources not previously available. Because of the changes made to the cost model, cost estimates provided in this edition are not comparable to previously published estimates.

Deaths Due to Unintentional Injuries, 2014

Type of event and age of victim

All unintentional injuries

The term "unintentional" covers most deaths from injury and poisoning. Excluded are homicides (including legal intervention), suicides, deaths for which none of these categories can be determined, and war deaths.

	Total	Change from 2013	Death rate[a]
Deaths	136,053	+4.2%	42.7

Age	0-4	5-14	15-24	25-44	45-64	65-74	75+
Deaths	2,377	1,480	11,836	33,405	38,640	11,909	36,406

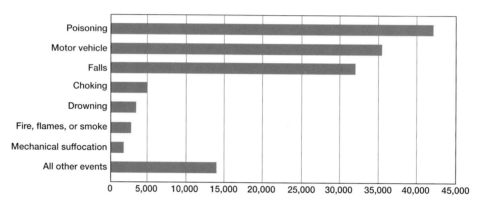

Poisoning

Includes deaths from drugs, medicines, other solid and liquid substances, and gases and vapors. Excludes poisonings from spoiled foods, *Salmonella*, etc., which are classified as disease deaths.

	Total	Change from 2013	Death rate[a]
Deaths	42,032	+8%	13.2

Age	0-4	5-14	15-24	25-44	45-64	65-74	75+
Deaths	37	31	3,492	18,450	18,022	1,410	590

Motor-vehicle incidents

Includes deaths involving mechanically or electrically powered highway-transport vehicles in motion (except those on rails), both on and off the highway or street.

	Total	Change from 2013	Death rate[a]
Deaths	35,398	+<0.5%	11.1

Age	0-4	5-14	15-24	25-44	45-64	65-74	75+
Deaths	473	829	6,709	10,518	10,024	3,153	3,692

Falls

Includes deaths from falls from one level to another or on the same level. Excludes falls in or from transport vehicles, or while boarding or alighting from them.

	Total	Change from 2013	Death rate[a]
Deaths	31,959	+6%	10.0

Age	0-4	5-14	15-24	25-44	45-64	65-74	75+
Deaths	32	21	174	789	3,898	3,938	23,107

See footnotes on page 13.

Type of event and age of victim

Choking

Includes deaths from unintentional ingestion or inhalation of food or other objects resulting in the obstruction of respiratory passages.

	Total	Change from 2013	Death rate[a]
Deaths	4,816	–1%	1.5

Age	0-4	5-14	15-24	25-44	45-64	65-74	75+
Deaths	95	23	39	228	887	789	2,755

Drowning

Includes non-transport-related drownings such as those resulting from swimming, playing in the water, or falling in. Excludes drownings in floods and other cataclysms, which are classified to the cataclysm, and boating-related drownings.

	Total	Change from 2013	Death rate[a]
Deaths	3,406	+<0.5%	1.1

Age	0-4	5-14	15-24	25-44	45-64	65-74	75+
Deaths	417	230	507	762	884	318	288

Fire, flames, or smoke

Includes deaths from exposure to fire, flames, or smoke, and from injuries in fires such as falls and struck by falling objects. Excludes burns from hot objects or liquids.

	Total	Change from 2013	Death rate[a]
Deaths	2,701	-2%	0.8

Age	0-4	5-14	15-24	25-44	45-64	65-74	75+
Deaths	130	117	104	381	859	475	635

Mechanical suffocation

Includes deaths from hanging and strangulation, and suffocation in enclosed or confined spaces; cave-ins; or by bed clothes, plastic bags, or similar materials.

	Total	Change from 2013	Death rate[a]
Deaths	1,764	+2%	0.6

Age	0-4	5-14	15-24	25-44	45-64	65-74	75+
Deaths	1,016	44	68	225	263	77	71

All other types

Most important types included are natural heat or cold; firearms; struck by or against object; machinery; electric current; and air, water, or rail transport.

	Total	Change from 2013	Death rate[a]
Deaths	13,977	+4%	4.4

Age	0-4	5-14	15-24	25-44	45-64	65-74	75+
Deaths	177	185	743	2,052	3,803	1,749	5,268

Note: Category descriptions have changed due to the adoption of the 10th revision of the International Classification of Diseases. See the Technical Appendix for comparability.
[a]*Deaths per 100,000 population.*
[b]*Deaths per 100,000 population in each age group.*

Unintentional injuries are the fourth leading cause of death overall and first among people in age groups from 1 to 44. By single years of age, unintentional injuries are the leading cause of death from age 1 to 42.

Causes are ranked for both sexes combined. Some leading causes for males and females separately may not be shown. Beginning with 1999 data, deaths are classified according to the 10th revision of the *International Classification of Diseases*. See the Technical Appendix for comparability.

Deaths and death rates by age and sex, 2013

Cause	Number of deaths			Death rates[a]		
	Total	Male	Female	Total	Male	Female
All ages[b]						
All causes	**2,596,993**	**1,306,034**	**1,290,959**	**821.5**	**839.1**	**804.4**
Heart disease	611,105	321,347	289,758	193.3	206.5	180.6
Cancer (malignant neoplasms)	584,881	307,559	277,322	185.0	197.6	172.8
Chronic lower respiratory diseases	149,205	70,317	78,888	47.2	45.2	49.2
Unintentional injuries	**130,557**	**81,916**	**48,641**	**41.3**	**52.6**	**30.3**
Poisoning	*38,851*	*25,080*	*13,771*	*12.3*	*16.1*	*8.6*
Motor-vehicle	*35,369*	*25,048*	*10,321*	*11.2*	*16.1*	*6.4*
Falls	*30,208*	*15,205*	*15,003*	*9.6*	*9.8*	*9.3*
Choking[c]	*4,864*	*2,615*	*2,249*	*1.5*	*1.7*	*1.4*
Drowning	*3,391*	*2,613*	*778*	*1.1*	*1.7*	*0.5*
All other unintentional injuries	*17,874*	*11,355*	*6,519*	*5.7*	*7.3*	*4.1*
Stroke (cerebrovascular disease)	128,978	53,691	75,287	40.8	34.5	46.9
Alzheimer's disease	84,767	25,836	58,931	26.8	16.6	36.7
Diabetes mellitus	75,578	39,841	35,737	23.9	25.6	22.3
Influenza and pneumonia	56,979	26,804	30,175	18.0	17.2	18.8
Nephritis and nephrosis	47,112	23,493	23,619	14.9	15.1	14.7
Suicide	41,149	32,055	9,094	13.0	20.6	5.7
Younger than 1						
All causes	**23,440**	**13,119**	**10,321**	**594.7**	**650.5**	**536.1**
Congenital anomalies	4,758	2,562	2,196	120.7	127.0	114.1
Short gestation, low birth weight, n.e.c.	4,202	2,297	1,905	106.6	113.9	99.0
Maternal complications of pregnancy	1,595	901	694	40.5	44.7	36.1
Sudden infant death syndrome	1,563	916	647	39.7	45.4	33.6
Unintentional injuries	**1,156**	**659**	**497**	**29.3**	**32.7**	**25.8**
Mechanical suffocation	*934*	*531*	*403*	*23.7*	*26.3*	*20.9*
Motor-vehicle	*68*	*34*	*34*	*1.7*	*1.7*	*1.8*
Choking[c]	*45*	*34*	*11*	*1.1*	*1.7*	*0.6*
Drowning	*23*	*15*	*8*	*0.6*	*0.7*	*0.4*
Fire, flames, or smoke	*17*	*7*	*10*	*0.4*	*0.3*	*0.5*
All other unintentional injuries	*69*	*38*	*31*	*1.8*	*1.9*	*1.6*
Complications of placenta, cord, membranes	953	530	423	24.2	26.3	22.0
Bacterial sepsis	578	337	241	14.7	16.7	12.5
Respiratory distress	522	296	226	13.2	14.7	11.7
Circulatory system disease	458	259	199	11.6	12.8	10.3
Neonatal hemorrhage	389	234	155	9.9	11.6	8.1
1-4 years						
All causes	**4,068**	**2,323**	**1,745**	**25.5**	**28.6**	**22.4**
Unintentional injuries	**1,316**	**831**	**485**	**8.3**	**10.2**	**6.2**
Motor-vehicle	*425*	*244*	*181*	*2.7*	*3.0*	*2.3*
Drowning	*393*	*274*	*119*	*2.5*	*3.4*	*1.5*
Fire, flames, or smoke	*128*	*74*	*54*	*0.8*	*0.9*	*0.7*
Choking[c]	*88*	*55*	*33*	*0.6*	*0.7*	*0.4*
Mechanical suffocation	*73*	*43*	*30*	*0.5*	*0.5*	*0.4*
All other unintentional injuries	*209*	*141*	*68*	*1.3*	*1.7*	*0.9*
Congenital anomalies	476	232	244	3.0	2.9	3.1
Homicide	337	184	153	2.1	2.3	2.0
Cancer (malignant neoplasms)	328	183	145	2.1	2.2	1.9
Heart disease	169	96	73	1.1	1.2	0.9
Influenza and pneumonia	102	53	49	0.6	0.7	0.6
Chronic lower respiratory diseases	64	38	26	0.4	0.5	0.3
Septicemia	53	32	21	0.3	0.4	0.3
Benign neoplasms	47	19	28	0.3	0.2	0.4
Perinatal period	45	29	16	0.3	0.4	0.2

See source and footnotes on page 16.

Deaths and death rates by age and sex, 2013 (cont.)

Cause	Number of deaths			Death rates[a]		
	Total	Male	Female	Total	Male	Female
5-14 years						
All causes	**5,340**	**3,077**	**2,263**	**13.0**	**14.6**	**11.2**
Unintentional injuries	**1,521**	**950**	**571**	**3.7**	**4.5**	**2.8**
Motor-vehicle	*852*	*498*	*354*	*2.1*	*2.4*	*1.8*
Drowning	*209*	*153*	*56*	*0.5*	*0.7*	*0.3*
Fire, flames, or smoke	*135*	*77*	*58*	*0.3*	*0.4*	*0.3*
Mechanical suffocation	*54*	*43*	*11*	*0.1*	*0.2*	*0.1*
Firearms	*39*	*31*	*8*	*0.1*	*0.1*	*0.0*
All other unintentional injuries	*232*	*148*	*84*	*0.6*	*0.7*	*0.4*
Cancer (malignant neoplasms)	895	471	424	2.2	2.2	2.1
Suicide	395	252	143	1.0	1.2	0.7
Congenital anomalies	340	176	164	0.8	0.8	0.8
Homicide	277	168	109	0.7	0.8	0.5
Heart disease	173	93	80	0.4	0.4	0.4
Chronic lower respiratory diseases	155	100	55	0.4	0.5	0.3
Influenza and pneumonia	128	70	58	0.3	0.3	0.3
Stroke (cerebrovascular disease)	89	44	45	0.2	0.2	0.2
Benign neoplasms	65	40	25	0.2	0.2	0.1
15-24 years						
All causes	**28,486**	**20,864**	**7,622**	**64.8**	**92.6**	**35.6**
Unintentional injuries	**11,619**	**8,545**	**3,074**	**26.4**	**37.9**	**14.3**
Motor-vehicle	*6,692*	*4,781*	*1,911*	*15.2*	*21.2*	*8.9*
Poisoning	*3,293*	*2,435*	*858*	*7.5*	*10.8*	*4.0*
Drowning	*501*	*446*	*55*	*1.1*	*2.0*	*0.3*
Falls	*205*	*161*	*44*	*0.5*	*0.7*	*0.2*
Fire, flames, or smoke	*137*	*91*	*46*	*0.3*	*0.4*	*0.2*
All other unintentional injuries	*791*	*631*	*160*	*1.8*	*2.8*	*0.7*
Suicide	4,878	3,903	975	11.1	17.3	4.5
Homicide	4,329	3,765	564	9.8	16.7	2.6
Cancer (malignant neoplasms)	1,496	859	637	3.4	3.8	3.0
Heart disease	941	628	313	2.1	2.8	1.5
Congenital anomalies	362	223	139	0.8	1.0	0.6
Influenza and pneumonia	197	114	83	0.4	0.5	0.4
Diabetes mellitus	193	120	73	0.4	0.5	0.3
Complicated pregnancy	178	0	178	0.4	0.0	0.8
Chronic lower respiratory diseases	155	101	54	0.4	0.4	0.3
25-34 years						
All causes	**45,463**	**31,462**	**14,001**	**106.1**	**145.4**	**66.0**
Unintentional injuries	**16,209**	**12,025**	**4,184**	**37.8**	**55.6**	**19.7**
Poisoning	*8,251*	*5,894*	*2,357*	*19.3*	*27.2*	*11.1*
Motor-vehicle	*5,955*	*4,491*	*1,464*	*13.9*	*20.8*	*6.9*
Drowning	*424*	*350*	*74*	*1.0*	*1.6*	*0.3*
Falls	*305*	*255*	*50*	*0.7*	*1.2*	*0.2*
Fire, flames, or smoke	*158*	*105*	*53*	*0.4*	*0.5*	*0.2*
All other unintentional injuries	*1,116*	*930*	*186*	*2.6*	*4.3*	*0.9*
Suicide	6,348	5,063	1,285	14.8	23.4	6.1
Homicide	4,236	3,555	681	9.9	16.4	3.2
Cancer (malignant neoplasms)	3,673	1,857	1,816	8.6	8.6	8.6
Heart disease	3,258	2,214	1,044	7.6	10.2	4.9
Diabetes mellitus	684	403	281	1.6	1.9	1.3
Chronic liver disease and cirrhosis	676	435	241	1.6	2.0	1.1
Human immunodeficiency virus infection	631	457	174	1.5	2.1	0.8
Stroke (cerebrovascular disease)	508	279	229	1.2	1.3	1.1
Influenza and pneumonia	449	253	196	1.0	1.2	0.9
35-44 years						
All causes	**69,573**	**43,072**	**26,501**	**172.0**	**213.8**	**130.5**
Unintentional injuries	**15,354**	**10,566**	**4,788**	**38.0**	**52.4**	**23.6**
Poisoning	*8,374*	*5,342*	*3,032*	*20.7*	*26.5*	*14.9*
Motor-vehicle	*4,612*	*3,413*	*1,199*	*11.4*	*16.9*	*5.9*
Falls	*522*	*408*	*114*	*1.3*	*2.0*	*0.6*
Drowning	*367*	*292*	*75*	*0.9*	*1.4*	*0.4*
Fire, flames, or smoke	*196*	*123*	*73*	*0.5*	*0.6*	*0.4*
All other unintentional injuries	*1,283*	*988*	*295*	*3.2*	*4.9*	*1.5*
Cancer (malignant neoplasms)	11,349	4,827	6,522	28.1	24.0	32.1
Heart disease	10,341	7,152	3,189	25.6	35.5	15.7
Suicide	6,551	5,003	1,548	16.2	24.8	7.6
Homicide	2,581	2,025	556	6.4	10.1	2.7
Chronic liver disease and cirrhosis	2,491	1,620	871	6.2	8.0	4.3
Diabetes mellitus	1,952	1,211	741	4.8	6.0	3.6
Stroke (cerebrovascular disease)	1,687	938	749	4.2	4.7	3.7
Human immunodeficiency virus infection	1,246	842	404	3.1	4.2	2.0
Influenza and pneumonia	881	464	417	2.2	2.3	2.1

See source and footnotes on page 16.

Deaths and death rates by age and sex, 2013 (cont.)

Cause	Number of deaths			Death rates[a]		
	Total	Male	Female	Total	Male	Female
45-54 years						
All causes	**177,724**	**107,997**	**69,727**	**406.1**	**500.7**	**314.1**
Cancer (malignant neoplasms)	46,185	22,966	23,219	105.5	106.5	104.6
Heart disease	35,167	24,830	10,337	80.3	115.1	46.6
Unintentional injuries	**20,357**	**13,591**	**6,766**	**46.5**	**63.0**	**30.5**
Poisoning	*10,651*	*6,397*	*4,254*	*24.3*	*29.7*	*19.2*
Motor-vehicle	*5,334*	*3,938*	*1,396*	*12.2*	*18.3*	*6.3*
Falls	*1,366*	*1,007*	*359*	*3.1*	*4.7*	*1.6*
Drowning	*464*	*355*	*109*	*1.1*	*1.6*	*0.5*
Fire, flames, or smoke	*366*	*243*	*123*	*0.8*	*1.1*	*0.6*
All other unintentional injuries	*2,176*	*1,651*	*525*	*5.0*	*7.7*	*2.4*
Chronic liver disease and cirrhosis	8,785	5,858	2,927	20.1	27.2	13.2
Suicide	8,621	6,393	2,228	19.7	29.6	10.0
Diabetes mellitus	5,899	3,633	2,266	13.5	16.8	10.2
Stroke (cerebrovascular disease)	5,425	3,067	2,358	12.4	14.2	10.6
Chronic lower respiratory diseases	4,619	2,142	2,477	10.6	9.9	11.2
Septicemia	2,445	1,304	1,141	5.6	6.0	5.1
Human immunodeficiency virus infection	2,378	1,760	618	5.4	8.2	2.8
55-64 years						
All causes	**338,127**	**206,325**	**131,802**	**860.0**	**1,088.4**	**647.4**
Cancer (malignant neoplasms)	113,324	62,810	50,514	288.2	331.3	248.1
Heart disease	72,568	50,680	21,888	184.6	267.3	107.5
Unintentional injuries	**17,057**	**11,658**	**5,399**	**43.4**	**61.5**	**26.5**
Poisoning	*6,388*	*3,973*	*2,415*	*16.2*	*21.0*	*11.9*
Motor-vehicle	*4,696*	*3,427*	*1,269*	*11.9*	*18.1*	*6.2*
Falls	*2,283*	*1,572*	*711*	*5.8*	*8.3*	*3.5*
Choking[c]	*600*	*361*	*239*	*1.5*	*1.9*	*1.2*
Fire, flames, or smoke	*556*	*355*	*201*	*1.4*	*1.9*	*1.0*
All other unintentional injuries	*2,534*	*1,970*	*564*	*6.4*	*10.4*	*2.8*
Chronic lower respiratory diseases	15,942	8,287	7,655	40.5	43.7	37.6
Diabetes mellitus	13,061	7,933	5,128	33.2	41.8	25.2
Chronic liver disease and cirrhosis	11,951	8,485	3,466	30.4	44.8	17.0
Stroke (cerebrovascular disease)	11,364	6,651	4,713	28.9	35.1	23.1
Suicide	7,135	5,373	1,762	18.1	28.3	8.7
Septicemia	5,345	2,892	2,453	13.6	15.3	12.0
Nephritis and nephrosis	4,947	2,800	2,147	12.6	14.8	10.5
65-74 years						
All causes	**454,429**	**257,898**	**196,531**	**1,802.1**	**2,186.0**	**1,464.6**
Cancer (malignant neoplasms)	155,552	85,669	69,883	616.9	726.2	520.8
Heart disease	98,432	62,634	35,798	390.3	530.9	266.8
Chronic lower respiratory diseases	35,603	17,925	17,678	141.2	151.9	131.7
Stroke (cerebrovascular disease)	18,722	10,033	8,689	74.2	85.0	64.8
Diabetes mellitus	17,279	9,857	7,422	68.5	83.6	55.3
Unintentional injuries	**10,967**	**7,014**	**3,953**	**43.5**	**59.5**	**29.5**
Falls	*3,586*	*2,184*	*1,402*	*14.2*	*18.5*	*10.4*
Motor-vehicle	*3,066*	*2,066*	*1,000*	*12.2*	*17.5*	*7.5*
Poisoning	*1,238*	*705*	*533*	*4.9*	*6.0*	*4.0*
Choking[c]	*742*	*449*	*293*	*2.9*	*3.8*	*2.2*
Fire, flames, or smoke	*412*	*230*	*182*	*1.6*	*1.9*	*1.4*
All other unintentional injuries	*1,923*	*1,380*	*543*	*7.6*	*11.7*	*4.0*
Nephritis and nephrosis	8,524	4,469	4,055	33.8	37.9	30.2
Septicemia	7,693	4,002	3,691	30.5	33.9	27.5
Influenza and pneumonia	7,441	4,131	3,310	29.5	35.0	24.7
Chronic liver disease and cirrhosis	7,087	4,531	2,556	28.1	38.4	19.0
75 years or older[b]						
All causes	**1,450,343**	**619,897**	**830,446**	**7,442.5**	**7,945.1**	**7,106.9**
Heart disease	389,747	172,844	216,903	2,000.0	2,215.3	1,856.3
Cancer (malignant neoplasms)	252,015	127,887	124,128	1,293.2	1,639.1	1,062.3
Chronic lower respiratory diseases	91,592	41,185	50,407	470.0	527.9	431.4
Stroke (cerebrovascular disease)	90,884	32,512	58,372	466.4	416.7	499.5
Alzheimer's disease	79,226	23,436	55,790	406.6	300.4	477.4
Influenza and pneumonia	40,591	17,587	23,004	208.3	225.4	196.9
Diabetes mellitus	36,474	16,665	19,809	187.2	213.6	169.5
Unintentional injuries	**35,001**	**16,077**	**18,924**	**179.6**	**206.1**	**162.0**
Falls	*21,880*	*9,580*	*12,300*	*112.3*	*122.8*	*105.3*
Motor-vehicle	*3,669*	*2,156*	*1,513*	*18.8*	*27.6*	*12.9*
Choking[c]	*2,751*	*1,338*	*1,413*	*14.1*	*17.1*	*12.1*
Fire, flames, or smoke	*655*	*348*	*307*	*3.4*	*4.5*	*2.6*
Poisoning	*591*	*297*	*294*	*3.0*	*3.8*	*2.5*
All other unintentional injuries	*5,455*	*2,358*	*3,097*	*28.0*	*30.2*	*26.5*
Nephritis and nephrosis	30,557	14,457	16,100	156.8	185.3	137.8
Parkinson's disease	21,311	12,480	8,831	109.4	160.0	75.6

Source: National Safety Council analysis of National Center for Health Statistics–Mortality Data for 2013 as compiled from data provided by the 57 vital statistics jurisdictions through the Vital Statistics Cooperative Program. Rates are National Safety Council estimates based on data from the National Center for Health Statistics and the U.S. Census Bureau.
[a]Deaths per 100,000 population in each age group. [b]Includes 132 deaths for which the age was unknown. [c]Inhalation or ingestion of food or other objects.

The rank of unintentional injuries as a cause of death varies with race and Hispanic origin. While ranking fourth overall (following heart disease, cancer, and chronic lower respiratory diseases), unintentional injuries rank third for Hispanics after cancer and heart disease and fifth for non-Hispanics after heart disease, cancer, chronic lower respiratory disease, and stroke.

By race, unintentional injuries rank fourth for whites, blacks, and for other non-black groups including Asians, Pacific Islanders, American Indians, and Alaskan Natives.

Unintentional-injury-related deaths and death rates by race, Hispanic origin, and sex, United States, 2013

| Race and sex | Total | | | Hispanic origin | | | | | |
| | | | | Non-Hispanic | | | Hispanic | | |
	Rank	Number	Rate	Rank	Number	Rate	Rank	Number	Rate
All races	4	130,557	41.3	5	118,080	45.1	3	12,015	22.2
Males	3	81,916	52.6	3	72,836	56.8	3	8,760	31.9
Females	6	48,641	30.3	6	45,244	33.8	5	3,255	12.2
White	4	112,803	45.9	4	100,773	50.9	3	11,664	(b)
Males	3	70,161	57.7	3	61,391	63.0	3	8,522	(b)
Females	6	42,642	34.4	6	39,382	39.2	5	3,142	(b)
Black	4	13,413	32.2	5	13,169	33.7	3	160	(b)
Males	3	9,017	45.3	3	8,845	47.4	3	111	(b)
Females	7	4,396	20.2	7	4,324	21.2	4	49	(b)
Not white or black[a]	4	4,341	15.0	4	4,138	16.5	3	191	(b)
Males	3	2,738	19.5	3	2,600	21.5	3	127	(b)
Females	4	1,603	10.7	4	1,538	11.8	3	64	(b)

Source: National Safety Council analysis of National Center for Health Statistics (NCHS)–Mortality Data for 2013, as compiled from data provided by the 57 vital statistics jurisdictions through the Vital Statistics Cooperative Program. Rates are National Safety Council estimates based on data from NCHS and the U.S. Census Bureau.
Note: Rates are deaths per 100,000 population in each race/sex/Hispanic origin group. Total column includes 462 deaths for which Hispanic origin was not determined.
[a]Includes American Indian, Alaskan Native, Asian, Native Hawaiian, and Pacific Islander.
[b]Race is not well-reported for persons of Hispanic origin. Population death rates are unreliable.

Leading causes of unintentional-injury-related death by race, Hispanic origin, and sex, United States, 2013

| Cause of death | All races | | | White | | | Black | | | Not white or black[a] | | |
	Both	Male	Female	Both	Male	Female	Both	Male	Female	Both	Male	Female
Total	130,557	81,916	48,641	112,803	70,161	42,642	13,413	9,017	4,396	4,341	2,738	1,603
Poisoning	38,851	25,080	13,771	34,035	21,874	12,161	3,823	2,558	1,265	993	648	345
Motor vehicle	35,369	25,048	10,321	29,118	20,662	8,456	4,731	3,431	1,300	1,520	955	565
Fall	30,208	15,205	15,003	27,912	13,880	14,032	1,415	836	579	881	489	392
Choking[b]	4,864	2,615	2,249	4,180	2,242	1,938	552	294	258	132	79	53
Drowning	3,391	2,613	778	2,603	1,983	620	532	433	99	256	197	59
Fires, flames, or smoke	2,760	1,653	1,107	2,136	1,297	839	549	311	238	75	45	30
Population (thousands)	316,129	155,652	160,477	245,499	121,674	123,825	41,624	19,905	21,719	29,006	14,073	14,933

| Cause of death | Non-Hispanic | | | Hispanic | | | Unknown | | |
	Both	Male	Female	Both	Male	Female	Both	Male	Female
Total	118,080	72,836	45,244	12,015	8,760	3,255	462	320	142
Poisoning	35,310	22,433	12,877	3,337	2,498	839	204	149	55
Motor vehicle	30,352	21,329	9,023	4,931	3,653	1,278	86	66	20
Fall	28,543	14,172	14,371	1,584	991	593	81	42	39
Choking[b]	4,567	2,421	2,146	286	188	98	11	6	5
Drowning	2,941	2,239	702	436	365	71	14	9	5
Fires, flames, or smoke	2,570	1,541	1,029	181	105	76	9	7	2
Population (thousands)	262,057	128,191	133,867	54,071	27,461	26,610	–	–	–

Source: National Safety Council analysis of National Center for Health Statistics (NCHS)–Mortality Data for 2013, as compiled from data provided by the 57 vital statistics jurisdictions through the Vital Statistics Cooperative Program. Rates are National Safety Council estimates based on data from NCHS and the U.S. Census Bureau.
Note: Dashes (–) indicate not applicable.
[a]Includes American Indian, Alaskan Native, Asian, Native Hawaiian, and Pacific Islander.
[b]Suffocation by inhalation or ingestion.

Leading Causes of Unintentional-Injury-Related Death by Age, 2013

Unintentional-injury-related deaths by age and event, United States, 2013

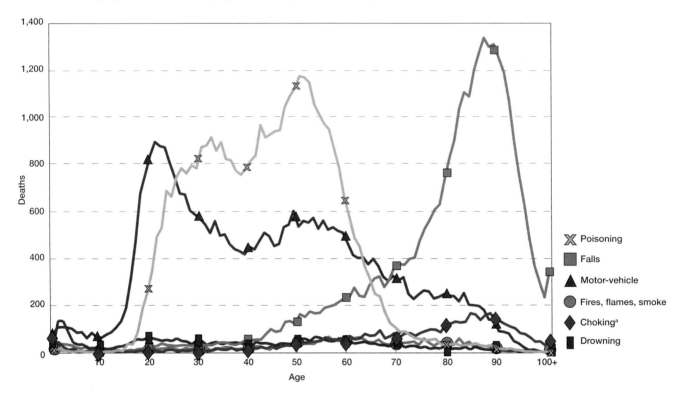

Poisonings; motor vehicle crashes; falls; choking (suffocation by inhalation or ingestion of food or other object); drownings; and fire, flames, or smoke were the six leading causes of unintentional-injury-related death in the United States in 2013. The graph above depicts the number of deaths attributed to the top six causes by single years of age through age 99 and an aggregate age group of people 100 and older.

In 2013, poisonings were the leading cause of unintentional-injury-related death for all ages combined for the third consecutive year and were the leading cause of unintentional-injury-related death for each single year of age from 26 to 62. Among infants younger than 1, mechanical suffocation was the leading cause of death, followed by motor vehicle deaths. Motor vehicle deaths also were the second leading cause of death among 1- and 2-year-olds, after drowning.

The distribution of 2013 poisoning fatalities shows a sharp increase during early adulthood into middle age, rising from 183 for 18-year-olds to 1,170 for 50-year-olds. The greatest number of poisoning fatalities in 2013 occurred among people 50 years old.

The second leading cause of unintentional-injury-related death overall in 2013 was motor vehicle crashes. Motor vehicle fatalities reached a high of 894 for 21-year-olds, and were the leading cause of unintentional-injury-related death for people age 3 to 25 and age 63 to 67. Poisoning was the second leading cause of unintentional-injury-related death for people age 15, from 17 to 25, and from 63 to 64. Motor vehicle fatalities were the second most common cause for every single year of age from less than age 1 to 2, 26 to 62, 68 to 87, and from age 89.

Falls were the third leading cause of unintentional-injury-related death in the United States in 2013. Falls were the leading cause of unintentional-injury-related death of people age 68 and older, and the second leading cause each single year of age from age 65-67. Deaths resulting from falls peaked at 1,332 for individuals age 87.

The fourth leading cause of unintentional-injury-related death in 2013 was choking.[a] Choking deaths peaked at ages 84 and 88 with 164 deaths. Choking was the second leading cause of unintentional-injury-related death for people age 88 and those age 90 and older.

Drowning was the fifth leading cause of unintentional-injury-related death in 2013 and peaked at 134 fatalities for 1-year-olds, resulting in the leading cause of death for this age group as well as people age 2. Drownings were the second leading cause of unintentional-injury-related death for children ages 3-6, 8-10, 12-14, and age 16 in 2013.

Fire, flames, or smoke was the sixth leading cause of unintentional-injury-related death in 2013. Fatalities due to fires, flames, or smoke peaked at 67 deaths among 56-year-olds.

Source: National Safety Council analysis of National Center for Health Statistics (NCHS)–Mortality Data for 2013, as compiled from data provided by the 57 vital statistics jurisdictions through the Vital Statistics Cooperative Program. Rates are National Safety Council estimates based on data from NCHS and the U.S. Census Bureau. See the Technical Appendix for ICD-10 codes for the leading causes and comparability with prior years.
[a]Inhalation or ingestion of food or other objects.

Unintentional-Injury-Related Death Rates by Age, 2013

Unintentional-injury-related deaths per 100,000 population by age and event, United States, 2013

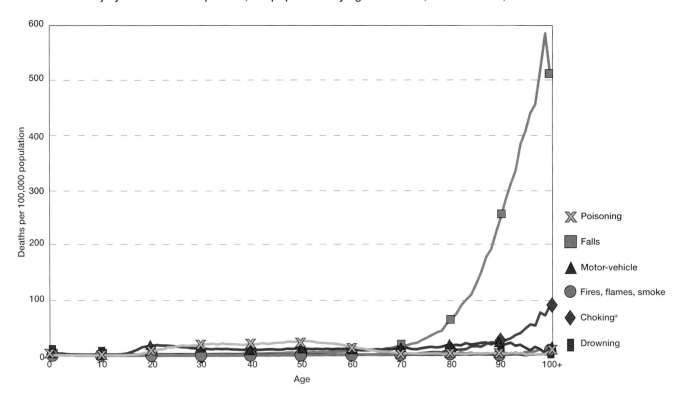

The graph above depicts U.S. death rates per 100,000 population for the six leading causes of unintentional-injury-related deaths in 2013 by age, through age 99 and an aggregate age group of people 100 and older.

Unintentional poisoning fatalities had the highest overall death rate, with an average of 12.3 deaths per 100,000 population. The poisoning death rate remained low until about age 15, when it started to increase steadily up to its peak rate of 26.0 at age 50 and 51 before falling again.

Motor vehicle crashes had the second highest overall death rate from unintentional injury in the United States, with an average rate of 11.2 deaths per 100,000 population. Historically, motor vehicle death rates peak for people in the 18-20 age group and, in 2013, there was such a peak among persons age 18-25 that reached a high of 19.6 for people age 21. However, in 2013 there was an even higher secondary peak among motor vehicle death rates that began at age 79 and extended into the early 90s, with the highest rate among people age 87, at a rate of 24.0. This peak rate is followed by a rate of 23.8 occurring at age 89, 23.5 for 92-year-olds, and 23.3 for 86-year-olds.

Although motor vehicle crashes were a significant problem for all ages, deaths resulting from falls for certain older ages had even higher death rates. Beginning at about age 67, the death rate from falls increased dramatically. The falls death rate surpassed that for motor vehicle for the first time at age 68 and remained higher throughout the remainder of the lifespan as it continued to rise steeply with increasing age, peaking for those age 99 with a rate of 583.1 per 100,000 population. The overall fatality rate for falls was 9.6.

Death rates due to choking on inhaled or ingested food or other objects were quite low for most ages. Rates rise rapidly beginning at about age 79. While relatively stable and low for all ages, the death rates for drownings showed peaks in the first few years of life and again at some very old ages. Death rates for fire, flames, or smoke were only slightly elevated at very young ages and began to climb at about age 75. The overall death rates per 100,000 U.S. population for choking; drowning; and fire, flames, or smoke did not exceed 1.5.

Source: National Safety Council analysis of National Center for Health Statistics (NCHS)–Mortality Data for 2013, as compiled from data provided by the 57 vital statistics jurisdictions through the Vital Statistics Cooperative Program. Rates are National Safety Council estimates based on data from NCHS and the U.S. Census Bureau. See the Technical Appendix for ICD-10 codes for the leading causes and comparability with prior years.
aInhalation or ingestion of food or other objects.

Unintentional-Injury-Related Deaths by Sex and Age, 2013

Unintentional-injury-related deaths by sex and age, United States, 2013

Males incurred more deaths due to unintentional injuries than females at all ages from birth to age 85 in 2013. The difference between the unintentional-injury-related death totals ranged from 18 more male deaths than female deaths at age 8 to 900 more deaths at age 24. The excess number of deaths for males compared to females was most evident from the late teen years to the mid-50s, when the gap begins to narrow. From age 85 on, deaths of females exceeded those of males by as little as 47 at age 86 to as much as 404 deaths nationwide at age 92.

Unintentional-injury-related deaths are at their lowest level for both sexes from about age 5 to about age 13. For males, the highest number of deaths (1,502) occurred at age 51, with high totals occurring from the late teens until the early 60s. For females, however, the highest totals occurred among the elderly throughout the 80s and into the early 90s. The greatest number of female deaths (1,112) occurred at age 89.

The graph above shows the number of unintentional-injury-related deaths in the United States during 2013 for each sex by single year of age from younger than 1 to age 99 and an aggregate age group of people 100 and older. It is based on death certificate data from the National Center for Health Statistics.

Source: National Safety Council analysis of National Center for Health Statistics (NCHS)--Mortality Data for 2013, as compiled from data provided by the 57 vital statistics jurisdictions through the Vital Statistics Cooperative Program. Rates are National Safety Council estimates based on data from NCHS and the U.S. Census Bureau. See the Technical Appendix for ICD-10 codes for the leading causes and comparability with prior years.

Unintentional-Injury-Related Death Rates by Sex and Age, 2013

Unintentional-injury-related deaths per 100,000 population by sex and age, 2013

Males have greater unintentional-injury-related death rates for each year of age compared to females. The graph above shows the unintentional-injury-related death rates for males and females by single year of age from younger than 1 to age 99 and an aggregate age group of people 100 and older. It is based on National Center for Health Statistics mortality data and U.S. Census Bureau population data.

Death rates for both sexes are lowest from birth until the mid-teen years, where rates rise rapidly. Rates then remain fairly constant until the early 70's, where they again rise steadily with increasing age. Across all ages, males had an overall death rate of 52.6 unintentional-injury-related deaths per 100,000 males, while the rate among females in the United States was 30.3. The overall unintentional-injury-related death rate for all ages and both sexes was 41.3 deaths per 100,000 population.

Source: National Safety Council analysis of National Center for Health Statistics (NCHS)–Mortality Data for 2013, as compiled from data provided by the 57 vital statistics jurisdictions through the Vital Statistics Cooperative Program. Rates are National Safety Council estimates based on data from NCHS and the U.S. Census Bureau. See the Technical Appendix for ICD-10 codes for the leading causes and comparability with prior years.

Mortality by selected external causes, United States, 2011-2013

Type of accident or manner of injury	2013[a]	2012	2011
All external causes of mortality, V01-Y89, *U01, *U03[b]	**195,713**	**192,988**	**190,048**
Deaths due to unintentional (accidental) injuries, V01-X59, Y85-Y86	**130,557**	**127,792**	**126,438**
Transport accidents, V01-V99, Y85	**37,938**	**39,045**	**38,023**
Motor-vehicle accidents, V02-V04, V09.0, V09.2, V12-V14, V19.0-V19.2, V19.4-V19.6, V20-V79, V80.3-V80.5, V81.0-V81.1, V82.0-V82.1, V83-V86, V87.0-V87.8, V88.0-V88.8, V89.0, V89.2	**35,369**	**36,415**	**35,303**
Pedestrian, V01-V09	5,974	6,020	5,622
Pedalcyclist, V10-V19	925	900	873
Motorcycle rider, V20-V29	4,230	4,643	4,344
Occupant of three-wheeled motor vehicle, V30-V39	7	7	4
Car occupant, V40-V49	6,625	7,632	8,415
Occupant of pick-up truck or van, V50-V59	1,474	1,729	1,929
Occupant of heavy transport vehicle, V60-V69	273	313	273
Bus occupant, V70-V79	29	38	50
Animal rider or occupant of animal-drawn vehicle, V80	91	106	129
Occupant of railway train or railway vehicle, V81	24	9	23
Occupant of streetcar, V82	1	2	1
Other and unspecified land transport accidents, V83-V89	16,716	15,997	14,590
Occupant of special industrial vehicle, V83	*10*	*7*	*2*
Occupant of special agricultural vehicle, V84	*81*	*94*	*120*
Occupant of special construction vehicle, V85	*22*	*12*	*15*
Occupant of all-terrain or other off-road motor vehicle, V86	*934*	*908*	*913*
Other and unspecified person, V87-V89	*15,669*	*14,976*	*13,540*
Water transport accidents, V90-V94	403	421	533
Drowning, V90, V92	*310*	*314*	*405*
Other and unspecified injuries, V91, V93-V94	*93*	*107*	*128*
Air and space transport accidents, V95-V97	412	432	494
Other and unspecified transport accidents and sequelae, V98-V99, Y85	754	796	743
Other specified transport accidents, V98	*0*	*0*	*0*
Unspecified transport accidents, V99	*0*	*2*	*0*
Nontransport unintentional (accidental) injuries, W00-X59, Y86	**92,619**	**88,747**	**88,415**
Falls, W00-W19	30,208	28,753	27,483
Fall on same level from slipping, tripping, and stumbling, W01	*710*	*727*	*800*
Other fall on same level, W00, W02-W03, W18	*9,631*	*8,989*	*8,661*
Fall involving bed, chair, other furniture, W06-W08	*1,170*	*1,138*	*1,113*
Fall on and from stairs and steps, W10	*2,233*	*2,127*	*2,101*
Fall on and from ladder or scaffolding, W11-W12	*420*	*481*	*465*
Fall from out of or through building or structure, W13	*504*	*481*	*452*
Other fall from one level to another, W09, W14-W17	*605*	*650*	*623*
Other and unspecified fall, W04-W05, W19	*14,935*	*14,160*	*13,268*
Exposure to inanimate mechanical forces, W20-W49	2,353	2,480	2,496
Struck by or striking against object, W20-W22	*811*	*859*	*827*
Caught between objects, W23	*88*	*106*	*137*
Contact with machinery, W24, W30-W31	*588*	*627*	*610*
Contact with sharp objects, W25-W29	*130*	*122*	*106*
Firearms discharge, W32-W34	*505*	*548*	*591*
Explosion and rupture of pressurized devices, W35-W38	*11*	*23*	*19*
Fireworks discharge, W39	*6*	*8*	*5*
Explosion of other materials, W40	*128*	*110*	*118*
Foreign body entering through skin or natural orifice, W44-W45	*37*	*32*	*31*
Other and unspecified inanimate mechanical forces, W41-W43, W49	*49*	*45*	*52*
Exposure to animate mechanical forces, W50-W64	133	144	130
Struck by or against another person, W50-W52	*12*	*15*	*10*
Bitten or struck by dog, W54	*35*	*34*	*34*
Bitten or struck by other mammals, W53, W55	*59*	*80*	*72*
Bitten or stung by nonvenomous insect and other arthropods, W57	*13*	*5*	*7*
Bitten or crushed by other reptiles, W59	*0*	*0*	*0*
Other and unspecified animate mechanical forces, W56, W58, W60, W64	*14*	*10*	*7*
Accidental drowning and submersion, W65-W74	3,391	3,551	3,556
Drowning and submersion while in or falling into bath-tub, W65-W66	*464*	*416*	*431*
Drowning and submersion while in or falling into swimming-pool, W67-W68	*651*	*691*	*652*
Drowning and submersion while in or falling into natural water, W69-W70	*1,810*	*1,844*	*1,782*
Other and unspecified drowning and submersion, W73-W74	*466*	*600*	*691*
Other accidental threats to breathing, W75-W84	6,601	6,238	6,242
Accidental suffocation and strangulation in bed, W75	*903*	*798*	*692*
Other accidental hanging and strangulation, W76	*247*	*264*	*233*
Threat to breathing due to cave-in, falling earth and other substances, W77	*27*	*16*	*16*
Inhalation of gastric contents, W78	*319*	*313*	*327*
Inhalation and ingestion of food causing obstruction of respiratory tract, W79	*1,177*	*1,138*	*1,173*
Inhalation and ingestion of other objects causing obstruction of respiratory tract, W80	*3,368*	*3,183*	*3,208*
Confined to or trapped in a low-oxygen environment, W81	*3*	*9*	*4*
Other and unspecified threats to breathing, W83-W84	*557*	*517*	*589*

See source and footnotes on page 23.

Mortality by selected external causes, United States, 2011-2013

Type of accident or manner of injury	2013[a]	2012	2011
Exposure to electric current, radiation, temperature, and pressure, W85-W99	273	287	324
Electric transmission lines, W85	66	61	72
Other and unspecified electric current, W86-W87	191	218	236
Radiation, W88-W91	0	0	0
Excessive heat or cold of man-made origin, W92-W93	5	3	4
High and low air pressure and changes in air pressure, W94	11	5	12
Other and unspecified man-made environmental factors, W99	0	0	0
Exposure to smoke, fire, and flames, X00-X09	2,760	2,464	2,746
Uncontrolled fire in building or structure, X00	2,266	1,941	2,176
Uncontrolled fire not in building or structure, X01	42	33	40
Controlled fire in building or structure, X02	14	22	19
Controlled fire not in building or structure, X03	22	36	38
Ignition of highly flammable material, X04	40	51	42
Ignition or melting of nightwear, X05	0	3	4
Ignition or melting of other clothing and apparel, X06	80	89	83
Other and unspecified smoke fire and flames, X08-X09	296	289	344
Contact with heat and hot substances, X10-X19	58	59	67
Contact with hot tap-water, X11	24	21	27
Other and unspecified heat and hot substances, X10, X12-X19	34	38	40
Contact with venomous animals and plants, X20-X29	91	83	94
Contact with venomous snakes and lizards, X20	4	6	9
Contact with venomous spiders, X21	7	7	3
Contact with hornets, wasps and bees, X23	62	59	71
Contact with other and unspecified venomous animal or plant, X22, X24-X29	18	11	11
Exposure to forces of nature, X30-X39	1,285	1,207	1,944
Exposure to excessive natural heat, X30	372	474	587
Exposure to excessive natural cold, X31	725	494	672
Lightning, X33	23	29	24
Earthquake and other earth movements, X34-X36	34	36	22
Cataclysmic storm, X37	63	138	584
Flood, X38	42	5	25
Exposure to other and unspecified forces of nature, X32, X39	26	31	30
Accidental poisoning by and exposure to noxious substances, X40-X49	38,851	36,332	36,280
Nonopioid analgesics, antipyretics, and antirheumatics, X40	233	210	220
Antiepileptic, sedative-hypnotic, antiparkinsonism, and psychotropic drugs n.e.c., X41	2,909	2,292	2,080
Narcotics and psychodysleptics [hallucinogens] n.e.c., X42	15,241	13,932	13,214
Other and unspecified drugs, medicaments, and biologicals, X43-X44	17,280	16,741	17,557
Alcohol, X45	2,244	2,176	2,155
Gases and vapors, X46-X47	753	792	866
Other and unspecified chemicals and noxious substances, X48-X49	191	189	188
Overexertion, travel, and privation, X50-X57	34	39	35
Accidental exposure to other and unspecified factors and sequelae, X58-X59, Y86	6,581	7,110	7,018
Intentional self-harm, X60-X84, Y87.0, *U03	**41,149**	**40,600**	**39,518**
Intentional self-poisoning, X60-X69	6,637	6,729	6,564
Intentional self-harm by hanging, strangulation, and suffocation, X70	10,062	10,088	9,913
Intentional self-harm by firearm, X72-X74	21,175	20,666	19,990
Other and unspecified means and sequelae, X71, X75-X84, Y87.0	3,275	3,117	3,051
Terrorism, *U03	0	0	0
Assault, X85-Y09, Y87.1, *U01	**16,121**	**16,688**	**16,238**
Assault by firearm, X93-X95	11,207	11,622	11,068
Assault by sharp object, X99	1,639	1,776	1,797
Other and unspecified means and sequelae, X85-X92, X96-X98, Y00-Y09, Y87.1	3,272	3,290	3,373
Terrorism, *U01	3	0	0
Event of undetermined intent, Y10-Y34, Y87.2, Y89.9	**4,587**	**4,737**	**4,773**
Poisoning, Y10-Y19	2,960	2,986	3,098
Hanging, strangulation, and suffocation, Y20	120	127	151
Drowning and submersion, Y21	238	278	287
Firearm discharge, Y22-Y24	281	256	248
Exposure to smoke, fire, and flames, Y26	132	153	111
Falling, jumping, or pushed from a high place, Y30	45	67	62
Other and unspecified means and sequelae, Y25, Y27-Y29, Y31-Y34,Y87.2, Y89.9	811	870	816
Legal intervention, Y35, Y89.0	**516**	**550**	**492**
Legal intervention involving firearm discharge, Y35.0	467	471	454
Legal execution, Y35.5	36	43	31
Other and unspecified means and sequelae, Y35.1-Y35.4, Y35.6-Y35.7, Y89.0	13	36	7
Operations of war and sequelae, Y36, Y89.1	**15**	**18**	**5**
Complications of medical and surgical care and sequelae, Y40-Y84, Y88.0-Y88.3	**2,768**	**2,603**	**2,584**

Source: National Center for Health Statistics–Mortality Data for 2013, as compiled from data provided by the 57 vital statistics jurisdictions through the Vital Statistics Cooperative Program. Deaths are classified on the basis of the 10th revision of The International Classification of Diseases (ICD-10), which became effective in 1999.
Note: "n.e.c." means not elsewhere classified.
[a]Latest official figures.
[b]Numbers following titles refer to external cause of injury and poisoning classifications in ICD-10.

Death by Age, Sex, and Type

Unintentional-injury-related deaths by age, sex, and type, United States, 2013[a]

Age and sex	Total[b]	Poisoning	Motor vehicle	Falls	Choking[c]	Drowning[d]	Fire, flames, or smoke	Mechanical suffocation	Natural heat or cold	All types	
										Males	Females
Total	130,557	38,851	35,369	30,208	4,864	3,391	2,760	1,737	1,097	81,916	48,641
Younger than 5	2,472	35	493	43	133	416	145	1,007	35	1,490	982
5-14	1,521	30	852	18	27	209	135	54	6	950	571
15-24	11,619	3,293	6,692	205	47	501	137	69	35	8,545	3,074
25-44	31,563	16,625	10,567	827	224	791	354	223	152	22,591	8,972
45-64	37,414	17,039	10,030	3,649	940	916	922	261	390	25,249	12,165
65-74	10,967	1,238	3,066	3,586	742	283	412	57	144	7,014	3,953
75 or older	35,001	591	3,669	21,880	2,751	275	655	66	335	16,077	18,924
Males	81,916	25,080	25,048	15,205	2,615	2,613	1,653	1,109	765		
Females	48,641	13,771	10,321	15,003	2,249	778	1,107	628	332		

Source: National Safety Council analysis of National Center for Health Statistics–Mortality Data for 2013, as compiled from data provided by the 57 vital statistics jurisdictions through the Vital Statistics Cooperative Program.
[a]Latest official figures.
[b]Includes types not shown separately.
[c]Inhalation or ingestion of food or other object obstructing breathing.
[d]Excludes water transport drownings.

Of the 130,557 unintentional-injury-related deaths in 2013, males accounted for 63% of all deaths. Females had the greatest share of deaths only in the 75 and older age group (54% female). Other than for falls, which is roughly split evenly between women and men, males are disproportionably represented over females. The largest differences in the proportion of fatalities were drowning (77% male) and motor vehicle deaths (71% male). The smallest difference between the proportion of male and female fatalities was choking (54% male).

Unintentional-injury-related death rates by type and sex, United States, 2013[a]

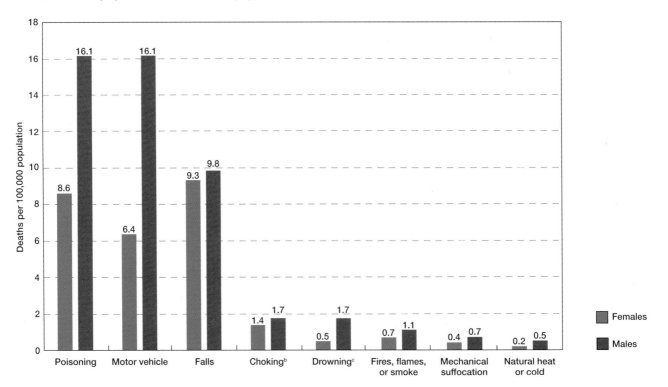

[a]Latest official figures.
[b]Inhalation or ingestion of food or other objects.
[c]Excludes water transport drownings.

Unintentional-injury-related deaths by month and type, United States, 2013[a]

Month	All types	Poisoning	Motor vehicle	Falls	Choking[b]	Drowning[c]	Fire, flames, or smoke	Mechanical suffocation	Natural heat or cold	Struck by or against	All other types
Total	130,557	38,851	35,369	30,208	4,864	3,391	2,760	1,737	1,097	811	11,469
January	11,305	3,396	2,642	2,823	522	155	345	159	179	58	1,026
February	10,035	3,231	2,296	2,490	412	133	298	133	125	55	862
March	10,909	3,419	2,791	2,596	437	180	257	149	87	62	931
April	10,386	3,188	2,719	2,428	386	197	259	155	34	72	948
May	10,797	3,239	2,988	2,437	375	334	193	148	33	71	979
June	11,071	3,174	3,181	2,369	348	572	171	133	93	66	964
July	11,305	3,153	3,119	2,462	369	637	151	157	174	74	1,009
August	11,316	3,188	3,378	2,451	419	417	161	152	48	73	1,029
September	10,701	3,076	3,184	2,450	336	309	164	127	44	64	947
October	10,831	3,109	3,173	2,603	405	184	210	122	34	71	920
November	10,888	3,272	3,076	2,495	417	153	248	163	82	71	911
December	11,013	3,406	2,822	2,604	438	120	303	139	164	74	943
Average	10,880	3,238	2,947	2,517	405	283	230	145	91	68	956

Source: National Safety Council analysis of National Center for Health Statistics–Mortality Data for 2013, as compiled from data provided by the 57 vital statistics jurisdictions through the Vital Statistics Cooperative Program.
[a]*Latest official figures.*
[b]*Inhalation or ingestion of food or other object obstructing breathing.*
[c]*Excludes water transport drownings.*

Unintentional-injury-related deaths by month and type, United States, 2013[a]

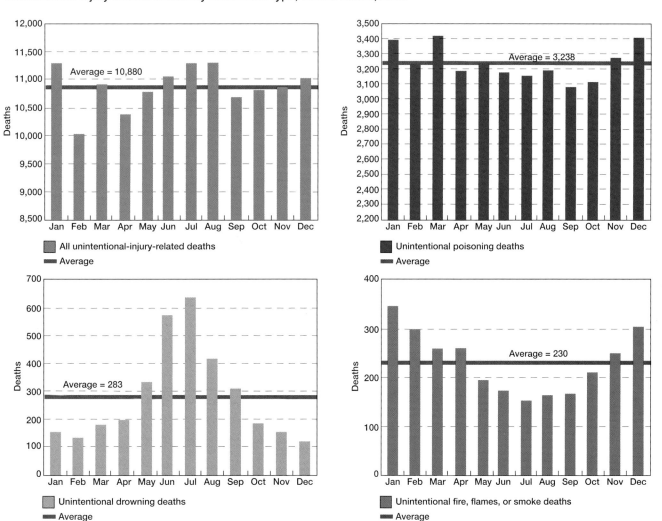

Cross-reference: See page 129 for motor vehicle deaths by month and page 165 for pedalcycle deaths by month.

The National Health Interview Survey, 2013

The National Health Interview Survey (NHIS), conducted by the National Center for Health Statistics, is a continuous, personal-interview sampling of households to obtain information about the health status of household members, including injuries experienced during the five weeks prior to the interview. Responsible family members residing in the household supplied the information used in the survey. In 2013, interviews were completed for 104,520 people living in 41,355 households throughout the United States. See page 27 for definitions.

Number of leading external causes of medically consulted injury and poisoning episodes by age, United States, 2013

	Population[a] (000)	External cause of injury and poisoning (number in thousands)						
		Falls	Struck by or against person or object	Transportation[b]	Overexertion	Cutting-piercing instructions	Other injury causes[b]	Poisoning[b]
All ages	310,929	14,951	5,344	3,810	4,508	2,073	9,195	583
Younger than 12	48,550	2,034	1,014	427[c]	225[c]	151[c]	943	[d]
12-17 years	24,894	965	966	158[c]	304[c]	106[c]	1,460	[d]
18-44 years	111,778	3,425	1,656	2,097	1,958	888	2,891	223[c]
45-64 years	82,299	3,869	1,148	891	1,531	611	2,636	142[c]
65-74 years	24,990	1,982	185[c]	[d]	238[c]	247[c]	823	[e]
75 or older	18,418	2,677	376[c]	[d]	252[c]	[d]	442[c]	[d]

[a]Civilian noninstitutionalized population.

[b]"Transportation" includes motor vehicle, bicycle, motorcycle, pedestrian, train, boat, or airplane. "Poisoning" does not include food poisoning or allergic reaction. "Other injury causes" includes fire/burn/scald-related, animal or insect bites, machinery, other (not specified), and unknown causes.

[c]Estimate does not meet standard of reliability or precision and should be used with caution.

[d]Estimate is not shown because it does not meet standard of reliability or precision.

[e]Quantity zero.

Leading external causes of injury and poisoning episodes by sex, United States, 2013

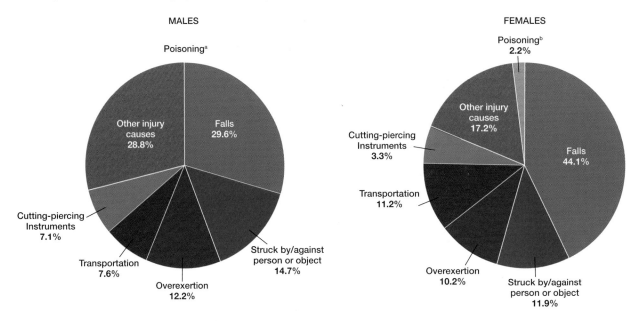

[a]The standard error of the poisoning estimate for males does not meet standard of reliability or precision.

[b]The standard error of the poisoning estimate for females does not meet standard of reliability or precision and should be used with caution.

Source: Adams, P.F., Martinez, M.E., & Benson, V. (2015). Tables of summary of health statistics for the U.S. population: 2013 National Health Interview Survey. Accessed October 23, 2015 at http://www.cdc.gov/nchs/nhis/SHS/tables.htm.

In 2013, an estimated 40.5 million medically consulted injury and poisoning episodes were recorded, of which 48.5% were among males and 51.5% among females. The overall injury rate was 129.39 episodes per 1,000 population, with males experiencing slightly higher rates (129.98 per 1,000 males) than females (128.09 per 1,000 females). Most injuries occurred in or around the home (51.5%), followed by injuries on streets, highways, sidewalks, and in parking lots and injuries at sport facilities, recreation areas, lakes, rivers, and pools (each with 11.5%). Nationwide, injuries in public areas such as schools, hospitals, streets, recreational facilities, industrial and trade areas, and public buildings together accounted for 42.0% of the total injuries.

Among the 19.6 million injuries reported for males, the single most common place of injury occurrence was at home,

with 27.2% occurring inside the home while injuries occurring outside contributed an additional 17.4%. About 58% of the injuries among females occurred at home. More than twice as many injuries to females occurred inside the home than outside, consistent with past findings. Streets, parking lots, sidewalks, and highways, along with sport facility, recreation area, lake, river, or pools, were the next most common locations for injuries among females, accounting for 12.5% and 8.0% of injuries, respectively. For males, sport facilities and recreational areas were the most common non-home places for injuries to occur (15.2%), followed by streets, parking lots, sidewalks, and highways (10.6%).

The 2013 NHIS injury definitions are listed below for comparability with prior years and other injury figures published in *Injury Facts*.

Number and percent of injury episodes by place of occurrence and sex, United States, 2013

Place of occurrence of injury episode	Both sexes No. of episodes (000)	Percent	Male No. of episodes (000)	Percent	Female No. of episodes (000)	Percent
Total episodes[a]	40,464	100.0	19,643	100.0	20,820	100.0
Home (inside)	13,509	33.4	5,347	27.2	8,162	39.2
Home (outside)	7,318	18.1	3,418	17.4	3,900	18.7
School, child care center, or preschool	3,347	8.3	1,862	9.5	1,485	7.1
Hospital or residential institution	855	2.1	193[b]	1.0[b]	662	3.2
Street, highway, sidewalk, or parking lot	4,671	11.5	2,078	10.6	2,593	12.5
Sport facility, recreation area, lake, river, or pool	4,646	11.5	2,988	15.2	1,658	8.0
Industrial, construction, or farm	1,374	3.4	1,167	5.9	207[b]	1.0[b]
Trade or service area	1,062	2.6	497	2.5	565[b]	2.7[b]
Other public building	1,038	2.6	526[b]	2.7[b]	512	2.5
Other (unspecified)	2,458	6.1	1,394	7.1	1,064	5.1

Source: Adams, P.F., Martinez, M.E., & Benson, V. (2015). Tables of summary of health statistics for the U.S. population: 2013 National Health Interview Survey. Accessed October 23, 2015 at www.cdc.gov/nchs/nhis/SHS/tables.htm.
[a]Numbers and percentages may not sum to respective totals due to rounding and unknowns.
[b]Estimate does not meet standard of reliability or precision and should be used with caution.

INJURY DEFINITIONS

National Health Interview Survey definitions. The 2013 National Health Interview Survey (NHIS) figures include medically consulted injury and poisoning episodes (e.g., call to a poison control center; use of an emergency vehicle or emergency room; visit to a doctor's office or other health clinic; or phone call to a doctor, nurse, or other health care professional) that reportedly occurred during the three months prior to the date of the interview and resulted in one or more conditions. Beginning in 2004, injury and poisoning estimates were calculated using only those episodes that occurred five weeks or less before the interview date. This reflects a change from 1997 to 2003, when NHIS data contained injury and poisoning episodes that were reported to occur within four months of the interview, and estimates were calculated using a three-month recall period. Also, an imputation procedure was performed for injury and poisoning episodes to assign a date of occurrence if it was not reported. Therefore, figures for 2004 and subsequent years are not comparable to estimates from prior years.

In the 2013 NHIS Injury and Poisoning file, an injury episode refers to the traumatic event in which the person was injured one or more times from an external

cause (e.g., a fall or a motor vehicle traffic incident). An injury condition is the acute condition or the physical harm caused by the traumatic event. Likewise, a poisoning episode refers to the event resulting from ingestion of or contact with harmful substances, as well as overdoses or wrong use of any drug or medication, while a poisoning condition is the acute condition or the physical harm caused by the event. Each episode must have at least one injury condition or poisoning classified according to the nature-of-injury codes 800-909.2, 909.4, 909.9, 910-994.9, 995.5-995.59, and 995.80-995.85 in the Ninth Revision of the International Classification of Diseases (ICD-9-CM). Poisoning episodes exclude food poisoning, sun poisoning, or poison ivy rashes.

National Safety Council definition of injury. A medically consulted injury is defined as one that is serious enough that a medical professional was consulted or is a recordable work injury based on OSHA definitions (see Glossary). All injury totals labeled "medically consulted" in *Injury Facts* are based on this definition.

The National Health Interview Survey, 2013 (cont.)

Of the 40.5 million medically consulted injuries in 2013, 34.1% were related to sports and leisure activities. Sports and leisure injuries accounted for 64.0% of all injury episodes among children younger than 12 and 67.5% of injury episodes among 12- to 17-year-olds.

The rate of injuries occurring during sports and leisure activities was substantially higher for males (51 cases per 1,000 males) than for females (40 cases per 1,000 females). The charts on this page illustrate these gender differences in terms of percentages and rates.

Number of injury episodes by age and activity at time of injury, United States, 2013

	Total Episodes[a] (000)	Activity at time of injury[b] (number in thousands)						
		Driving[c]	Working at paid job	Working around the house or yard	Attending school	Sports	Leisure activities	Other[d]
All ages	**40,464**	**2,358**	**4,215**	**6,774**	**1,315**	**6,131**	**7,652**	**12,039**
Younger than 12	4,881	(e)	0	(e)	610	993	2,133	1,119
12-17 years	4,039	(e)	(e)	149[f]	559	2,330	398[f]	630
18-44 years	13,137	1,495	2,356	1,532	(e)	1,987	2,234	3,515
45-64 years	10,828	624	1,696	2,883	0	528	1,716	3,277
65-74 years	3,562	(e)	(e)	1,006	0	293[f]	634	1,333
75 or older	4,018	(e)	(e)	1,165	0	0	536[f]	2,164

Percent and rates of injury episodes by sex and activity at time of injury, United States, 2013

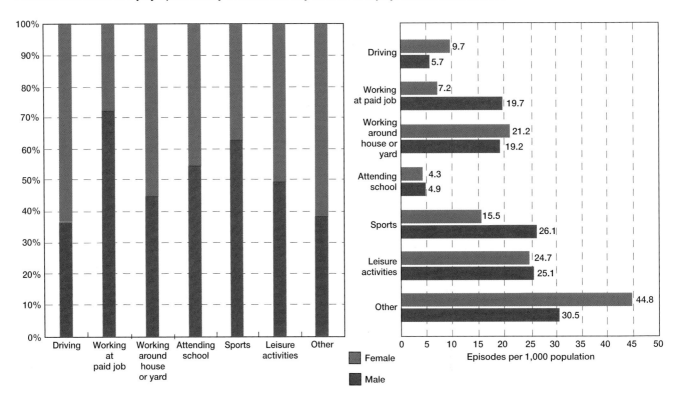

Source: Adams, P.F., Martinez, M.E., & Benson, V. (2015). Tables of summary of health statistics for the U.S. population: 2013 National Health Interview Survey. Accessed October 23, 2015 at http://www.cdc.gov/nchs/nhis/SHS/tables.htm.
[a]*Numbers may not sum to respective totals due to rounding and unknowns.*
[b]*Activity at time of injury and poisoning episodes is based on the question, "What was [person] doing when the injury/poisoning happened?" Respondents could indicate up to two activities.*
[c]*Driving includes both drivers and passengers.*
[d]*"Other" includes unpaid work such as housework, shopping, volunteer work, sleeping, resting, eating, drinking, cooking, hands-on care from another person, and other unspecified activities.*
[e]*Estimate is not shown because it does not meet standard of reliability or precision.*
[f]*Estimate does not meet standard of reliability or precision and should be used with caution.*

A body of evidence has accumulated pointing to socioeconomic factors such as income, wealth, and education as the fundamental causes of a wide range of health outcomes. In general, people with the highest levels of income and education are healthier than those with median income and education, who, in turn, tend to be in better health than the poor and least educated.[a]

Lower socioeconomic status is known to contribute to increased rates of fatal injuries. Although research provides some evidence of links between socioeconomic status and nonfatal injuries, studies based on morbidity data provide results somewhat less consistent than those of mortality studies. Nonetheless, numerous studies show considerable differences between socioeconomic groups even for nonfatal injuries.[b] The National Health Interview Survey provides an opportunity to look at the occurrence of unintentional injuries in the U.S. population as a function of socioeconomic position using two socioeconomic status measures – family income and education.[c]

Although NHIS data indicate that all people are affected by injuries, families whose poverty status was poor (below the poverty threshold) had substantially higher injury rates than families whose poverty status was near poor (100% to less than 200% of the poverty threshold) and not poor (200% of the poverty threshold and greater). Similarly, those with a bachelor's degree or higher had the lowest medically consulted injury rate in 2013 (114.77 injuries per 1,000 population). In contrast, those with some college had the highest injury rate (180.73 per 1,000 population). The finding that individuals with some college education have the highest rate of medically consulted injuries is consistent with past NHIS findings but does not seem to support the typical socioeconomic status pattern.

[a]Braveman, P. & Gottlieb, L. (2014). The social determinants of health: It's time to consider the causes of the causes. Public Health Reports, 2014 Supplement 2, Vol. 129, pp. 19-31.

[b]Laflamme, L., Burrows, S., & Hasselberg, M. (2009). Socioeconomic differences in injury risks—A review of findings and a discussion of potential countermeasures. Denmark: World Health Organization—Europe.

[c]Education data are shown for people 25 and older.

Percentages and rates of medically consulted injuries by poverty status, United States, 2013

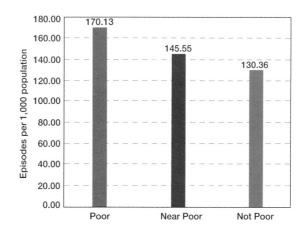

Percentages and rates of medically consulted injuries by level of education, United States, 2013

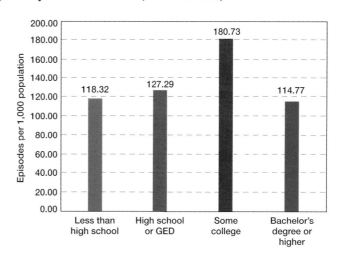

Source: Adams, P.F., Martinez, M.E., & Benson, V. (2015). Tables of summary of health statistics for the U.S. population: 2013 National Health Interview Survey. Accessed October 23, 2015 at http://www.cdc.gov/nchs/nhis/SHS/tables.htm.

Injury-Related Hospital Emergency Department Visits, 2011

■ *Over 40 million visits to hospital emergency departments in 2011 were due to injuries.*

About 29% of all hospital emergency department visits in the United States were injury-related, according to information from the 2011 National Hospital Ambulatory Medical Care Survey conducted for the National Center for Health Statistics. Approximately 136.3 million visits were made to emergency departments in 2011, of which about 40.2 million were injury-related. This resulted in an annual rate of about 44.5 emergency department visits per 100 people, of which about 13.1 visits per 100 people were injury-related.

Males had a higher overall rate of injury-related visits than females. For males, about 14.2 visits per 100 people were recorded; for females, the rate was 12.1 per 100 people. Males also had higher rates of injury-related visits than females for those younger than 15 through age 64, while females had higher rates for age groups beginning at age 65. Those ages 15-24 had the highest rate of injury-related visits for males, while those 75 and older had the highest rate for females.

Falls and motor vehicle incidents were the leading causes of injury-related emergency department visits, accounting for

26% and 10% of the total, respectively. In total, over 11.3 million visits to emergency departments were made in 2011 due to unintentional falls, and over 4.1 million were made due to motor vehicle incidents. The next leading types were struck against or struck accidentally by objects or people, with nearly 3.5 million visits (8% of the total), and incidents involving cutting or piercing instruments or objects, which accounted for about 2.4 million visits (over 5% of the total).

The upper extremities were the most frequent body site of injuries treated in hospital emergency departments, followed by injuries to the lower extremities and those to the head and neck. These three body sites accounted for about 42% of injury-related visits. Injury visits with multiple injury diagnoses accounted for another 2%. The most commonly mentioned specific body sites for injuries were wrist, hand, and fingers, followed by the vertebral column, lower leg and ankle, and foot and toes.

Number and percent distribution of emergency department visits by cause of injury, United States, 2011

Cause of injury and E-code[a]	No. of visits (000)	Percent
All visits related to injury, poisoning, and adverse effects	42,997	100.0
All injury visits	40,220	93.5
Unintentional injuries, E800-E848, E850-E869, E880-E929	31,013	72.1
Falls, E880.0-E886.9, E888	11,324	26.3
Total motor vehicle, E810-E819, E820-E825 (.0-.5, .7-.9)	4,142	9.6
Motor vehicle traffic, E810-E819	*3,828*	*8.9*
Motor vehicle, nontraffic, E820-E825(.0-.5, .7-.9)	*314*	*0.7*
Struck against or struck accidentally by objects or persons, E916-E917	3,482	8.1
Cutting or piercing instruments or objects, E920	2,369	5.5
Overexertion and strenuous movements, E927	2,210	5.1
Natural and environmental factors, E900-E909, E928.0-E928.2	2,091	4.9
Poisoning, E850-E869	946	2.2
Foreign body, E914-E915	780	1.8
Caught accidentally in or between objects, E918	405	0.9
Pedalcycle, nontraffic, and other, E800-E807(.3), E820-E825(.6), E826.1, E826.9	400	0.9
Fire and flames, hot substances or object, caustic or corrosive material, and steam, E890-E899, E924	393	0.9
Other transportation, E800-807(.0-.2, .8-.9), E826(.0, .2-.8), E827-E829, E831, E833-E845	(b)	(b)
Suffocation, E911-E913	(b)	(b)

Cause of injury and E-code[a]	No. of visits (000)	Percent
Machinery, E919	179	0.4
Other mechanism[c], E830, E832, E846-E848, E910, E921-E923, E925-E926, E928(.3-.5, .8), E929(.0-.5, .8)	2,046	4.8
Mechanism unspecified, E887, E928.9, E929.9	(b)	(b)
Intentional injuries, E950-E979, E990-E999	2,984	6.9
Assault, E960-E969, E979	2,061	4.8
Unarmed fight or brawl, striking by blunt or thrown object, E960.0, E968.2	*1,240*	*2.9*
Cutting or piercing instrument, E966	*127*	*0.3*
Other and unspecified mechanism[d], E960.1, E961-E964, E965, E967-E968.1, E968.3-E969, E979	*693*	*1.6*
Self-inflicted injury, E950-E959	836	1.9
Poisoning by solid or liquid substances, gases, and vapors, E950-E952	*509*	*1.2*
Other and unspecified mechanism[e], E953-E959	*327*	*0.8*
Other causes of violence, E970-E978, E990-E999	(b)	(b)
Injuries of undetermined intent, E980-E989	510	1.2
Adverse effects of medical treatment, E870-E879, E930-E949	1,888	4.4
Medical and surgical complications, E870-E879	1,157	2.7
Adverse drug effects, E930-E949	731	1.7
Alcohol and drug use[f]	134	0.3
Unknown[g]	6,468	15.0

Source: National Hospital Ambulatory Medical Care Survey: 2011 Emergency Department Summary Tables. Accessed December 2, 2014, at www.cdc.gov/nchs/data/ahcd/nhamcs_emergency/2011_ed_web_tables.pdf. Note: Sum of parts may not add to total due to rounding.
[a]*Based on "Supplementary Classification of External Causes of Injury and Poisoning" in the International Classification of Diseases, 9th Revision, Clinical Modification (ICD-9-CM).*
[b]*Figure did not meet standard of reliability or precision.*

[c]*Includes drowning, firearms, and other mechanism.*
[d]*Includes assault by firearms and explosives, and other mechanism.*
[e]*Includes injury by cutting and piercing instruments, suffocation, and other and unspecified mechanism.*
[f]*Alcohol and drug abuse are not contained in the "Supplementary Classification of External Causes of Injury and Poisoning," but are frequently recorded as a cause of injury or poisoning.*
[g]*Includes illegible entries and blanks.*

Injury-Related Hospital Emergency
Department Visits, 2011 (cont.)

Rate[a] of injury-related[b] visits to emergency departments by patient age and sex, 2011

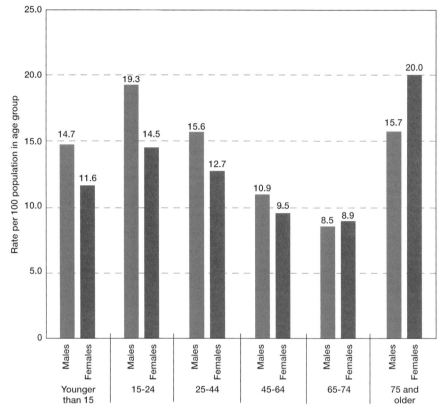

[a]Number of visits per 100 population in each age group.
[b]Injury-related includes injuries or poisoning; adverse effects and complications are excluded.

Percent of injury-related[a] emergency department visits by body site of primary diagnosis, United States, 2011

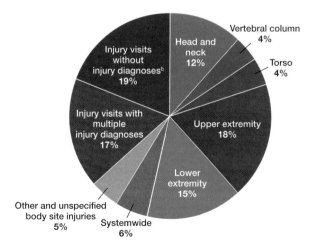

[a] Injury-related includes injuries or poisoning; adverse effects and complications are excluded.
[b]"Injury visits without injury diagnoses" includes musculoskeletal conditions; skin conditions; symptoms, signs,
and ill-defined conditions; mental disorders; observation and evaluation; all other diagnoses; and unknown diagnoses.

Leading Causes of Fatal Unintentional Injuries

Poisoning is the leading cause of fatal unintentional injuries in the United States, according to the latest data from the National Center for Health Statistics. A total of 38,851 poisoning fatalities occurred in 2013, accounting for about 30% of all unintentional-injury-related deaths. Poisoning fatalities were the leading cause of unintentional-injury-related deaths in age groups from 25-34 through 55-64. Suffocation was the leading cause of unintentional-injury-related deaths for people younger than 1, while drowning was the leading cause for those 1-4 years old. Motor vehicle traffic fatalities were the leading cause of death in the 5-9 through 15-24 age groups. The leading cause of death for people age 65 and older was falls. Taken together, poisoning, motor vehicle traffic, and falls accounted for more than three-quarters of all unintentional-injury-related deaths. In addition to these three causes, drowning was a leading cause of unintentional-injury-related deaths for most age groups.

Leading causes of fatal unintentional injuries by age group, United States, 2013

Rank	All ages	Younger than 1	1-4	5-9	10-14	15-24	25-34	35-44	45-54	55-64	65 or older
						Age group					
1	Poisoning 38,851	Suffocation 979	Drowning 393	Motor vehicle traffic 342	Motor vehicle traffic 414	Motor vehicle traffic 6,510	Poisoning 8,251	Poisoning 8,374	Poisoning 10,651	Poisoning 6,388	Falls 25,464
2	Motor vehicle traffic 33,804	Motor vehicle traffic 66	Motor vehicle traffic 327	Drowning 116	Drowning 93	Poisoning 3,293	Motor vehicle traffic 5,776	Motor vehicle traffic 4,448	Motor vehicle traffic 5,082	Motor vehicle traffic 4,502	Motor vehicle traffic 6,333
3	Falls 30,208	Drowning 23	Suffocation 161	Fire/burn 87	Other land transport 49	Drowning 501	Drowning 424	Falls 522	Falls 1,366	Falls 2,283	Unspecified 4,316
4	Suffocation 6,601	Natural/ environment 19	Fire/burn 129	Suffocation 44	Fire/burn 48	Falls 205	Falls 305	Drowning 367	Suffocation 478	Suffocation 723	Suffocation 3,616
5	Unspecified 5,407	Fire/burn 17	Pedestrian, other 90	Other land transport 29	Suffocation 37	Other land transport 179	Suffocation 184	Suffocation 263	Drowning 464	Fire/burn 564	Poisoning 1,824
6	Drowning 3,391	Falls 15	Natural/ environment 43	Natural/ environment 22	Firearms 24	Fire/burn 138	Other specified 179	Other specified 212	Fire/burn 373	Drowning 452	Fire/burn 1,103
7	Fire/burn 2,818	Unspecified 10	Struck by/ against 33	Pedetrian, other 18	Poisoning 21	Pedetrian, other 125	Fire/burn 159	Fire/burn 197	Unspecified 294	Unspecified 436	Other specified, n.e.c.[a] 635
8	Natural/ environment 1,535	Other specified 6	Poisoning 29	Firearms 15	Other transport 14	Suffocation 116	Other land transport 157	Other land transport 154	Other specified 292	Natural/ environment 307	Natural/ environment 601
9	Other specified 1,325	Poisoning 6	Falls 28	Other transport 15	Pedetrian, other 14	Firearms 107	Pedetrian, other 128	Unspecified 154	Other land transport 243	Other specified 283	Drowning 554
10	Other land transport 1,278	Struck by/ against 5	Firearms 27	Struck by/ against 13	Falls 11	Other transport 89	Other transport 113	Natural/ environment 143	Natural/ environment 242	Other specified, n.e.c.[a] 209	Other land transport 292

All causes of fatal unintentional injury

	All ages	Younger than 1	1-4	5-9	10-14	15-24	25-34	35-44	45-54	55-64	65 or older
Number	130,557	1,156	1,316	746	775	11,619	16,209	15,354	20,357	17,057	45,968[b]
Per 100,000 population	41.3	29.3	8.3	3.6	3.7	26.4	37.8	37.9	46.5	43.4	102.8[b]

Source: Centers for Disease Control and Prevention, National Center for Injury Prevention and Control. Web-based Injury Statistics Query and Reporting System (WISQARS), data accessed July 21, 2015, at www.cdc.gov/injury/wisqars/index.html.
[a]*"n.e.c." means not elsewhere classified.*
[b]*Includes 26 cases with age unknown.*

KEY

☐ Poisoning	☐ Falls	▨ Drowning	▨ Overexertion
☐ Motor vehicle traffic/occupant	▨ Suffocation	☐ Stuck by/ against	■ Cut/pierce

Falls are the leading cause of nonfatal unintentional injuries that are treated in hospital emergency departments, according to data from the All Injury Program, a cooperative program involving the National Center for Injury Prevention and Control, the Centers for Disease Control and Prevention, and the Consumer Product Safety Commission. More than 8.7 million people were treated in an emergency department for fall-related injuries in 2013. Falls were the leading cause of nonfatal injuries for all age groups except for the 10- to 14 and 15- to 24-year-old age groups, for which struck by or against an object or person was the leading cause. Struck by or against, overexertion, and motor vehicle crashes involving vehicle occupants also were leading causes for most age groups (please see color key at the bottom of the opposite page).

Leading causes of nonfatal unintentional injuries treated in hospital emergency departments by age group, United States, 2013[a]

Rank	All ages	Younger than 1	1-4	5-9	10-14	15-24	25-34	35-44	45-54	55-64	65 or older
										Age group	
1	Falls 8,771,656	Falls 134,229	Falls 852,884	Falls 624,890	Struck by/against 561,690	Struck by/against 905,659	Falls 742,177	Falls 704,264	Falls 913,871	Falls 930,521	Falls 2,495,397
2	Struck by/against 4,214,125	Struck by/against 28,786	Struck by/against 336,917	Struck by/against 403,522	Falls 558,177	Falls 814,829	Overexertion 638,745	Overexertion 530,422	Overexertion 461,114	Overexertion 266,126	Stuck by/against 281,279
3	Overexertion 3,256,567	Other bite/sting[b] 12,186	Other bite/sting[b] 158,587	Cut/pierce 112,633	Overexertion 294,669	Overexertion 672,946	Struck by/against 599,340	Struck by/against 444,089	Struck by/against 390,931	Struck by/against 261,840	Overexertion 212,293
4	Motor vehicle occupant 2,462,684	Foreign body 10,650	Foreign body 139,597	Other bite/sting[b] 107,975	Cut/pierce 114,285	Motor vehicle occupant 627,565	Motor vehicle occupant 526,303	Motor vehicle occupant 374,231	Other specified[c] 385,221	Motor vehicle occupant 227,620	Motor vehicle occupant 197,646
5	Cut/pierce 2,077,775	Other specified[c] 10,511	Cut/pierce 83,575	Overexertion 93,612	Pedalcyclist 84,732	Cut/pierce 431,691	Cut/pierce 402,197	Other specified[c] 300,154	Motor vehicle occupant 343,470	Other specified[c] 212,168	Cut/pierce 156,693
6	Other specified[c] 1,767,630	Fire/burn 9,816	Overexertion 81,588	Pedalcyclist 74,831	Unknown/unspecified 84,668	Other specified[c] 321,914	Other specified[c] 336,990	Cut/pierce 297,769	Cut/pierce 282,353	Cut/pierce 189,440	Poisoning 100,988
7	Other bite/sting[b] 1,174,267	Inhalation/suffocation 8,294	Other specified[c] 65,120	Foreign body 63,450	Motor vehicle occupant 73,692	Other bite/sting[b] 177,665	Other bite/sting[b] 180,922	Poisoning 175,870	Poisoning 237,328	Poisoning 153,767	Other bite/sting[b] 90,850
8	Poisoning 1,055,960	Cut/pierce 7,139	Fire/burn 52,884	Motor vehicle occupant 58,114	Other bite/sting[b] 64,848	Unknown/unspecified 163,923	Poisoning 180,448	Other bite/sting[b] 138,410	Other bite/sting[b] 143,349	Other bite/sting[b] 97,474	Other specified[c] 86,729
9	Unknown/unspecified 819,878	Unknown/unspecified 5,735	Unknown/unspecified 41,297	Dog bite 43,499	Other transport[d] 35,609	Poisoning 152,962	Unknown/unspecified 129,308	Unknown/unspecified 106,498	Unknown/unspecified 110,102	Unknown/unspecified 67,974	Unknown/unspecified 74,864
10	Foreign body 567,745	Overexertion 4,985	Poisoning 32,443	Unknown/unspecified 35,303	Dog bite 33,064	Pedalcyclist 96,744	Other transport[d] 75,861	Other transport[d] 59,765	Other transport[d] 60,811	Other transport[d] 45,746	Other transport[d] 68,022

All causes of unintentional injury

	All ages	Younger than 1	1-4	5-9	10-14	15-24	25-34	35-44	45-54	55-64	65 or older
Number	28,649,449	243,085	1,966,824	1,718,720	2,015,002	4,811,835	4,187,790	3,429,102	3,649,414	2,673,206	3,954,471[e]
Per 100,000 population	9,062.6	6,166.9	12,349.5	8,355.2	9,757.7	10,947.3	9,774.4	8,476.8	8,338.2	6,799.2	8,845.9[e]

Source: NEISS All Injury Program, Office of Statistics and Programming, National Center for Injury Prevention and Control, the Centers for Disease Control and Prevention, and Consumer Product Safety Commission.
[a]See color key on opposite page.
[b]Other than dog bite.
[c]Injury associated with any other specified cause that does not fit another category. Includes electric current, explosions, fireworks, radiation, animal scratch, etc. Excludes all causes listed in the table and bb/pellet gunshot, drowning and near drowning, firearm gunshot, suffocation, machinery, natural and environmental conditions, pedestrians, and motorcyclists.
[d]Includes occupant of any transport vehicle other than a motor vehicle or motorcycle (e.g., airplane, space vehicle, railcar, boat, all-terrain vehicle, animal and animal-drawn conveyances, battery-powered carts, ski lifts, and other cable cars not on rails).
[e]Includes 2,944 cases with age unknown.

Disasters are front-page news, even though the lives lost in the United States are relatively few when compared to the day-to-day life losses from unintentional injuries (see "While You Speak!" on page 5). Listed below are the U.S. disasters, of which the National Safety Council is aware, that occurred in 2014 and took five or more lives.

Disaster deaths, United States, 2014

Type and location	No. of deaths	Date of disaster
Major disasters (25 or more deaths)		
Debris flow/ mudslide, Washington	43	March 22
Other disasters (5-24 deaths)		
Tornado, Arkansas	16	April 27
Lake-effect snow, New York	13	November 17-19
Tornado, Mississippi	11	April 28
Motor vehicle traffic crash, California	10	April 10
Winter storm, Alabama	9	January 28
Mixed-occupancy building fire, New York	8	March
Passenger jet crash resulting in fire, Massachusetts	7	May
Motor vehicle traffic crash, New Mexico	7	May 22
Mixed-occupancy building fire, Massachusetts	7	July
Single-family home fire, Indiana	6	February
Motor vehicle traffic crash, California	6	February 9
Single-family home fire, New Jersey	6	June
Motor vehicle traffic crash, Montana	6	June 19
Motor vehicle traffic crash, Kentucky	6	June 26
Motor vehicle traffic crash, Utah	6	July 6
Single-family home fire, North Carolina	6	August
Motor vehicle traffic crash, Texas	6	August 10
Motor vehicle traffic crash, Texas	6	August 31
Single-family home fire, Pennsylvania	6	October
Rooming house fire, Maine	6	November
Single-family home fire, Oklahoma	5	January
Single-family home fire, Iowa	5	January
Motor vehicle traffic crash, Iowa	5	January 10
Two-family home fire, Minnesota	5	February
Motor vehicle traffic crash, California	5	February 15
Motor vehicle traffic crash, Florida	5	February 9
Motor vehicle traffic crash, Missouri	5	March 23
Motor vehicle traffic crash, Arizona	5	March 28

Type and location	No. of deaths	Date of disaster
Other disasters (5-24 deaths)		
Motor vehicle traffic crash, Arizona	5	March 29
Motor vehicle traffic crash, Pennsylvania	5	April 16
Motor vehicle traffic crash, Texas	5	April 19
Motor vehicle traffic crash, New York	5	May 10
Motor vehicle traffic crash, California	5	May 11
Motor vehicle traffic crash, California	5	May 21
Motor vehicle traffic crash, Louisiana	5	May 30
Motor vehicle traffic crash, Texas	5	June 29
Motor vehicle traffic crash, Georgia	5	June 30
Motor vehicle traffic crash, Illinois	5	July 21
Motor vehicle traffic crash, New York	5	August 23
Motor vehicle traffic crash, Pennsylvania	5	September 20
Motor vehicle traffic crash, California	5	October 3
Motor vehicle traffic crash, California	5	October 4
Motor vehicle traffic crash, Maryland	5	October 10
Single-family home fire, Louisiana	5	November
Single-family home fire, Texas	5	November
Motor vehicle traffic crash, Arkansas	5	November 4
Motor vehicle traffic crash, California	5	November 15
Motor vehicle traffic crash, Louisiana	5	November 19
Motor vehicle traffic crash, Iowa	5	November 22
Motor vehicle traffic crash, Oklahoma	5	Novemenber 22
Motor vehicle traffic crash, Texas	5	November 29
Apartment building fire, Texas	5	December
Single-family home fire, New Jersey	5	December
Apartment building fire, South Carolina	5	December
Car crash associated with heavy rain, West Virginia	5	December 6
Tornado, Mississippi	5	December 23
Motor vehicle traffic crash, California	5	December 26
Motor vehicle traffic crash, Indiana	5	December 26
Motor vehicle traffic crash, Missouri	5	December 27

Source: The National Climatic Data Center, National Fire Protection Association, and National Highway Traffic Safety Administration.
Note: Some death totals are estimates and may differ among sources.

Injuries may be divided into three broad groups – unintentional, intentional, and undetermined intent. Most of *Injury Facts* presents data on unintentional injuries. This page and the next two present data on intentional injuries.

Under the World Health Organization's Safe Communities initiative, for which the National Safety Council is the affiliate support center in the United States, injury prevention is not limited to unintentional injuries. Data on intentional inju-

ries are presented here to support Safe Communities and to provide context to the unintentional-injury data provided in *Injury Facts*.

Intentional injuries may be divided into four subgroups – intentional self-harm (suicide), assault (homicide), legal intervention, and operations of war. The diagram below illustrates the injury groupings and shows the death totals for 2013.

Injury deaths by intent, United States, 2013

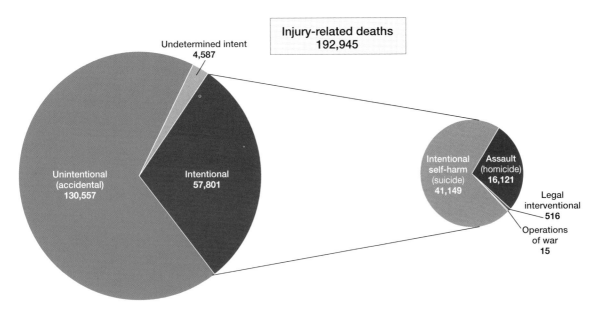

Intentional self-harm includes suicide and attempted suicide by purposely self-inflicted poisoning or injury. The most common methods of intentional self-harm that result in death are firearms; hanging, strangulation, and suffocation; and poisoning.

Assault includes homicide and injuries inflicted by another person with intent to injure or kill (excluding legal intervention and operations of war). The most common means of

homicide are firearms; sharp objects; and hanging, strangulation, and suffocation.

Legal intervention includes legal execution. Operations of war include injuries to military personnel and civilians caused by war and civil insurrection. The death must have occurred in the United States. In the vital statistics system, war deaths (and other deaths) occurring outside the United States are counted by the country in which they occurred.

Intentional Injuries by Age and Sex

The three most frequent causes of injury death are also among the top 20 causes of all deaths in the United States in 2013. Unintentional (accidental) injuries ranked 4th, intentional self-harm (suicide) ranked 10th, and assault (homicide) ranked 16th.

Intentional self-harm ranked as high as second (after unintentional injuries) for people ages 13-17, 19, and 21-35, and ranked third for those 12, 18, and 20. Suicide deaths were highest at age 52 (944) and ranked fifth at this age after cancer, heart disease, unintentional injuries, and chronic liver disease. Assault ranked as high as second (after unintentional injuries) for people 18 and 20 years old. It ranked third among people 1, 2, 16, 17, 19, and 21-30 years old. Homicide deaths were highest at age 22 (640). For people 16-30 years old, unintentional, homicide, and suicide are the three leading causes of death. The graph below shows the number of deaths due to injuries by single year of age from 0 to 100.

Injury deaths by age, United States, 2013

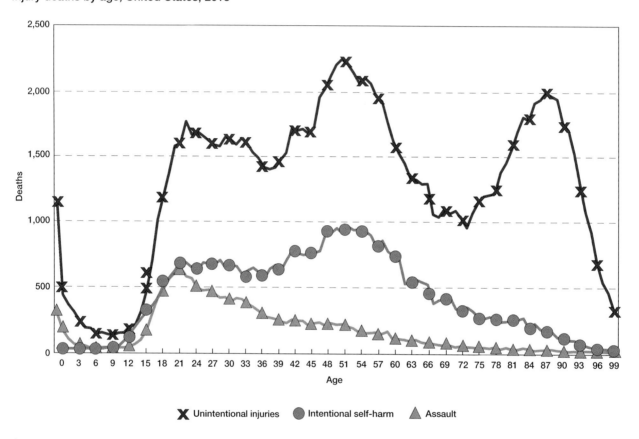

Source: National Safety Council analysis of National Center for Health Statistics–Mortality Data for 2013, as compiled from data provided by the 57 vital statistics jurisdictions through the Vital Statistics Cooperative Program.

Males have higher death rates than females for injuries of all intents. Males also have higher nonfatal injury rates than females for unintentional injuries and assault. Females, however, have a higher injury rate than males for intentional self-harm.

Death and nonfatal injury rates by intent and sex, United States, 2013

Sex	Deaths per 100,000 population			Nonfatal injuries per 100,000 population		
	Unintentional	Homicide	Suicide	Unintentional	Assault	Self-harm
Both sexes	41.3	5.1	13.0	9,063	520	156
Males	52.6	8.2	20.6	9,803	642	130
Females	30.3	2.1	5.7	8,344	402	182
Ratio of male to female	1.7	3.9	3.6	1.2	1.6	0.7

Source: National Safety Council analysis of National Center for Health Statistics (NCHS)–Mortality Data for 2013, as compiled from data provided by the 57 vital statistics jurisdictions through the Vital Statistics Cooperative Program. Rates are National Safety Council estimates based on data from NCHS and the U.S. Census Bureau.

The graph below shows the trends from 1992 to 2013 in injury deaths and death rates. Unintentional-injury-related deaths and death rates increased by 55.5% and 26.2%, respectively. Suicide deaths increased 35.0%, while the death rate increased 9.6%. Homicide deaths and death rates decreased 35.9% and 48.0%, respectively, over the 1992-2013 period. Age-adjusted death rates, which remove the effects of the changing age distribution of the population, increased 18.1% for unintentional injuries, increased 5.2% for suicide, and decreased 45.2% for homicide.

Injury deaths and death rates, United States, 1992-2013

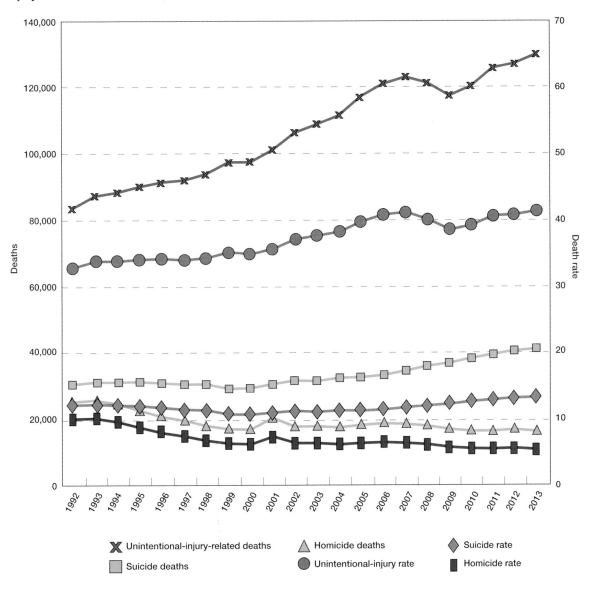

*Deaths per 100,000 population.

Source: National Safety Council analysis of National Center for Health Statistics (NCHS)—Mortality Data for 2013, as compiled from data provided by the 57 vital statistics jurisdictions through the Vital Statistics Cooperative Program. Rates are National Safety Council estimates based on data from NCHS and the U.S. Census Bureau.

Cross-reference: See page 168 for additional information on firearm related deaths.

■ *Motor vehicle crashes are the leading cause of injury-related deaths among children.*

Unintentional injuries are a major public health concern affecting children and adolescents in the United States. They are the underlying cause of death in over one-third of childhood mortality cases for people 1-19 years old, and about 38% of the deaths among 15- to 19-year-olds.

Fatal injuries in the first year of life numbered 1,160 in 2013, or approximately 29 deaths per 100,000 population. Mechanical suffocation constituted the majority (80%) of all injury-related mortality cases for infants. Motor vehicle crashes were the second leading cause of injury mortality. In addition, 282 infant deaths that year were attributed to homicide (for more information on intentional injuries, see pages 35-37).

In the second year of life, the risk of fatal injury is reduced by more than half. In 2013, 429 fatal injury cases, or about 11 deaths per 100,000 population, were recorded among 1-year-old children. Drowning was the leading cause of injury death in this age group, followed by motor vehicle crashes.

In the following three-year period (ages 2-4) the injury mortality rate dropped even lower, averaging about 7 deaths per 100,000 population in 2013. Drowning was the leading cause for 2-year-olds, followed by motor vehicle crashes and fire,

flames, or smoke. For 3- and 4-year-olds, motor vehicle crashes were the number one cause of injury mortality, followed by drowning and fires, flames, or smoke.

From the age of 5 to early adolescence (ages 12-14), the injury mortality rate shows a general U-shaped pattern, reaching its lowest level at around age 10. Motor vehicle crashes, unintentional drowning, and incidents related to fire, flames, or smoke were the leading causes of injury mortality for children 5-14 years old in 2013.

Teens (15-19 years) made up 27% of the U.S. population between the ages of 1 and 19 and 56% of all injury mortality cases in that age group. Most importantly, about 66% of teen injury deaths are attributed to motor vehicle crashes. Of the 3,652 injury deaths among teens in 2013, 2,408 occurred in crashes. The overall injury rate for this age group was 17.3 per 100,000 population and it varied from a low of 7.2 for 15-year-olds to a high of 27.2 for 19-year-olds.

For all children and adolescents younger than 19, the injury mortality rate by age can be described as a J-shaped relationship, peaking during infancy and again in the late teen years.

Unintentional injury deaths by event, ages 0-19, United States, 2013

Age	Population (000)	Total	Rates[a]	Motor vehicle	Drowning	Poisoning	Fire, flames, or smoke	Mechanical suffocation	Choking[b]	Firearms	Falls	All Other
<1 year	3,942	1,160	29.4	69	24	6	17	934	45	3	15	47
1-19 years	**78,306**	**6,489**	**8.3**	**3,685**	**843**	**646**	**316**	**157**	**132**	**121**	**108**	**481**
1 year	3,956	429	10.8	107	134	18	25	45	42	0	11	47
2 years	3,989	356	8.9	109	132	7	37	11	21	5	6	28
3 years	3,990	300	7.5	107	86	4	35	10	10	12	6	30
4 years	3,992	231	5.8	102	41	0	31	7	15	10	5	20
5 years	4,122	177	4.3	85	32	5	21	3	2	4	3	22
6 years	4,142	172	4.2	87	33	3	18	2	3	4	1	21
7 years	4,108	130	3.2	62	16	0	27	7	5	2	1	10
8 years	4,095	140	3.4	84	18	0	11	3	3	3	0	18
9 years	4,103	127	3.1	66	17	1	10	15	1	2	2	13
10 years	4,073	118	2.9	64	16	2	8	3	2	8	1	14
11 years	4,056	136	3.4	77	13	3	14	6	5	2	1	15
12 years	4,156	139	3.3	87	16	2	8	5	2	4	3	12
13 years	4,218	185	4.4	107	23	9	12	8	2	3	3	18
14 years	4,147	197	4.8	133	25	5	6	2	2	7	3	14
15 years	4,147	300	7.2	189	32	34	8	4	1	7	7	18
16 years	4,158	461	11.1	315	43	33	12	6	1	9	4	38
17 years	4,191	690	16.5	472	55	84	6	6	5	9	12	41
18 years	4,286	1,011	23.6	676	52	183	13	7	6	14	14	46
19 years	4,377	1,190	27.2	756	59	253	14	7	4	16	25	56
0-4 years	**19,869**	**2,476**	**12.5**	**494**	**417**	**35**	**145**	**1,007**	**133**	**30**	**43**	**172**
5-9 years	**20,570**	**746**	**3.6**	**384**	**116**	**9**	**87**	**30**	**14**	**15**	**7**	**84**
10-14 years	**20,650**	**775**	**3.8**	**468**	**93**	**21**	**48**	**24**	**13**	**24**	**11**	**73**
15-19 years	**21,159**	**3,652**	**17.3**	**2,408**	**241**	**587**	**53**	**30**	**17**	**55**	**62**	**199**

Source: National Safety Council analysis of National Center for Health Statistics (NCHS)–Mortality Data for 2013 as compiled from data provided by the 57 vital statistics jurisdictions through the Vital Statistics Cooperative Program. Rates are National Safety Council estimates based on data from NCHS and the U.S. Census Bureau.

Note: Data do not include "age unknown" cases, which totaled 22 in 2013.

[a]Deaths per 100,000 population in each age group.

[b]Suffocation by inhalation or ingestion of food or other object.

■ *Injury mortality and fall-related mortality rates increase with age.*

Unintentional injuries cause significant mortality among adults in the United States. In 2013 alone, injuries were responsible for nearly 122,900 deaths among Americans 20 and older.

The leading causes of injury mortality include poisoning, motor vehicle crashes, falls, choking, drowning, and fire, flames and smoke. Poisoning (31%), motor vehicle crashes (26%), and falls (24%), the three leading causes of injury mortality, combined to account for over four-fifths of all fatal unintentional injuries sustained by adults older than 20 in 2013.

Age plays an important role in the occurrence of injuries. Motor vehicle crashes are the leading cause of injury mortality through the early to mid-20s. Starting with the mid-20s, incidences of poisoning become the leading cause of death, with prevalence peaking in the early 50s. Beginning in the late 60s, motor vehicle crashes once again take over as the leading cause of injury mortality until superseded by falls beginning in the early 70s.

The increase in the incidence of fatal falls appears to be the driving force behind a surge in the overall injury mortality rate in later life. The highest fall mortality rates occur among adults beginning at age 70 and older. As the table below illustrates, the number of injury-related deaths per 100,000 population in 2013 increased from 49 for 70- to 74-year-olds to 425 for 90- to 94-year-olds – a nearly nine-fold increase.

A 2015 report from the National Trauma Data Bank (NTDB) summarized data from 860,694 records of fatal and nonfatal incidents with valid trauma diagnoses submitted to the NTDB from over 746 hospitals in 2014.[a] By selected mechanism of injury, falls were the only injury type that showed consistent increases in the number of incidents from younger to older adults, increasing over 850% from young adults age 20-24 to those older than 84. The motor vehicle traffic; struck by or against; transport, other; firearm; and cut/pierce categories all increased in incidence from the 20-24 to the 25-34 age group, but then generally declined with age, with the average decline in the number of incidents averaging 92% from the 20-24 age group to the older than 84 age group. Case fatality rates generally increased with age for all of the selected mechanisms of injury, with the greatest increases from the youngest to oldest adults observed for the struck by or against, fall, and cut/pierce categories.

[a]National Trauma Data Bank 2015 – Annual Report, accessed 9/24/15 at https://www.facs.org/quality-programs/trauma/ntdb/docpub.

Unintentional-injury-related deaths by event, age 20 or older, United States, 2013

| Age | Population (000) | Unintentional injury deaths | | | | | | | | | | | |
		Total	Rates[a]	Poisoning	Motor vehicle	Falls	Choking[b]	Drowning	Fire, flames, or smoke	Natural heat or cold	Mechanical suffocation	Firearms	All other
20-24	22,795	7,967	35.0	2,706	4,284	143	30	260	84	23	39	52	346
25-29	21,580	8,120	37.6	3,852	3,279	141	32	232	78	23	50	44	389
30-34	21,264	8,089	38.0	4,399	2,676	164	45	192	80	33	57	38	405
35-39	19,604	7,240	36.9	3,933	2,248	194	57	189	93	43	65	24	394
40-44	20,849	8,114	38.9	4,441	2,364	328	90	178	103	53	51	24	482
45-49	21,208	9,482	44.7	5,117	2,590	555	126	179	160	70	60	35	590
50-54	22,559	10,875	48.2	5,534	2,744	811	214	285	206	106	78	45	852
55-59	21,194	9,813	46.3	4,210	2,640	1,023	274	250	279	113	67	32	925
60-64	18,122	7,244	40.0	2,178	2,056	1,260	326	202	277	101	56	27	761
65-69	14,609	5,769	39.5	881	1,717	1,577	368	157	209	76	29	18	737
70-74	10,608	5,198	49.0	357	1,349	2,009	374	126	203	68	28	17	667
75-79	7,678	6,148	80.1	221	1,239	3,044	479	99	220	79	15	4	748
80-84	5,769	8,290	143.7	157	1,156	4,942	667	76	216	83	11	14	968
85-89	3,804	9,747	256.2	141	860	6,395	752	63	127	83	23	3	1,300
90-94	1,726	7,341	425.3	58	348	5,149	536	28	58	64	12	4	1,084
95-99	443	2,911	657.1	8	56	2,007	256	5	29	16	4	0	530
100 and older	67	538	803.0	1	6	341	61	0	2	4	1	0	122
20 and older	233,879	122,886	52.5	38,194	31,612	30,083	4,687	2,521	2,424	1,038	646	381	11,300
25 and older	211,084	114,919	54.4	35,488	27,328	29,940	4,657	2,261	2,340	1,015	607	329	10,954
35 and older	168,240	98,710	58.7	27,237	21,373	29,635	4,580	1,837	2,182	959	500	247	10,160
45 and older	127,787	83,356	65.2	18,863	16,761	29,113	4,433	1,470	1,986	863	384	199	9,284
55 and older	84,020	62,999	75.0	8,212	11,427	27,747	4,093	1,006	1,620	687	246	119	7,842
65 and older	44,704	45,942	102.8	1,824	6,731	25,464	3,493	554	1,064	473	123	60	6,156
75 and older	19,487	34,975	179.5	586	3,665	21,878	2,751	271	652	329	66	25	4,752

Source: National Safety Council analysis of National Center for Health Statistics—Mortality Data for 2013, as compiled from data provided by the 57 vital statistics jurisdictions through the Vital Statistics Cooperative Program. Rates are National Safety Council estimates based on data from NCHS and the U.S. Census Bureau.
Note: Data do not include "age unknown" cases, which totaled 22 in 2013.
[a]Deaths per 100,000 population in each age group.
[b]Suffocation by inhalation or ingestion of food or other object.

The table on the following pages was prepared in response to frequent inquiries asking questions such as, "What are the odds of being killed by lightning?" or "What are the chances of dying in a plane crash?"

The odds given in the table are statistical averages over the whole U.S. population and do not necessarily reflect the chances of death for a particular person from a particular external cause. Any individual's odds of dying from various external causes are affected by the activities in which they participate, where they live and drive, what kind of work they do, among other factors.

The table has four columns. The first column gives the manner of injury such as motor-vehicle crash, fall, fire, etc. The second column gives the total number of deaths nationwide due to the manner of injury in 2013 (the latest year for which data are available). The third column gives the odds of dying in one year due to the manner of injury. The fourth column gives the lifetime odds of dying from the manner of injury. Statements about the odds or chances of dying from a given cause of death may be made as follows:

- The odds of dying from (manner of injury) in 2013 were 1 in (value given in the one-year odds column).
- The life-time odds of dying from (manner of injury) for a person born in 2013 were 1 in (value given in the lifetime odds column).

For example, referring to the first line of the table:
- The odds of dying from an injury in 2013 were 1 in 1,615.
- The lifetime odds of dying from an injury for a person born in 2013 were 1 in 20.

The one year odds are approximated by dividing the 2013 population (316,159,818) by the number of deaths. The lifetime odds are approximated by dividing the one-year odds by the life expectancy of a person born in 2013 (78.8 years). Please note that odds based on less than 20 deaths are likely to be unstable from year to year and are therefore not included in the table and figure on the following pages.

The figure on page 43 visually represents the lifetime odds of death for selected causes from the odds table. The total lifetime odds of death from any cause are 1 in 1, or 100%, and thus the largest shaded area representing the total odds actually extends off the page in all directions to infinity. The circles for selected causes are sized according to their relative lifetime probabilities, with the least probable event – death from a lightning strike – depicted using the smallest box.

Source: National Safety Council estimates based on data from National Center for Health Statistics—Mortality Data for 2013, as compiled from data provided by the 57 vital statistics jurisdictions through the Vital Statistics Cooperative Program. Population and life expectancy data are from the U.S. Census Bureau. Deaths are classified on the basis of the Tenth Revision of the World Health Organization's "The International Classification of Diseases" (ICD). Numbers following titles refer to External Cause of Morbidity and Mortality classifications in ICD-10.

Odds of death due to injury, United States, 2013[a]

Type of accident or manner of injury	Deaths	One-year odds	Lifetime odds
All external causes of mortality, V01-Y89, *U01, *U03[b]	**195,713**	**1,615**	**20**
Deaths due to unintentional (accidental) injuries, V01-X59, Y85-Y86	**130,557**	**2,421**	**31**
Transport accidents, V01-V99, Y85	**37,938**	**8,333**	**106**
Motor vehicle accidents, V02-V04, V09.0, V09.2, V12-V14, V19.0-V19.2, V19.4-V19.6, V20-V79, V80.3-V80.5, V81.0-V81.1, V82.0-V82.1, V83-V86, V87.0-V87.8, V88.0-V88.8, V89.0, V89.2	**35,369**	**8,938**	**113**
Pedestrian, V01-V09	5,974	52,917	672
Pedalcyclist, V10-V19	925	341,761	4,337
Motorcycle rider, V20-V29	4,230	74,735	948
Occupant of three-wheeled motor vehicle, V30-V39	7	(c)	(c)
Car occupant, V40-V49	6,625	47,718	606
Occupant of pick-up truck or van, V50-V59	1,474	214,470	2,722
Occupant of heavy transport vehicle, V60-V69	273	1,157,981	14,695
Bus occupant, V70-V79	29	10,900,994	138,337
Animal rider or occupant of animal-drawn vehicle, V80	91	3,473,943	44,086
Occupant of railway train or railway vehicle, V81	24	13,172,035	167,158
Occupant of streetcar, V82	1	(c)	(c)
Other and unspecified land transport accidents, V83-V89	16,716	18,912	240
Occupant of special industrial vehicle, V83	*10*	*(c)*	*(c)*
Occupant of special agricultural vehicle, V84	*81*	*3,902,825*	*49,528*
Occupant of special construction vehicle, V85	*22*	*14,369,493*	*182,354*
Occupant of all-terrain or other off-road motor vehicle, V86	*934*	*338,468*	*4,295*
Other and unspecified person, V87-V89	*15,669*	*20,175*	*256*
Water transport accidents, V90-V94	403	784,439	9,955
Drowning, V90, V92	*310*	*1,019,770*	*12,941*
Other and unspecified injuries, V91, V93-V94	*93*	*3,399,235*	*43,137*
Air and space transport accidents, V95-V97	412	767,303	9,737
Other and unspecified transport accidents and sequelae, V98-V99, Y85	754	419,269	5,321
Other specified transport accidents, V98	*0*	*(c)*	*(c)*
Unspecified transport accidents, V99	*0*	*(c)*	*(c)*
Nontransport unintentional (accidental) injuries, W00-X59, Y86	**92,619**	**3,413**	**43**
Falls, W00-W19	30,208	10,465	133
Fall on same level from slipping, tripping, and stumbling, W01	*710*	*445,252*	*5,650*
Other fall on same level, W00, W02-W03, W18	*9,631*	*32,824*	*417*
Fall involving bed, chair, or other furniture, W06-W08	*1,170*	*270,196*	*3,429*
Fall on and from stairs and steps, W10	*2,233*	*141,571*	*1,797*
Fall on and from ladder or scaffolding, W11-W12	*420*	*752,688*	*9,552*
Fall from out of or through building or structure, W13	*504*	*627,240*	*7,960*
Other fall from one level to another, W09, W14-W17	*605*	*522,527*	*6,631*
Other and unspecified fall, W04-W05, W19	*14,935*	*21,167*	*269*
Exposure to inanimate mechanical forces, W20-W49	2,353	134,351	1,705
Struck by or striking against object, W20-W22	*811*	*389,801*	*4,947*
Caught between objects, W23	*88*	*3,592,373*	*45,588*
Contact with machinery, W24, W30-W31	*588*	*537,634*	*6,823*
Contact with sharp objects, W25-W29	*130*	*2,431,760*	*30,860*
Firearms discharge, W32-W34	*505*	*625,998*	*7,944*
Explosion and rupture of pressurized devices, W35-W38	*11*	*(c)*	*(c)*
Fireworks discharge, W39	*6*	*(c)*	*(c)*
Explosion of other materials, W40	*128*	*2,469,757*	*31,342*
Foreign body entering through skin or natural orifice, W44-W45	*37*	*8,544,023*	*108,427*
Other and unspecified inanimate mechanical forces, W41-W43, W49	*49*	*6,451,609*	*81,873*
Exposure to animate mechanical forces, W50-W64	133	2,376,909	30,164
Struck by or against another person, W50-W52	*12*	*(c)*	*(c)*
Bitten or struck by dog, W54	*35*	*9,032,253*	*114,622*
Bitten or struck by other mammals, W53, W55	*59*	*5,358,116*	*67,996*
Bitten or stung by nonvenomous insect and other arthropods, W57	*13*	*(c)*	*(c)*
Bitten or crushed by other reptiles, W59	*0*	*(c)*	*(c)*
Other and unspecified animate mechanical forces, W56, W58, W60, W64	*14*	*(c)*	*(c)*
Accidental drowning and submersion, W65-W74	3,391	93,226	1,183
Drowning and submersion while in or falling into bath-tub, W65-W66	*464*	*681,312*	*8,646*
Drowning and submersion while in or falling into swimming-pool, W67-W68	*651*	*485,605*	*6,162*
Drowning and submersion while in or falling into natural water, W69-W70	*1,810*	*174,657*	*2,216*
Other and unspecified drowning and submersion, W73-W74	*466*	*678,388*	*8,609*
Other accidental threats to breathing, W75-W84	6,601	47,891	608
Accidental suffocation and strangulation in bed, W75	*903*	*350,087*	*4,443*
Other accidental hanging and strangulation, W76	*247*	*1,279,874*	*16,242*
Threat to breathing due to cave-in, falling earth and other substances, W77	*27*	*11,708,476*	*148,585*
Inhalation of gastric contents, W78	*319*	*990,999*	*12,576*
Inhalation and ingestion of food causing obstruction of respiratory tract, W79	*1,177*	*268,589*	*3,408*
Inhalation and ingestion of other objects causing obstruction of respiratory tract, W80	*3,368*	*93,862*	*1,191*
Confined to or trapped in a low-oxygen environment, W81	*3*	*(c)*	*(c)*
Other and unspecified threats to breathing, W83-W84	*557*	*567,556*	*7,202*

See source and footnotes on page 42.

Odds of death due to injury, United States, 2013[a] (cont.)

Type of accident or manner of injury	Deaths	One-year odds	Lifetime odds
Exposure to electric current, radiation, temperature, and pressure, W85-W99	273	1,157,981	14,695
Electric transmission lines, W85	66	4,789,831	60,785
Other and unspecified electric current, W86-W87	191	1,655,125	21,004
Radiation, W88-W91	0	0	0
Excessive heat or cold of man-made origin, W92-W93	5	(c)	(c)
High and low air pressure and changes in air pressure, W94	11	(c)	(c)
Other and unspecified man-made environmental factors, W99	0	0	0
Exposure to smoke, fire, and flames, X00-X09	2,760	114,539	1,454
Uncontrolled fire in building or structure, X00	2,266	139,510	1,770
Uncontrolled fire not in building or structure, X01	42	7,526,877	95,519
Controlled fire in building or structure, X02	14	(c)	(c)
Controlled fire not in building or structure, X03	22	14,369,493	182,354
Ignition of highly flammable material, X04	40	7,903,221	100,295
Ignition or melting of nightwear, X05	0	(c)	(c)
Ignition or melting of other clothing and apparel, X06	80	3,951,610	50,147
Other and unspecified smoke fire and flames, X08-X09	296	1,068,003	13,553
Contact with heat and hot substances, X10-X19	58	5,450,497	69,169
Contact with hot tap-water, X11	24	13,172,035	167,158
Other and unspecified heat and hot substances, X10, X12-X19	34	9,297,907	117,994
Contact with venomous animals and plants, X20-X29	91	3,473,943	44,086
Contact with venomous snakes and lizards, X20	4	(c)	(c)
Contact with venomous spiders, X21	7	(c)	(c)
Contact with hornets, wasps and bees, X23	62	5,098,852	64,706
Contact with other and unspecified venomous animal or plant, X22, X24-X29	18	(c)	(c)
Exposure to forces of nature, X30-X39	1,285	246,015	3,122
Exposure to excessive natural heat, X30	372	849,809	10,784
Exposure to excessive natural cold, X31	725	436,040	5,533
Lightning, X33	23	13,744,732	174,426
Earthquake and other earth movements, X34-X36	34	9,297,907	117,994
Cataclysmic storm, X37	63	5,017,918	63,679
Flood, X38	42	7,526,877	95,519
Exposure to other and unspecified forces of nature, X32, X39	26	12,158,802	154,300
Accidental poisoning by and exposure to noxious substances, X40-X49	38,851	8,137	103
Nonopioid analgesics, antipyretics, and antirheumatics, X40	233	1,356,776	17,218
Antiepileptic, sedative-hypnotic, antiparkinsonism, and psychotropic drugs n.e.c., X41	2,909	108,673	1,379
Narcotics and psychodysleptics [hallucinogens] n.e.c., X42	15,241	20,742	263
Other and unspecified drugs, medicaments, and biologicals, X43-X44	17,280	18,294	232
Alcohol, X45	2,244	140,877	1,788
Gases and vapors, X46-X47	753	419,826	5,328
Other and unspecified chemicals and noxious substances, X48-X49	191	1,655,125	21,004
Overexertion, travel, and privation, X50-X57	34	9,297,907	117,994
Accidental exposure to other and unspecified factors and sequelae, X58-X59, Y86	6,581	48,037	610
Intentional self-harm, X60-X84, Y87.0, *U03	**41,149**	**7,683**	**97**
Intentional self-poisoning, X60-X69	6,637	47,631	604
Intentional self-harm by hanging, strangulation, and suffocation, X70	10,062	31,418	399
Intentional self-harm by firearm, X72-X74	21,175	14,929	189
Other and unspecified means and sequelae, X71, X75-X84, Y87.0	3,275	96,528	1,225
Terrorism, *U03	0	(c)	(c)
Assault, X85-Y09, Y87.1, *U01	**16,121**	**19,610**	**249**
Assault by firearm, X93-X95	11,207	28,208	358
Assault by sharp object, X99	1,639	192,879	2,448
Other and unspecified means and sequelae, X85-X92, X96-X98, Y00-Y09, Y87.1	3,272	96,616	1,226
Terrorism, *U01	3	(c)	(c)
Event of undetermined intent, Y10-Y34, Y87.2, Y89.9	**4,587**	**68,918**	**875**
Poisoning, Y10-Y19	2,960	106,800	1,355
Hanging, strangulation, and suffocation, Y20	120	2,634,407	33,432
Drowning and submersion, Y21	238	1,328,272	16,856
Firearm discharge, Y22-Y24	281	1,125,014	14,277
Exposure to smoke, fire, and flames, Y26	132	2,394,915	30,392
Falling, jumping, or pushed from a high place, Y30	45	7,025,085	89,151
Other and unspecified means and sequelae, Y25, Y27-Y29, Y31-Y34, Y87.2, Y89.9	811	389,801	4,947
Legal intervention, Y35, Y89.0	**516**	**612,653**	**7,775**
Legal intervention involving firearm discharge, Y35.0	467	676,935	8,591
Legal execution, Y35.5	36	8,781,357	111,439
Other and unspecified means and sequelae, Y35.1-Y35.4, Y35.6-Y35.7, Y89.0	13	(c)	(c)
Operations of war and sequelae, Y36, Y89.1	**15**	**(c)**	**(c)**
Complications of medical and surgical care and sequelae, Y40-Y84, Y88.0-Y88.3	**2,768**	**114,208**	**1,449**

Source: National Center for Health Statistics–Mortality Data for 2013, as compiled from data provided by the 57 vital statistics jurisdictions through the Vital Statistics Cooperative Program. Deaths are classified on the basis of the Tenth Revision of The International Classification of Diseases (ICD-10), which became effective in 1999.

Note: "n.e.c." means not elsewhere classified.

[a] *Latest official figures.*

[b] *Numbers following titles refer to external cause of injury and poisoning classifications in ICD-10.*

[c] *Rates based on less than 20 deaths are likely to be unstable from year to year and therefore are not included.*

The Odds of Dying From... (cont.)

Lifetime odds of death for selected causes, United States, 2013[a]

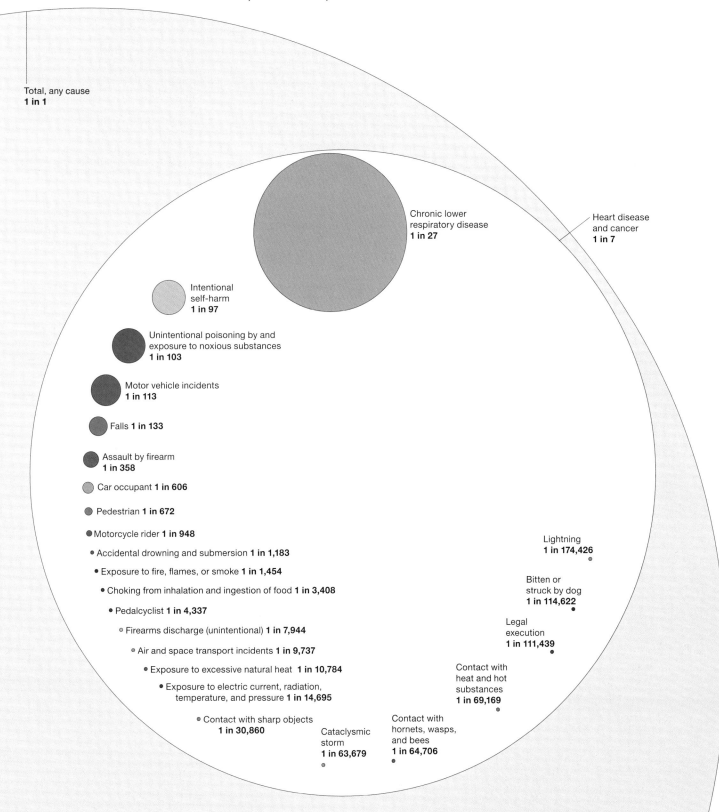

Total, any cause
1 in 1

Chronic lower
respiratory disease
1 in 27

Heart disease
and cancer
1 in 7

Intentional
self-harm
1 in 97

Unintentional poisoning by and
exposure to noxious substances
1 in 103

Motor vehicle incidents
1 in 113

Falls **1 in 133**

Assault by firearm
1 in 358

Car occupant **1 in 606**

Pedestrian **1 in 672**

Motorcycle rider **1 in 948**

Accidental drowning and submersion **1 in 1,183**

Exposure to fire, flames, or smoke **1 in 1,454**

Choking from inhalation and ingestion of food **1 in 3,408**

Pedalcyclist **1 in 4,337**

Firearms discharge (unintentional) **1 in 7,944**

Air and space transport incidents **1 in 9,737**

Exposure to excessive natural heat **1 in 10,784**

Exposure to electric current, radiation,
temperature, and pressure **1 in 14,695**

Contact with sharp objects
1 in 30,860

Cataclysmic
storm
1 in 63,679

Contact with
hornets, wasps,
and bees
1 in 64,706

Lightning
1 in 174,426

Bitten or
struck by dog
1 in 114,622

Legal
execution
1 in 111,439

Contact with
heat and hot
substances
1 in 69,169

Trends in Unintentional-Injury-Related Death Rates

Age-adjusted rates, which eliminate the effect of shifts in the age distribution of the population, decreased 56% from 1912 to 2014 – from 100.4 to 40.4 deaths per 100,000 population. The adjusted rates, which are shown in the graphs on the opposite page, are standardized to the year 2000 standard U.S. population. The break in the lines at 1948 shows the estimated effect of changes in the International Classification of Diseases (ICD). The break in the lines at 1992 resulted from the adoption of the Bureau of Labor Statistics Census of Fatal Occupational Injuries for work-related deaths. Another change in the ICD in 1999 also affects the trends. See the Technical Appendix for comparability.

The table below shows the change in the age distribution of the population since 1910.

The age-adjusted death rate for all unintentional injuries increased and decreased significantly several times during the period from 1910 to 1940 (top of facing page). Since 1940, there were some setbacks, such as in the early 1960s, but the overall trend through the early 1990s was positive. However, since 1992 the overall age-adjusted death rate has demonstrated an increasing trend. The age-adjusted death rates for unintentional-injury-related deaths in the work and home classes declined fairly steadily since they became available in the late 1920s, and the home class rates have increased since the early 1990s. The rates in the public class declined for three decades, rose in the 1960s, and then continued declining until leveling out in the 1990s to present. The age-adjusted motor-vehicle death rate rose steadily from 1910 to the late 1930s as the automobile became more widely used. A sharp drop in use occurred during World War II and a sharp rise in rates occurred in the 1960s, with death rates reflecting economic cycles and a long-term downward trend since then.

United States population, selected years

Year	All ages	Younger than 15	15-24	25-44	45-64	65 or older
Number (in thousands)						
1910	91,973[a]	29,499	18,121	26,810	13,424	3,950
2000[b]	274,634	58,964	38,077	81,892	60,991	34,710
2014	318,857	61,068	43,980	84,030	83,536	46,243
Percent						
1910	100.0%	32.1%	19.7%	29.2%	14.6%	4.3%
2000[b]	100.0%	21.5%	13.9%	29.8%	22.2%	12.6%
2014	100.0%	19.2%	13.8%	26.4%	26.2%	14.5%

Looking at individual leading causes (bottom chart on next page), at the turn of the last century falls were the leading cause of unintentional-injury-related death, while motor vehicle and poisoning deaths were only minor concerns. Today, although falls continue to be a major concern, poisonings and motor vehicle incidents have become the two leading causes of unintentional-injury-related deaths.

Source: For 1910: U.S. Census Bureau. (1960). Historical Statistics of the United States, Colonial Times to 1957. Series A 71-85. Washington, DC: U.S. Government Printing Office. For 2000: Anderson, R.N., & Rosenberg, H.M. (1998). Age standardization of death rates: Implementation of the year 2000 standard. National Vital Statistics Reports, Issue 47, No. 3 p. 13. For 2013: U.S. Census Bureau.
[a] Includes 169,000 people with age unknown.
[b] This is the population used for standardization (age adjustment) and differs slightly from the actual 2000 population, which totaled 275,306,000.

Trends in Unintentional-Injury-Related Death Rates
(cont.)

Age-adjusted death rates by class of injury, United States, 1910-2014

[a] Deaths per 100,000 population adjusted to the year 2000 standard population. The break at 1948 shows the estimated effect of classification changes. The break at 1992 is due to the adoption of the Bureau of Labor Statistics' Census of Fatal Occupational Injuries for work-related deaths.

Age-adjusted death rates by leading cause of unintentional injury, United States, 1910-2014

[a] Deaths per 100,000 population adjusted to the year 2000 standard population. Breaks in graph lines signify changes in fatal injury coding.

Principal classes of unintentional-injury-related deaths, United States, 1903-2014

Year	Total[a]		Motor vehicle		Work		Home		Public non-motor vehicle	
	Deaths	Rate[b]	Deaths	Rate[b]	Deaths	Rate[b]	Deaths	Rate[b]	Deaths	Rate[b]
1903	70,600	87.2	(c)	–	(c)	–	(c)	–	(c)	–
1904	71,500	86.6	(c)	–	(c)	–	(c)	–	(c)	–
1905	70,900	84.2	(c)	–	(c)	–	(c)	–	(c)	–
1906	80,000	93.2	400	0.5	(c)	–	(c)	–	(c)	–
1907	81,900	93.6	700	0.8	(c)	–	(c)	–	(c)	–
1908	72,300	81.2	800	0.9	(c)	–	(c)	–	(c)	–
1909	72,700	80.1	1,300	1.4	(c)	–	(c)	–	(c)	–
1910	77,900	84.4	1,900	2.0	(c)	–	(c)	–	(c)	–
1911	79,300	84.7	2,300	2.5	(c)	–	(c)	–	(c)	–
1912	78,400	82.5	3,100	3.3	(c)	–	(c)	–	(c)	–
1913	82,500	85.5	4,200	4.4	(c)	–	(c)	–	(c)	–
1914	77,000	78.6	4,700	4.8	(c)	–	(c)	–	(c)	–
1915	76,200	76.7	6,600	6.6	(c)	–	(c)	–	(c)	–
1916	84,800	84.1	8,200	8.1	(c)	–	(c)	–	(c)	–
1917	90,100	88.2	10,200	10.0	(c)	–	(c)	–	(c)	–
1918	85,100	82.1	10,700	10.3	(c)	–	(c)	–	(c)	–
1919	75,500	71.9	11,200	10.7	(c)	–	(c)	–	(c)	–
1920	75,900	71.2	12,500	11.7	(c)	–	(c)	–	(c)	–
1921	74,000	68.4	13,900	12.9	(c)	–	(c)	–	(c)	–
1922	76,300	69.4	15,300	13.9	(c)	–	(c)	–	(c)	–
1923	84,400	75.7	18,400	16.5	(c)	–	(c)	–	(c)	–
1924	85,600	75.6	19,400	17.1	(c)	–	(c)	–	(c)	–
1925	90,000	78.4	21,900	19.1	(c)	–	(c)	–	(c)	–
1926	91,700	78.7	23,400	20.1	(c)	–	(c)	–	(c)	–
1927	92,700	78.4	25,800	21.8	(c)	–	(c)	–	(c)	–
1928	95,000	79.3	28,000	23.4	19,000	15.8	30,000	24.9	21,000	17.4
1929	98,200	80.8	31,200	25.7	20,000	16.4	30,000	24.6	20,000	16.4
1930	99,100	80.5	32,900	26.7	19,000	15.4	30,000	24.4	20,000	16.3
1931	97,300	78.5	33,700	27.2	17,500	14.1	29,000	23.4	20,000	16.1
1932	89,000	71.3	29,500	23.6	15,000	12.0	29,000	23.2	18,000	14.4
1933	90,932	72.4	31,363	25.0	14,500	11.6	29,500	23.6	18,500	14.7
1934	100,977	79.9	36,101	28.6	16,000	12.7	34,000	26.9	18,000	14.2
1935	99,773	78.4	36,369	28.6	16,500	13.0	32,000	25.2	18,000	14.2
1936	110,052	85.9	38,089	29.7	18,500	14.5	37,000	28.9	19,500	15.2
1937	105,205	81.7	39,643	30.8	19,000	14.8	32,000	24.8	18,000	14.0
1938	93,805	72.3	32,582	25.1	16,000	12.3	31,000	23.9	17,000	13.1
1939	92,623	70.8	32,386	24.7	15,500	11.8	31,000	23.7	16,000	12.2
1940	96,885	73.4	34,501	26.1	17,000	12.9	31,500	23.9	16,500	12.5
1941	101,513	76.3	39,969	30.0	18,000	13.5	30,000	22.5	16,500	12.4
1942	95,889	71.6	28,309	21.1	18,000	13.4	30,500	22.8	16,000	12.0
1943	99,038	73.8	23,823	17.8	17,500	13.0	33,500	25.0	17,000	12.7
1944	95,237	71.7	24,282	18.3	16,000	12.0	32,500	24.5	16,000	12.0
1945	95,918	72.4	28,076	21.2	16,500	12.5	33,500	25.3	16,000	12.1
1946	98,033	70.0	33,411	23.9	16,500	11.8	33,000	23.6	17,500	12.5
1947	99,579	69.4	32,697	22.8	17,000	11.9	34,500	24.1	18,000	12.6
1948 (5th Rev.)[d]	98,001	67.1	32,259	22.1	16,000	11.0	35,000	24.0	17,000	11.6
1948 (6th Rev.)[d]	93,000	63.7	32,259	22.1	16,000	11.0	31,000	21.2	16,000	11.0
1949	90,106	60.6	31,701	21.3	15,000	10.1	31,000	20.9	15,000	10.1
1950	91,249	60.3	34,763	23.0	15,500	10.2	29,000	19.2	15,000	9.9
1951	95,871	62.5	36,996	24.1	16,000	10.4	30,000	19.6	16,000	10.4
1952	96,172	61.8	37,794	24.3	15,000	9.6	30,500	19.6	16,000	10.3
1953	95,032	60.1	37,955	24.0	15,000	9.5	29,000	18.3	16,500	10.4
1954	90,032	55.9	35,586	22.1	14,000	8.7	28,000	17.4	15,500	9.6
1955	93,443	56.9	38,426	23.4	14,200	8.6	28,500	17.3	15,500	9.4
1956	94,780	56.6	39,628	23.7	14,300	8.5	28,000	16.7	16,000	9.6
1957	95,307	55.9	38,702	22.7	14,200	8.3	28,000	16.4	17,500	10.3
1958	90,604	52.3	36,981	21.3	13,300	7.7	26,500	15.3	16,500	9.5
1959	92,080	52.2	37,910	21.5	13,800	7.8	27,000	15.3	16,500	9.3
1960	93,806	52.1	38,137	21.2	13,800	7.7	28,000	15.6	17,000	9.4
1961	92,249	50.4	38,091	20.8	13,500	7.4	27,000	14.8	16,500	9.0
1962	97,139	52.3	40,804	22.0	13,700	7.4	28,500	15.3	17,000	9.2
1963	100,669	53.4	43,564	23.1	14,200	7.5	28,500	15.1	17,500	9.3
1964	105,000	54.9	47,700	25.0	14,200	7.4	28,000	14.6	18,500	9.7
1965	108,004	55.8	49,163	25.4	14,100	7.3	28,500	14.7	19,500	10.1
1966	113,563	58.1	53,041	27.1	14,500	7.4	29,500	15.1	20,000	10.2
1967	113,169	57.3	52,924	26.8	14,200	7.2	29,000	14.7	20,500	10.4
1968	114,864	57.6	54,862	27.5	14,300	7.2	28,000	14.0	21,500	10.8
1969	116,385	57.8	55,791	27.7	14,300	7.1	27,500	13.7	22,500	11.2
1970	114,638	56.2	54,633	26.8	13,800	6.8	27,000	13.2	23,500	11.5
1971	113,439	54.8	54,381	26.3	13,700	6.6	26,500	12.8	23,500	11.4
1972	115,448	55.2	56,278	26.9	14,000	6.7	26,500	12.7	23,500	11.2
1973	115,821	54.8	55,511	26.3	14,300	6.8	26,500	12.5	24,500	11.6

See source and footnotes on page 47.

Principal Classes of Unintentional-Injury-Related Deaths (cont.)

Principal classes of unintentional-injury-related deaths, United States, 1903-2014 (cont.)

Year	Total[a] Deaths	Total[a] Rate[b]	Motor vehicle Deaths	Motor vehicle Rate[b]	Work Deaths	Work Rate[b]	Home Deaths	Home Rate[b]	Public non-motor vehicle Deaths	Public non-motor vehicle Rate[b]
1974	104,622	49.0	46,402	21.8	13,500	6.3	26,000	12.2	23,000	10.8
1975	103,030	47.8	45,853	21.3	13,000	6.0	25,000	11.6	23,000	10.6
1976	100,761	46.3	47,038	21.6	12,500	5.7	24,000	11.0	21,500	10.0
1977	103,202	47.0	49,510	22.5	12,900	5.9	23,200	10.6	22,200	10.1
1978	105,561	47.5	52,411	23.6	13,100	5.9	22,800	10.3	22,000	9.9
1979	105,312	46.9	53,524	23.8	13,000	5.8	22,500	10.0	21,000	9.4
1980	105,718	46.5	53,172	23.4	13,200	5.8	22,800	10.0	21,300	9.4
1981	100,704	43.9	51,385	22.4	12,500	5.4	21,700	9.5	19,800	8.6
1982	94,082	40.6	45,779	19.8	11,900	5.1	21,200	9.2	19,500	8.4
1983	92,488	39.6	44,452	19.0	11,700	5.0	21,200	9.1	19,400	8.3
1984	92,911	39.4	46,263	19.6	11,500	4.9	21,200	9.0	18,300	7.8
1985	93,457	39.3	45,901	19.3	11,500	4.8	21,600	9.1	18,800	7.9
1986	95,277	39.7	47,865	19.9	11,100	4.6	21,700	9.0	18,700	7.8
1987	95,020	39.2	48,290	19.9	11,300	4.7	21,400	8.8	18,400	7.6
1988	97,100	39.7	49,078	20.1	11,000	4.5	22,700	9.3	18,400	7.5
1989	95,028	38.5	47,575	19.3	10,900	4.4	22,500	9.1	18,200	7.4
1990	91,983	36.9	46,814	18.8	10,100	4.0	21,500	8.6	17,400	7.0
1991	89,347	35.4	43,536	17.3	9,800	3.9	22,100	8.8	17,600	7.0
1992	86,777	34.0	40,982	16.1	4,968[e]	1.9[e]	24,000[e]	9.4[e]	19,000[e]	7.4[e]
1993	90,523	35.1	41,893	16.3	5,035	2.0	26,100	10.1	19,700	7.6
1994	91,437	35.1	42,524	16.3	5,338	2.1	26,300	10.1	19,600	7.5
1995	93,320	35.5	43,363	16.5	5,018	1.9	27,200	10.3	20,100	7.6
1996	94,948	35.8	43,649	16.5	5,058	1.9	27,500	10.4	21,000	7.9
1997	95,644	35.7	43,458	16.2	5,162	1.9	27,700	10.3	21,700	8.1
1998	97,835	36.2	43,501	16.1	5,120	1.9	29,000	10.7	22,600	8.4
1999[f]	97,860	35.9	42,401	15.5	5,185	1.9	30,500	11.2	22,200	8.1
2000	97,900	35.6	43,354	15.7	5,022	1.8	29,200	10.6	22,700	8.2
2001	101,537	35.6	43,788	15.4	5,042	1.8	33,200	11.6	21,800	7.6
2002	106,742	37.1	45,380	15.8	4,726	1.6	36,400	12.6	22,500	7.8
2003	109,277	37.6	44,757	15.4	4,725	1.6	38,800	13.3	23,200	8.0
2004	112,012	38.1	44,933	15.3	5,000	1.7	41,700	14.2	22,700	7.7
2005	117,809	39.7	45,343	15.3	4,987	1.7	46,400	15.6	23,400	7.9
2006	121,599	40.8	45,316	15.2	5,092	1.7	49,600	16.6	23,900	8.0
2007	123,706	41.1	43,945	14.6	4,833	1.6	53,500	17.8	23,700	7.9
2008	121,902	40.0	39,790	13.1	4,425	1.5	55,200	18.1	24,500	8.0
2009	118,046	38.5	36,216	11.8	3,744	1.2	55,800	18.2	24,000	7.8
2010	120,859	39.0	35,332	11.4	3,902	1.3	58,100	18.7	25,300	8.2
2011	126,438	40.6	35,303	11.3	3,975	1.3	62,400	20.0	26,400	8.5
2012	127,792	40.7	36,415	11.6	3,904	1.2	62,800	20.0	26,600	8.5
2013[g]	130,557	41.3	35,369	11.2	4,023	1.3	65,700	20.8	27,300	8.6
2014[h]	136,053	42.7	35,398	11.1	4,008	1.3	69,500	21.8	29,100	9.1

Changes										
2005 to 2014	15%	8%	−22%	−27%	−20%	−24%	50%	40%	24%	15%
2013 to 2014	4%	3%	<1%	<−1%	<−1%	0%	6%	5%	7%	6%

Total deaths and average death rates										
Since 2005	1,244,761	40.4	388,427	12.7	42,893	1.4	579,000	18.8	254,200	8.3
Since 1995	2,158,516	38.4	783,648	14.3	87,933	1.6	873,000	15.1	454,600	8.1
Since 1985	3,177,785	38.0	1,281,469	15.6	179,024	2.3	1,106,100	13.3	641,500	7.9
Since 1975	4,181,554	39.6	1,770,856	17.1	304,324	3.1	1,331,700	12.5	849,500	8.2

Source: Total and motor vehicle deaths, 1903-1932 based on National Center for Health Statistics (NCHS) death registration states; 1933-1948 (5th Rev.), 1949-1963, 1965-2012 are NCHS totals for the United States. Work deaths for 1992-2013 are from the Bureau of Labor Statistics Census of Fatal Occupational Injuries. All other figures are National Safety Council estimates.

[a] *Duplications between motor vehicle, work, and home are eliminated in the total column.*

[b] *Rates are deaths per 100,000 population.*

[c] *Data insufficient to estimate yearly totals.*

[d] *In 1948, a revision was made in the International Classification of Diseases. The first figures for 1948 are comparable with those for earlier years, the second with those for later years.*

[e] *Adoption of the Census of Fatal Occupational Injuries figure for the work class necessitated adjustments to the home and public classes. See the Technical Appendix for details.*

[f] *In 1999, a revision was made in the International Classification of Diseases. See the Technical Appendix for comparability with earlier years.*

[g] *Revised.*

[h] *Preliminary.*

Unintentional-Injury-Related Deaths by Age

Unintentional-injury-related deaths by age, United States, 1903-2014

Year	All ages	Younger than 5 years	5-14 years	15-24 years	25-44 years	45-64 years	65-74 years	75 years and older[a]
1903	70,600	9,400	8,200	10,300	20,100	12,600	10,000	
1904	71,500	9,700	9,000	10,500	19,900	12,500	9,900	
1905	70,900	9,800	8,400	10,600	19,600	12,600	9,900	
1906	80,000	10,000	8,400	13,000	24,000	13,600	11,000	
1907	81,900	10,500	8,300	13,400	24,900	14,700	10,100	
1908	72,300	10,100	7,600	11,300	20,500	13,100	9,700	
1909	72,700	9,900	7,400	10,700	21,000	13,300	10,400	
1910	77,900	9,900	7,400	11,900	23,600	14,100	11,000	
1911	79,300	11,000	7,500	11,400	22,400	15,100	11,900	
1912	78,400	10,600	7,900	11,500	22,200	14,700	11,500	
1913	82,500	9,800	7,400	12,200	24,500	16,500	12,100	
1914	77,000	10,600	7,900	11,000	21,400	14,300	11,800	
1915	76,200	10,300	8,200	10,800	20,500	14,300	12,100	
1916	84,800	11,600	9,100	7,700	24,900	17,800	13,700	
1917	90,100	11,600	9,700	11,700	24,400	18,500	14,200	
1918	85,100	10,600	10,100	10,600	21,900	17,700	14,200	
1919	75,500	10,100	10,000	10,200	18,600	13,800	12,800	
1920	75,900	10,200	9,900	10,400	18,100	13,900	13,400	
1921	74,000	9,600	9,500	9,800	18,000	13,900	13,200	
1922	76,300	9,700	9,500	10,000	18,700	14,500	13,900	
1923	84,400	9,900	9,800	11,000	21,500	16,900	15,300	
1924	85,600	10,200	9,900	11,900	20,900	16,800	15,900	
1925	90,000	9,700	10,000	12,400	22,200	18,700	17,000	
1926	91,700	9,500	9,900	12,600	22,700	19,200	17,800	
1927	92,700	9,200	9,900	12,900	22,900	19,700	18,100	
1928	95,000	8,900	9,800	13,100	23,300	20,600	19,300	
1929	98,200	8,600	9,800	14,000	24,300	21,500	20,000	
1930	99,100	8,200	9,100	14,000	24,300	22,200	21,300	
1931	97,300	7,800	8,700	13,500	23,100	22,500	21,700	
1932	89,000	7,100	8,100	12,000	20,500	20,100	21,200	
1933	90,932	6,948	8,195	12,225	21,005	20,819	21,740	
1934	100,977	7,034	8,272	13,274	23,288	24,197	24,912	
1935	99,773	6,971	7,808	13,168	23,411	23,457	24,958	
1936	110,052	7,471	7,866	13,701	24,990	26,535	29,489	
1937	105,205	6,969	7,704	14,302	23,955	24,743	27,532	
1938	93,805	6,646	6,593	12,129	20,464	21,689	26,284	
1939	92,628	6,668	6,378	12,066	20,164	20,842	26,505	
1940	96,885	6,851	6,466	12,763	21,166	21,840	27,799	
1941	101,513	7,052	6,702	14,346	22,983	22,509	27,921	
1942	95,889	7,220	6,340	13,732	21,141	20,764	26,692	
1943	99,038	8,039	6,636	15,278	20,212	20,109	28,764	
1944	95,237	7,912	6,704	14,750	19,115	19,097	27,659	
1945	95,918	7,741	6,836	12,446	19,393	20,097	29,405	
1946	98,033	7,949	6,545	13,366	20,705	20,249	29,219	
1947	99,579	8,219	6,069	13,166	21,155	20,513	30,457	
1948 (5th Rev.)[b]	98,001	8,387	5,859	12,595	20,274	19,809	31,077	
1948 (6th Rev.)[b]	93,000	8,350	5,850	12,600	20,300	19,300	9,800	16,800
1949	90,106	8,469	5,539	11,522	19,432	18,302	9,924	16,918
1950	91,249	8,389	5,519	12,119	20,663	18,665	9,750	16,144
1951	95,871	8,769	5,892	12,366	22,363	19,610	10,218	16,653
1952	96,172	8,871	5,980	12,787	21,950	19,892	10,026	16,667
1953	95,032	8,678	6,136	12,837	21,422	19,479	9,927	16,553
1954	90,032	8,380	5,939	11,801	20,023	18,299	9,652	15,938
1955	93,443	8,099	6,099	12,742	29,911	19,199	9,929	16,464
1956	94,780	8,173	6,319	13,545	20,986	19,207	10,160	16,393
1957	95,307	8,423	6,454	12,973	20,949	19,495	10,076	16,937
1958	90,604	8,789	6,514	12,744	19,658	18,095	9,431	15,373
1959	92,080	8,748	6,511	13,269	19,666	18,937	9,475	15,474
1960	93,806	8,950	6,836	13,457	19,600	19,385	9,689	15,829
1961	92,249	8,622	6,717	13,431	19,273	19,134	9,452	15,620
1962	97,139	8,705	6,751	14,557	19,955	20,335	10,149	16,687
1963	100,669	8,688	6,962	15,889	20,529	21,262	10,194	17,145
1964	100,500	8,670	7,400	17,420	22,080	22,100	10,400	16,930
1965	108,004	8,586	7,391	18,688	22,228	22,900	10,430	17,781
1966	113,563	8,507	7,958	21,030	23,134	24,022	10,706	18,206
1967	113,169	7,825	7,874	21,645	23,255	23,826	10,645	18,099
1968	114,864	7,263	8,369	23,012	23,684	23,896	10,961	17,679
1969	116,385	6,973	8,186	24,668	24,410	24,192	10,643	17,313
1970	114,638	6,594	8,203	24,336	23,979	24,164	10,644	16,718
1971	113,439	6,496	8,143	24,733	23,535	23,240	10,494	16,798
1972	115,448	6,142	8,242	25,762	23,852	23,658	10,446	17,346
1973	115,821	6,037	8,102	26,550	24,750	23,059	10,243	17,080

See source and footnotes on page 49.

Unintentional-injury-related deaths by age, United States, 1903-2014 (cont.)

Year	All ages	Younger than 5 years	5-14 years	15-24 years	25-44 years	45-64 years	65-74 years	75 years and older[a]
1974	104,622	5,335	7,037	24,200	22,547	20,334	9,323	15,846
1975	103,030	4,948	6,818	24,121	22,877	19,643	9,220	15,403
1976	100,761	4,692	6,308	24,316	22,399	19,000	8,823	15,223
1977	103,202	4,470	6,305	25,619	23,460	19,167	9,006	15,175
1978	105,561	4,766	6,118	26,622	25,024	18,774	9,072	15,185
1979	105,312	4,429	5,689	26,574	26,097	18,346	9,013	15,164
1980	105,718	4,479	5,224	26,206	26,722	18,140	8,997	15,950
1981	100,704	4,130	4,866	23,582	26,928	17,339	8,639	15,220
1982	94,082	4,108	4,504	21,306	25,135	15,907	8,224	14,898
1983	92,488	3,999	4,321	19,756	24,996	15,444	8,336	15,636
1984	92,911	3,652	4,198	19,801	25,498	15,273	8,424	16,065
1985	93,457	3,746	4,252	19,161	25,940	15,251	8,583	16,524
1986	95,277	3,843	4,226	19,975	27,201	14,733	8,499	16,800
1987	95,020	3,871	4,198	18,695	27,484	14,807	8,686	17,279
1988	97,100	3,794	4,215	18,507	28,279	15,177	8,971	18,157
1989	95,028	3,770	4,090	16,738	28,429	15,046	8,812	18,143
1990	91,983	3,496	3,650	16,241	27,663	14,607	8,405	17,921
1991	89,347	3,626	3,660	15,278	26,526	13,693	8,137	18,427
1992	86,777	3,286	3,388	13,662	25,808	13,882	8,165	18,586
1993	90,523	3,488	3,466	13,966	27,277	14,434	8,125	19,767
1994	91,437	3,406	3,508	13,898	27,012	15,200	8,279	20,134
1995	93,320	3,067	3,544	13,842	27,660	16,004	8,400	20,803
1996	94,948	2,951	3,433	13,809	27,092	16,717	8,780	22,166
1997	95,644	2,770	3,371	13,367	27,129	17,521	8,578	22,908
1998	97,835	2,689	3,254	13,349	27,172	18,286	8,892	24,193
1999[c]	97,860	2,743	3,091	13,656	27,121	18,924	8,208	24,117
2000	97,900	2,707	2,979	14,113	27,182	19,783	7,698	23,438
2001	101,537	2,690	2,836	14,411	27,784	21,002	7,835	24,979
2002	106,742	2,587	2,718	15,412	29,279	23,020	8,086	25,640
2003	109,277	2,662	2,618	15,272	29,307	25,007	8,081	26,330
2004	112,012	2,693	2,666	15,449	29,503	26,593	8,116	26,992
2005	117,809	2,747	2,415	15,753	30,916	29,192	8,632	28,154
2006	121,599	2,757	2,258	16,229	32,488	31,121	8,420	28,326
2007	123,706	2,873	2,194	15,897	31,908	32,508	8,753	29,573
2008	121,902	2,784	1,859	14,089	30,653	33,136	8,994	30,387
2009	118,046	2,674	1,680	12,454	29,159	32,945	8,976	30,158
2010	120,859	2,504	1,643	12,341	29,365	33,690	9,407	31,909
2011	126,438	2,540	1,635	12,330	30,748	35,907	10,014	33,264
2012	127,792	2,522	1,550	11,908	30,885	36,216	10,558	34,153
2013[d]	130,557	2,472	1,521	11,619	31,563	37,414	10,967	35,001
2014[e]	136,053	2,377	1,480	11,836	33,405	38,640	11,909	36,406
Changes								
2005 to 2014	15%	–13%	–39%	–25%	8%	32%	38%	29%
2013 to 2014	4%	–4%	–3%	2%	6%	3%	9%	4%

Source: 1903-1932 based on National Center for Health Statistics (NCHS) data for registration states; 1933-1948 (5th Rev.), 1949-1963, 1965-2014 are NCHS totals. All other figures are National Safety Council estimates. See Technical Appendix for comparability.

[a] Includes age unknown. In 2014, they numbered 20.

[b] In 1948, a revision was made in the International Classification of Diseases. The first figures for 1948 are comparable with those for earlier years, the second with those for later years.

[c] In 1999, a revision was made in the International Classification of Diseases. See the Technical Appendix for comparability with earlier years.

[d] Revised.

[e] Preliminary.

Unintentional-Injury-Related Death Rates by Age

Unintentional-injury-related death rates[a] by age, United States, 1903-2014

Year	Standardized rate[b]	All ages	Younger than 5 years	5-14 years	15-24 years	25-44 years	45-64 years	65-74 years	75 years and older[c]
1903	99.4	87.2	98.7	46.8	65.0	87.4	111.7	299.8	
1904	103.4	86.6	99.1	50.9	64.9	84.6	108.1	290.0	
1905	98.4	84.2	98.6	47.0	64.1	81.4	106.2	282.5	
1906	114.2	93.2	99.1	46.5	77.1	97.3	111.7	306.0	
1907	112.4	93.6	102.7	45.5	78.0	98.8	117.8	274.2	
1908	99.7	81.2	97.5	41.2	64.4	79.5	102.2	256.7	
1909	97.4	80.1	94.2	39.6	59.9	79.6	101.0	268.2	
1910	103.0	84.4	92.8	39.1	65.3	87.3	104.0	276.0	
1911	104.7	84.7	101.9	39.3	62.1	81.4	108.7	292.1	
1912	100.4	82.5	97.1	40.5	62.3	79.2	103.2	275.8	
1913	103.5	85.5	88.4	37.4	65.2	85.6	112.5	281.7	
1914	95.9	78.6	94.3	38.9	58.5	73.2	94.6	268.1	
1915	92.1	76.7	90.8	39.7	57.3	69.0	92.1	268.8	
1916	101.4	84.1	101.4	43.3	40.8	82.5	112.1	297.6	
1917	106.7	88.2	108.4	45.3	62.1	79.8	113.8	301.2	
1918	101.2	82.1	91.0	46.5	58.7	72.2	106.3	294.2	
1919	87.7	71.9	87.2	45.9	55.3	60.1	81.8	262.0	
1920	87.8	71.2	87.4	44.9	55.5	56.9	85.6	289.5	
1921	84.3	68.4	80.8	42.4	51.4	55.5	79.4	259.8	
1922	86.9	69.4	80.6	41.5	51.4	57.1	81.4	265.1	
1923	94.5	75.7	82.0	42.4	55.6	64.5	92.6	282.8	
1924	93.3	75.6	82.9	42.4	58.6	61.7	90.2	283.5	
1925	97.2	78.4	78.6	42.3	59.7	64.7	97.8	293.9	
1926	97.7	78.7	77.9	41.4	59.9	65.4	98.2	298.7	
1927	97.5	78.4	75.9	41.0	60.2	65.2	98.0	295.4	
1928	99.6	79.3	74.4	40.4	59.9	65.6	99.9	306.2	
1929	101.2	80.8	73.3	40.0	63.1	67.7	102.1	308.9	
1930	101.8	80.5	71.8	36.9	62.3	67.0	102.9	317.9	
1931	99.2	78.5	69.9	35.2	59.7	63.0	102.1	313.3	
1932	90.5	71.3	65.1	32.8	52.7	55.6	89.3	296.9	
1933	91.1	72.4	65.5	33.4	53.6	56.3	90.8	295.3	
1934	100.5	79.9	68.1	33.9	57.8	61.8	103.3	328.5	
1935	97.9	78.4	68.5	32.2	56.9	61.6	98.0	319.8	
1936	108.1	85.9	74.4	32.9	58.8	65.3	108.6	367.4	
1937	100.7	81.7	69.6	32.7	60.9	62.1	99.3	333.4	
1938	89.4	72.3	65.3	28.5	51.3	52.5	85.4	308.9	
1939	86.7	70.8	62.9	28.2	50.7	51.2	81.0	300.0	
1940	89.1	73.4	64.8	28.8	53.5	53.2	83.4	305.7	
1941	90.7	76.3	65.0	29.7	60.9	57.2	84.8	297.4	
1942	84.3	71.6	63.9	27.9	59.8	52.4	77.1	275.5	
1943	86.3	73.8	66.9	29.0	69.7	50.3	73.6	287.8	
1944	82.5	71.7	63.2	29.1	72.9	48.9	68.9	268.6	
1945	83.4	72.4	59.8	29.5	64.5	50.5	71.6	277.6	
1946	81.0	70.0	60.2	28.1	61.7	48.8	70.9	267.9	
1947	80.5	69.4	57.4	25.8	59.6	49.0	70.6	270.7	
1948 (5th Rev.)[d]	79.5	67.1	56.3	24.6	56.8	46.2	66.8	267.4	
1948 (6th Rev.)[d]	72.5	63.7	56.0	24.5	56.8	46.2	65.1	122.4	464.3
1949	69.0	60.6	54.4	23.0	52.2	43.5	60.6	120.4	450.7
1950	68.1	60.3	51.4	22.6	55.0	45.6	60.5	115.8	414.7
1951	70.1	62.5	50.8	23.6	57.7	49.0	62.7	117.1	413.6
1952	69.0	61.8	51.5	22.5	60.9	47.7	62.7	111.1	399.8
1953	67.0	60.1	49.5	22.1	61.4	46.4	60.5	106.7	383.6
1954	62.2	55.9	46.7	20.5	56.4	43.0	55.9	100.7	354.4
1955	63.4	56.9	43.9	20.7	60.1	44.7	57.7	100.8	350.2
1956	63.0	56.6	43.3	20.2	63.3	44.7	56.7	100.6	335.6
1957	62.2	55.9	43.5	19.9	59.5	44.6	56.6	97.5	333.3
1958	57.5	52.3	44.5	19.6	56.2	42.0	51.7	89.3	292.6
1959	57.4	52.2	43.6	18.9	56.5	42.1	53.2	87.7	284.7
1960	57.3	52.1	44.0	19.1	55.6	42.0	53.6	87.6	281.4
1961	55.4	50.4	42.0	18.1	54.0	41.2	52.1	83.8	267.9
1962	57.5	52.3	42.6	18.0	55.0	42.7	54.6	88.5	277.7
1963	58.6	53.4	42.8	18.2	57.2	44.0	56.3	87.9	277.0
1964	60.0	54.9	43.1	19.1	59.9	47.3	57.6	88.9	263.9
1965	61.9	55.8	43.4	18.7	61.6	47.7	58.8	88.5	268.7
1966	63.0	58.1	44.4	19.9	66.9	49.6	60.7	89.8	267.4
1967	62.1	57.3	42.2	19.4	66.9	49.7	59.2	88.5	257.4
1968	62.0	57.6	40.6	20.5	69.2	50.1	58.5	90.2	244.0
1969	61.8	57.8	40.2	20.0	71.8	51.2	58.4	86.6	232.0
1970	59.8	56.2	38.4	20.1	68.0	49.8	57.6	85.2	219.6
1971	58.1	54.8	37.7	20.1	66.1	48.4	54.7	82.7	213.2
1972	58.0	55.2	35.9	20.6	67.6	47.5	55.2	80.8	214.2
1973	57.1	54.8	35.8	20.6	68.2	48.0	53.3	77.3	206.3

See source and footnotes on page 51.

Unintentional-injury-related death rates[a] by age, United States, 1903-2014 (cont.)

Year	Standardized rate[b]	All ages	Younger than 5 years	5-14 years	15-24 years	25-44 years	45-64 years	65-74 years	75 years and older[c]
1974	50.9	49.0	32.4	18.2	60.9	42.7	46.7	68.7	186.7
1975	49.3	47.8	30.7	17.8	59.5	42.3	44.9	66.2	175.5
1976	47.3	46.3	30.0	16.7	58.9	40.3	43.2	62.0	168.4
1977	47.6	47.0	28.7	17.0	61.3	40.9	43.4	61.5	164.0
1978	47.8	47.5	30.3	16.9	63.1	42.3	42.4	60.5	159.7
1979	47.0	46.9	27.6	16.1	62.6	42.7	41.3	58.8	154.8
1980	46.5	46.5	27.2	15.0	61.7	42.3	40.8	57.5	158.6
1981	44.0	43.9	24.4	14.2	55.9	41.2	39.0	54.4	147.4
1982	40.6	40.6	23.8	13.2	51.2	37.3	35.8	50.9	140.0
1983	39.6	39.6	22.8	12.7	48.2	36.0	34.7	50.8	142.8
1984	39.4	39.4	20.6	12.4	48.9	35.7	34.3	50.7	142.8
1985	39.2	39.3	21.0	12.6	47.9	35.3	34.2	50.9	143.0
1986	39.4	39.7	21.4	12.6	50.5	36.1	33.0	49.6	141.5
1987	39.0	39.2	21.4	12.4	48.1	35.7	33.0	49.8	141.6
1988	39.5	39.7	20.9	12.3	48.5	36.1	33.4	50.9	145.3
1989	38.4	38.5	20.4	11.8	44.8	35.7	32.8	49.3	141.5
1990	36.8	36.9	18.5	10.4	44.0	34.2	31.6	46.4	136.5
1991	35.3	35.4	18.9	10.2	42.0	32.3	29.3	44.5	136.7
1992	34.0	34.0	16.8	9.3	37.8	31.3	28.7	44.2	134.5
1993	35.0	35.1	17.7	9.4	38.8	33.0	29.1	43.6	139.9
1994	35.0	35.1	17.3	9.4	38.4	32.5	29.9	44.3	139.2
1995	35.0	35.5	15.7	9.3	38.2	33.2	30.6	44.8	140.6
1996	35.3	35.8	15.3	8.9	38.1	32.3	31.1	47.0	145.9
1997	35.1	35.7	14.5	8.7	36.5	32.5	31.6	46.3	146.2
1998	35.5	36.2	14.2	8.3	35.9	32.6	31.9	48.3	151.1
1999[e]	35.2	35.9	14.5	7.8	36.1	32.7	32.0	45.0	147.7
2000	34.8	35.6	14.3	7.5	36.7	33.0	32.3	42.3	140.8
2001	35.7	35.6	13.9	6.9	36.1	32.7	32.6	42.8	146.8
2002	37.1	37.1	13.2	6.6	37.9	34.7	34.6	44.2	148.2
2003	37.6	37.6	13.5	6.4	37.0	34.8	36.4	44.0	149.6
2004	38.1	38.1	13.4	6.5	37.1	35.1	37.6	43.9	151.4
2005	39.5	39.7	13.5	6.0	37.4	36.8	40.1	46.3	155.2
2006	40.4	40.8	13.5	5.6	38.5	38.9	41.6	44.5	154.4
2007	40.5	41.1	13.9	5.5	37.5	38.2	42.4	45.2	159.2
2008	39.4	40.0	13.2	4.6	32.8	36.8	42.6	44.7	162.8
2009	37.7	38.5	12.6	4.1	28.9	35.1	41.5	43.2	160.6
2010	38.1	39.0	11.7	4.0	28.6	35.3	41.7	44.1	168.2
2011	39.3	40.6	12.6	4.0	28.2	37.3	43.4	44.5	175.9
2012	39.1	40.7	12.6	3.8	27.1	37.3	43.7	47.0	178.3
2013[f]	39.4	41.3	12.4	3.7	26.4	37.9	45.0	45.7	179.6
2014[g]	40.4	42.7	12.0	3.6	26.9	39.8	46.3	45.1	183.5
Changes									
2005 to 2014		8%	−11%	−40%	−28%	8%	15%	−3%	18%
2013 to 2014		3%	−3%	−3%	2%	5%	3%	−1%	2%
2014 population (thousands)									
Total[h]		318,857	19,877	41,191	43,980	84,030	83,536	26,398	19,845
Male		156,936	10,156	21,030	22,523	42,129	40,747	12,349	8,002
Female		161,921	9,721	20,161	21,456	41,900	42,790	14,049	11,843

Source: All figures are National Safety Council estimates. See Technical Appendix for comparability.

[a] Rates are deaths per 100,000 resident population in each age group.

[b] Adjusted to the year 2000 standard population to remove the influence of changes in age distribution between 1903 and 2014.

[c] Includes age unknown.

[d] In 1948, a revision was made in the International Classification of Diseases. The first figures for 1948 are comparable with those for earlier years, the second with those for later years.

[e] In 1999, a revision was made in the International Classification of Diseases. See the Technical Appendix for comparability.

[f] Revised.

[g] Preliminary.

[h] Sum of parts may not equal total due to rounding.

Principal Types of Unintentional-Injury-Related Deaths

Principal types of unintentional-injury-related deaths, United States, 1903-1998

Year	Total	Motor vehicle	Falls	Drowning[a]	Fire, flames, or smoke[b]	Choking[b]	Firearms	Poison (solid or liquid)	Poison (gas or vapor)	All other
1903	70,600	(c)	(c)	9,200	(c)	(c)	2,500	(c)	(c)	58,900
1904	71,500	(c)	(c)	9,300	(c)	(c)	2,800	(c)	(c)	59,400
1905	70,900	(c)	(c)	9,300	(c)	(c)	2,000	(c)	(c)	59,600
1906	80,000	400	(c)	9,400	(c)	(c)	2,100	(c)	(c)	68,100
1907	81,900	700	(c)	9,000	(c)	(c)	1,700	(c)	(c)	70,500
1908	72,300	800	(c)	9,300	(c)	(c)	1,900	(c)	(c)	60,300
1909	72,700	1,300	(c)	8,500	(c)	(c)	1,600	(c)	(c)	61,300
1910	77,900	1,900	(c)	8,700	(c)	(c)	1,900	(c)	(c)	65,400
1911	79,300	2,300	(c)	9,000	(c)	(c)	2,100	(c)	(c)	65,900
1912	78,400	3,100	(c)	8,600	(c)	(c)	2,100	(c)	(c)	64,600
1913	82,500	4,200	15,100	10,300	8,900	(c)	2,400	3,200	(c)	38,400
1914	77,000	4,700	15,000	8,700	9,100	(c)	2,300	3,300	(c)	33,900
1915	76,200	6,600	15,000	8,600	8,400	(c)	2,100	2,800	(c)	32,700
1916	84,800	8,200	15,200	8,900	9,500	(c)	2,200	2,900	(c)	37,900
1917	90,100	10,200	15,200	7,600	10,800	(c)	2,300	2,800	(c)	41,200
1918	85,100	10,700	13,200	7,000	10,200	(c)	2,500	2,700	(c)	38,800
1919	75,500	11,200	11,900	9,100	9,100	(c)	2,800	3,100	(c)	28,300
1920	75,900	12,500	12,600	6,100	9,300	(c)	2,700	3,300	(c)	29,400
1921	74,000	13,900	12,300	7,800	7,500	(c)	2,800	2,900	(c)	26,800
1922	76,300	15,300	13,200	7,000	8,300	(c)	2,900	2,800	(c)	26,800
1923	84,400	18,400	14,100	6,800	9,100	(c)	2,900	2,800	2,700	27,600
1924	85,600	19,400	14,700	7,400	7,400	(c)	2,900	2,700	2,900	28,200
1925	90,000	21,900	15,500	7,300	8,600	(c)	2,800	2,700	2,800	28,400
1926	91,700	23,400	16,300	7,500	8,800	(c)	2,800	2,600	3,200	27,100
1927	92,700	25,800	16,500	8,100	8,200	(c)	3,000	2,600	2,700	25,800
1928	95,000	28,000	17,000	8,600	8,400	(c)	2,900	2,800	2,800	24,500
1929	98,200	31,200	17,700	7,600	8,200	(c)	3,200	2,600	2,800	24,900
1930	99,100	32,900	18,100	7,500	8,100	(c)	3,200	2,600	2,500	24,200
1931	97,300	33,700	18,100	7,600	7,100	(c)	3,100	2,600	2,100	23,000
1932	89,000	29,500	18,600	7,500	7,100	(c)	3,000	2,200	2,100	19,000
1933	90,932	31,363	18,962	7,158	6,781	(c)	3,014	2,135	1,633	19,886
1934	100,977	36,101	20,725	7,077	7,456	(c)	3,033	2,148	1,643	22,794
1935	99,773	36,369	21,378	6,744	7,253	(c)	2,799	2,163	1,654	21,413
1936	110,052	38,089	23,562	6,659	7,939	(c)	2,817	2,177	1,665	27,144
1937	105,205	39,643	22,544	7,085	7,214	(c)	2,576	2,190	1,675	22,278
1938	93,805	32,582	23,239	6,881	6,491	(c)	2,726	2,077	1,428	18,381
1939	92,623	32,386	23,427	6,413	6,675	(c)	2,618	1,963	1,440	17,701
1940	96,885	34,501	23,356	6,202	7,521	(c)	2,375	1,847	1,583	19,500
1941	101,513	39,969	22,764	6,389	6,922	(c)	2,396	1,731	1,464	19,878
1942	95,889	28,309	22,632	6,696	7,901	(c)	2,678	1,607	1,741	24,325
1943	99,038	23,823	24,701	7,115	8,726	921	2,282	1,745	2,014	27,711
1944	95,237	24,282	22,989	6,511	8,372	896	2,392	1,993	1,860	25,942
1945	95,918	28,076	23,847	6,624	7,949	897	2,385	1,987	2,120	22,033
1946	98,033	33,411	23,109	6,442	7,843	1,076	2,801	1,961	1,821	19,569
1947	99,579	32,697	24,529	6,885	8,033	1,206	2,439	1,865	1,865	14,060
1948 (5th Rev.)[d]	98,001	32,259	24,836	6,428	7,743	1,315	2,191	1,753	2,045	19,611
1948 (6th Rev.)[d]	93,000	32,259	22,000	6,500	6,800	1,299	2,330	1,600	2,020	17,192
1949	90,106	31,701	22,308	6,684	5,982	1,341	2,326	1,634	1,617	16,513
1950	91,249	34,763	20,783	6,131	6,405	1,350	2,174	1,584	1,769	16,290
1951	95,871	36,996	21,376	6,489	6,788	1,456	2,247	1,497	1,627	17,395
1952	96,172	37,794	20,945	6,601	6,922	1,434	2,210	1,440	1,397	17,429
1953	95,032	37,955	20,631	6,770	6,579	1,603	2,277	1,391	1,223	16,603
1954	90,032	35,586	19,771	6,334	6,083	1,627	2,271	1,339	1,223	15,798
1955	93,443	38,426	20,192	6,344	6,352	1,608	2,120	1,431	1,163	15,807
1956	94,780	39,628	20,282	6,263	6,405	1,760	2,202	1,422	1,213	15,605
1957	95,307	38,702	20,545	6,613	6,269	2,043	2,369	1,390	1,143	16,233
1958	90,604	36,981	18,248	6,582[e]	7,291[e]	2,191[e]	2,172	1,429	1,187	14,523
1959	92,080	37,910	18,774	6,434	6,898	2,189	2,258	1,661	1,141	14,815
1960	93,806	38,137	19,023	6,529	7,645	2,397	2,334	1,679	1,253	14,809
1961	92,249	38,091	18,691	6,525	7,102	2,499	2,204	1,804	1,192	14,141
1962	97,139	40,804	19,589	6,439	7,534	1,813	2,092	1,833	1,376	15,659
1963	100,669	43,564	19,335	6,347	8,172	1,949	2,263	2,061	1,489	15,489
1964	105,000	47,700	18,941	6,709	7,379	1,865	2,275	2,100	1,360	16,571
1965	108,004	49,163	19,984	6,799	7,347	1,836	2,344	2,110	1,526	16,895
1966	113,563	53,041	20,066	7,084	8,084	1,831	2,558	2,283	1,648	16,968
1967	113,169	52,924	20,120	7,076	7,423	1,980	2,896	2,506	1,574	16,670
1968	114,864	54,862	18,651	7,372[e]	7,335	3,100[e]	2,394[e]	2,583	1,526	17,041
1969	116,385	55,791	17,827	7,699	7,163	3,712	2,309	2,967	1,549	16,368
1970	114,638	54,633	16,926	7,860	6,718	2,753	2,406	3,679	1,620	18,043
1971	113,439	54,381	16,755	7,396	6,776	2,877	2,360	3,710	1,646	17,538
1972	115,448	56,278	16,744	7,586	6,714	2,830	2,442	3,728	1,690	17,436
1973	115,821	55,511	16,506	8,725	6,503	3,013	2,618	3,683	1,652	17,610

See source and footnotes on page 53.

Principal Types of Unintentional-Injury-Related Deaths (cont.)

Principal types of unintentional-injury-related deaths, United States, 1903-1998 (cont.)

Year	Total	Motor vehicle	Falls	Drowning[a]	Fire, flames, or smoke[b]	Choking[b]	Firearms	Poison (solid or liquid)	Poison (gas or vapor)	All other
1974	104,622	46,402	16,339	7,876	6,236	2,991	2,513	4,016	1,518	16,731
1975	103,030	45,853	14,896	8,000	6,071	3,106	2,380	4,694	1,577	16,453
1976	100,761	47,038	14,136	6,827	6,338	3,033	2,059	4,161	1,569	15,600
1977	103,202	49,510	13,773	7,126	6,357	3,037	1,982	3,374	1,596	16,447
1978	105,561	52,411	13,690	7,026	6,163	3,063	1,806	3,035	1,737	16,630
1979	105,312	53,524	13,216	6,872	5,991	3,243	2,004	3,165	1,472	15,825
1980	105,718	53,172	13,294	7,257	5,822	3,249	1,955	3,089	1,242	16,638
1981	100,704	51,385	12,628	6,277	5,697	3,331	1,871	3,243	1,280	14,992
1982	94,082	45,779	12,077	6,351	5,210	3,254	1,756	3,474	1,259	14,922
1983	92,488	44,452	12,024	6,353	5,028	3,387	1,695	3,382	1,251	14,916
1984	92,911	46,263	11,937	5,388	5,010	3,541	1,668	3,808	1,103	14,193
1985	93,457	45,901	12,001	5,316	4,938	3,551	1,649	4,091	1,079	14,931
1986	95,277	47,865	11,444	5,700	4,835	3,692	1,452	4,731	1,009	14,549
1987	95,020	48,290	11,733	5,100	4,710	3,688	1,440	4,415	900	14,744
1988	97,100	49,078	12,096	4,966	4,965	3,805	1,501	5,353	873	14,463
1989	95,028	47,575	12,151	4,015	4,716	3,578	1,489	5,603	921	14,980
1990	91,983	46,814	12,313	4,685	4,175	3,303	1,416	5,055	748	13,474
1991	89,347	43,536	12,662	4,818	4,120	3,240	1,441	5,698	736	13,096
1992	86,777	40,982	12,646	3,542	3,958	3,182	1,409	6,449	633	13,976
1993	90,523	41,893	13,141	3,807	3,900	3,160	1,521	7,877	660	14,564
1994	91,437	42,524	13,450	3,942	3,986	3,065	1,356	8,309	685	14,120
1995	93,320	43,363	13,986	4,350	3,761	3,185	1,225	8,461	611	14,378
1996	94,948	43,649	14,986	3,959	3,741	3,206	1,134	8,872	638	14,763
1997	95,644	43,458	15,447	4,051	3,490	3,275	981	9,587	576	14,779
1998	97,835	43,501	16,274	4,406	3,255	3,515	866	10,255	546	15,217

Principal types of unintentional-injury-related deaths, United States, 1999-2014

Year	Total	Motor vehicle	Falls	Poisoning	Choking[b]	Drowning[f]	Fire, flames, or smoke[b]	Mechanical suffocation	Firearms	All other
1999[g]	97,860	42,401	13,162	12,186	3,885	3,529	3,348	1,618	824	16,907
2000	97,900	43,354	13,322	12,757	4,313	3,482	3,377	1,335	776	15,184
2001	101,537	43,788	15,019	14,078	4,185	3,281	3,309	1,370	802	15,705
2002	106,742	45,380	16,257	17,550	4,128	3,447	3,159	1,389	762	13,670
2003	109,277	44,757	17,229	19,457	4,272	3,306	3,369	1,309	730	14,850
2004	112,012	44,933	18,807	20,950	4,470	3,308	3,229	1,421	649	14,245
2005	117,809	45,343	19,656	23,617	4,386	3,582	3,197	1,514	789	15,725
2006	121,599	45,316	20,823	27,531	4,332	3,579	3,109	1,580	642	14,687
2007	123,706	43,945	22,631	29,846	4,344	3,443	3,286	1,653	613	14,558
2008	121,902	39,790	24,013	31,116	4,366	3,548	2,912	1,759	592	14,398
2009	118,046	36,216	24,792	31,758	4,370	3,517	2,756	1,569	554	13,068
2010	120,859	35,332	26,009	33,041	4,570	3,782	2,782	1,595	606	13,748
2011	126,438	35,303	27,483	36,280	4,708	3,556	2,746	1,534	591	14,237
2012	127,792	36,415	28,756	36,332	4,634	3,551	2,464	1,604	548	13,488
2013[h]	130,557	35,369	30,208	38,851	4,864	3,391	2,760	1,737	505	12,872
2014	136,053	35,398	31,959	42,032	4,816	3,406	2,701	1,764	586	13,391
Changes										
2005 to 2014	15%	−22%	63%	78%	10%	−5%	−16%	17%	−26%	−15%
2013 to 2014	4%	<1%	6%	8%	−1%	<1%	−2%	2%	16%	4%

Source: National Center for Health Statistics and National Safety Council. See Technical Appendix for comparability.
[a] Includes drowning in water transport incidents.
[b] Fires, flames, or smoke includes burns by fire and deaths resulting from conflagration regardless of nature of injury. Choking is the inhalation of food or other object obstructing breathing.
[c] Comparable data not available.
[d] In 1948, a revision was made in the International Classification of Diseases. The first figures for 1948 are comparable with those for earlier years, the second with those for later years.
[e] Data are not comparable to previous years shown due to classification changes in 1958 and 1968.
[f] Excludes water transport drownings.
[g] In 1999, a revision was made in the International Classification of Diseases. See the Technical Appendix for comparability.
[h] Revised.

Unintentional-Injury-Related Death Rates for Principal Types

Unintentional-injury-related death rates[a] for principal types, United States, 1903-1998

Year	Total	Motor vehicle	Falls	Drowning[b]	Fire, flames, or smoke[c]	Choking[c]	Firearms	Poison (solid or liquid)	Poison (gas or vapor)	All other
1903	87.2	(d)	(d)	11.4	(d)	(d)	3.1	(d)	(d)	72.7
1904	86.6	(d)	(d)	11.3	(d)	(d)	3.4	(d)	(d)	71.9
1905	84.2	(d)	(d)	11.1	(d)	(d)	2.4	(d)	(d)	70.7
1906	93.2	0.5	(d)	11.0	(d)	(d)	2.4	(d)	(d)	79.3
1907	93.6	0.8	(d)	10.4	(d)	(d)	2.0	(d)	(d)	80.4
1908	81.2	0.9	(d)	10.5	(d)	(d)	2.1	(d)	(d)	67.7
1909	80.1	1.4	(d)	9.4	(d)	(d)	1.8	(d)	(d)	67.5
1910	84.4	2.0	(d)	9.4	(d)	(d)	2.1	(d)	(d)	70.9
1911	84.7	2.5	(d)	9.6	(d)	(d)	2.2	(d)	(d)	70.4
1912	82.5	3.3	(d)	9.0	(d)	(d)	2.2	(d)	(d)	68.0
1913	85.5	4.4	15.5	10.6	9.1	(d)	2.5	3.3	(d)	40.1
1914	78.6	4.8	15.1	8.8	9.1	(d)	2.3	3.3	(d)	35.2
1915	76.7	6.6	14.9	8.6	8.4	(d)	2.1	2.8	(d)	33.3
1916	84.1	8.1	14.9	8.7	9.3	(d)	2.2	2.8	(d)	38.1
1917	88.2	10.0	14.7	7.4	10.5	(d)	2.2	2.7	(d)	40.7
1918	82.1	10.3	12.8	6.8	9.9	(d)	2.4	2.6	(d)	37.3
1919	71.9	10.7	11.4	6.9	8.7	(d)	2.7	3.0	(d)	28.5
1920	71.2	11.7	11.8	5.7	8.7	(d)	2.5	3.1	(d)	27.7
1921	68.4	12.9	11.3	7.2	6.9	(d)	2.6	2.7	(d)	24.8
1922	69.4	13.9	12.0	6.4	7.5	(d)	2.6	2.5	(d)	24.5
1923	75.7	16.5	12.6	6.1	8.1	(d)	2.6	2.5	2.4	24.9
1924	75.6	17.1	12.9	6.5	8.4	(d)	2.5	2.4	2.5	23.3
1925	78.4	19.1	13.4	6.3	7.4	(d)	2.4	2.3	2.4	25.1
1926	78.7	20.1	13.9	6.4	7.5	(d)	2.4	2.2	2.7	23.5
1927	78.4	21.8	13.9	6.8	6.9	(d)	2.5	2.2	2.3	22.0
1928	79.3	23.4	14.1	7.1	7.0	(d)	2.4	2.3	2.3	20.7
1929	80.8	25.7	14.5	6.2	6.7	(d)	2.6	2.1	2.3	20.7
1930	80.5	26.7	14.7	6.1	6.6	(d)	2.6	2.1	2.0	19.7
1931	78.5	27.2	14.6	6.1	5.7	(d)	2.5	2.1	1.7	18.6
1932	71.3	23.6	14.9	6.0	5.7	(d)	2.4	1.8	1.7	15.2
1933	72.4	25.0	15.1	5.7	5.4	(d)	2.4	1.7	1.3	15.8
1934	79.9	28.6	16.4	5.6	5.9	(d)	2.4	1.7	1.3	18.0
1935	78.4	28.6	16.8	5.3	5.7	(d)	2.2	1.7	1.3	16.8
1936	85.9	29.7	18.4	5.2	6.2	(d)	2.2	1.7	1.3	21.2
1937	81.7	30.8	17.5	5.5	5.6	(d)	2.0	1.7	1.3	17.3
1938	72.3	25.1	17.9	5.3	5.0	(d)	2.1	1.6	1.1	14.2
1939	70.8	24.7	17.9	4.9	5.1	(d)	2.0	1.5	1.1	13.6
1940	73.4	26.1	17.7	4.7	5.7	(d)	1.8	1.4	1.2	14.8
1941	76.3	30.0	17.1	4.8	5.2	(d)	1.8	1.3	1.1	15.0
1942	71.6	21.1	16.9	5.0	5.9	(d)	2.0	1.2	1.3	18.2
1943	73.8	17.8	18.4	5.3	6.5	0.7	1.7	1.3	1.5	20.6
1944	71.7	18.3	17.3	4.9	6.3	0.7	1.8	1.5	1.4	19.5
1945	72.4	21.2	18.0	5.0	6.0	0.7	1.8	1.5	1.6	16.6
1946	70.0	23.9	16.5	4.6	5.6	0.8	2.0	1.4	1.3	13.9
1947	69.4	22.8	17.1	4.8	5.6	0.8	1.7	1.3	1.3	14.0
1948 (5th Rev.)[e]	67.1	22.1	17.0	4.4	5.3	0.9	1.5	1.2	1.4	13.3
1948 (6th Rev.)[e]	63.7	22.1	15.1	4.5	4.7	0.9	1.6	1.1	1.4	12.3
1949	60.6	21.3	15.0	4.5	4.0	0.9	1.6	1.1	1.1	11.1
1950	60.3	23.0	13.7	4.1	4.2	0.9	1.4	1.1	1.2	10.7
1951	62.5	24.1	13.9	4.2	4.4	1.0	1.5	1.0	1.1	11.3
1952	61.8	24.3	13.5	4.2	4.5	0.9	1.4	0.9	0.9	11.2
1953	60.1	24.0	13.0	4.3	4.2	1.0	1.4	0.9	0.8	10.2
1954	55.9	22.1	12.3	3.9	3.8	1.0	1.4	0.8	0.8	9.8
1955	56.9	23.4	12.3	3.9	3.9	1.0	1.3	0.9	0.7	9.5
1956	56.6	23.7	12.1	3.7	3.8	1.1	1.3	0.8	0.7	9.4
1957	55.9	22.7	12.1	3.9	3.7	1.2	1.4	0.8	0.7	9.4
1958	52.3	21.3	10.5	3.8[f]	4.2[f]	1.3[f]	1.3	0.8	0.7	8.4
1959	52.2	21.5	10.6	3.7	3.9	1.2	1.3	0.9	0.7	8.4
1960	52.1	21.2	10.6	3.6	4.3	1.3	1.3	0.9	0.7	8.2
1961	50.4	20.8	10.2	3.6	3.9	1.4	1.2	1.0	0.7	7.6
1962	52.3	22.0	10.5	3.5	4.1	1.0	1.1	1.0	0.7	8.4
1963	53.4	23.1	10.3	3.4	4.3	1.0	1.2	1.1	0.8	8.2
1964	54.9	25.0	9.9	3.5	3.9	1.0	1.2	1.1	0.7	8.4
1965	55.8	25.4	10.3	3.5	3.8	1.0	1.2	1.1	0.8	8.7
1966	58.1	27.1	10.3	3.6	4.8	0.9	1.3	1.2	0.8	8.1
1967	57.3	26.8	10.2	3.6	3.8	1.0	1.5	1.3	0.8	8.3
1968	57.6	27.5	9.4	3.7[f]	3.7[f]	1.6[f]	1.2[f]	1.3	0.8	8.4
1969	57.8	27.7	8.9	3.8	3.6	1.8	1.2	1.5	0.8	8.5
1970	56.2	26.8	8.3	3.9	3.3	1.4	1.2	1.8	0.8	8.7
1971	54.8	26.3	8.1	3.6	3.3	1.4	1.1	1.8	0.8	8.4
1972	55.2	26.9	8.0	3.6	3.2	1.4	1.2	1.8	0.8	8.3
1973	54.8	26.3	7.8	4.1	3.1	1.4	1.2	1.7	0.8	8.4

See source and footnotes on page 55.

Unintentional-injury-related death rates[a] for principal types, United States, 1903-1998 (cont.)

Year	Total	Motor vehicle	Falls	Drowning[b]	Fire, flames, or smoke[c]	Choking[c]	Firearms	Poison (solid or liquid)	Poison (gas or vapor)	All other
1974	49.0	21.8	7.7	3.7	2.9	1.4	1.2	1.8	0.7	7.8
1975	47.8	21.3	6.9	3.7	2.8	1.4	1.1	2.2	0.7	7.7
1976	46.3	21.6	6.5	3.1	2.9	1.4	0.9	1.9	0.7	7.3
1977	47.0	22.5	6.3	3.2	2.9	1.4	0.9	1.5	0.7	7.6
1978	47.5	23.6	6.2	3.2	2.8	1.4	0.8	1.4	0.8	7.3
1979	46.9	23.8	5.9	3.1	2.7	1.4	0.9	1.4	0.7	7.0
1980	46.5	23.4	5.9	3.2	2.6	1.4	0.9	1.4	0.5	7.2
1981	43.9	22.4	5.5	2.7	2.5	1.5	0.8	1.4	0.6	6.5
1982	40.6	19.8	5.2	2.7	2.2	1.4	0.8	1.5	0.5	6.5
1983	39.6	19.0	5.1	2.7	2.2	1.4	0.7	1.4	0.5	6.6
1984	39.4	19.6	5.1	2.3	2.1	1.5	0.7	1.6	0.5	6.0
1985	39.3	19.3	5.0	2.2	2.1	1.5	0.7	1.7	0.5	6.3
1986	39.7	19.9	4.8	2.4	2.0	1.5	0.6	2.0	0.4	6.1
1987	39.2	19.9	4.8	2.1	1.9	1.5	0.6	1.8	0.4	6.2
1988	39.7	20.1	4.9	2.0	2.0	1.6	0.6	2.2	0.4	5.9
1989	38.5	19.3	4.9	1.9	1.9	1.4	0.6	2.3	0.4	5.8
1990	36.9	18.8	4.9	1.9	1.7	1.3	0.6	2.0	0.3	5.4
1991	35.4	17.3	5.0	1.8	1.6	1.3	0.6	2.3	0.3	5.2
1992	34.0	16.1	5.0	1.4	1.6	1.2	0.6	2.5	0.2	5.4
1993	35.1	16.3	5.1	1.5	1.5	1.2	0.6	3.1	0.3	5.5
1994	35.1	16.3	5.2	1.5	1.5	1.2	0.5	3.2	0.3	5.4
1995	35.5	16.5	5.3	1.7	1.4	1.2	0.5	3.2	0.2	5.5
1996	35.8	16.5	5.6	1.5	1.4	1.2	0.4	3.3	0.2	5.7
1997	35.7	16.2	5.8	1.5	1.3	1.2	0.4	3.6	0.2	5.5
1998	36.2	16.1	6.0	1.6	1.2	1.3	0.3	3.8	0.2	5.7

Unintentional-injury-related death rates[a] for principal types, United States, 1999-2014

Year	Total	Motor vehicle	Falls	Poisoning	Choking[c]	Drowning[g]	Fire, flames, or smoke[c]	Mechanical suffocation	Firearms	All other
1999[h]	35.9	15.5	4.8	4.5	1.4	1.3	1.2	0.6	0.3	6.3
2000	35.6	15.7	4.8	4.6	1.6	1.3	1.2	0.5	0.3	5.5
2001	35.6	15.4	5.3	4.9	1.5	1.2	1.2	0.5	0.3	5.5
2002	37.1	15.8	5.6	6.4	1.4	1.2	1.1	0.5	0.3	4.7
2003	37.6	15.4	5.9	6.7	1.5	1.1	1.2	0.4	0.3	5.1
2004	38.1	15.3	6.4	7.1	1.5	1.1	1.1	0.5	0.2	4.9
2005	39.7	15.3	6.6	8.0	1.5	1.2	1.1	0.5	0.3	5.3
2006	40.8	15.2	7.0	9.2	1.5	1.2	1.0	0.5	0.2	4.9
2007	41.1	14.6	7.5	9.9	1.4	1.1	1.1	0.5	0.2	4.8
2008	40.0	13.1	7.9	10.2	1.4	1.2	1.0	0.6	0.2	4.7
2009	38.5	11.8	8.1	10.3	1.4	1.1	0.9	0.5	0.2	4.1
2010	39.0	11.4	8.4	10.7	1.5	1.2	0.9	0.5	0.2	4.4
2011	40.6	11.3	8.8	11.6	1.5	1.1	0.9	0.5	0.2	4.6
2012	40.7	11.6	9.2	11.6	1.5	1.1	0.8	0.5	0.2	4.3
2013[i]	41.3	11.2	9.6	12.3	1.5	1.1	0.9	0.5	0.2	4.1
2014	42.7	11.1	10.0	13.2	1.5	1.1	0.8	0.6	0.2	4.3
Changes										
2005 to 2014	8%	−27%	52%	65%	0%	−8%	−27%	20%	−33%	−19%
2013 to 2014	3%	−1%	4%	7%	0%	0%	−11%	20%	0%	5%

Source: National Safety Council estimates. See Technical Appendix for comparability.

[a] Deaths per 100,000 population.

[b] Includes drowning in water transport incidents.

[c] Fires, flames, or smoke includes burns by fire and deaths resulting from conflagration regardless of nature of injury. Choking is the inhalation of food or other object obstructing breathing.

[d] Comparable data not available.

[e] In 1948, a revision was made in the International Classification of Diseases. The first figures for 1948 are comparable with those for earlier years, the second with those for later years.

[f] Data are not comparable to previous years shown due to classification changes in 1958 and 1968.

[g] Excludes water transport drownings.

[h] In 1999, a revision was made in the International Classification of Diseases. See the Technical Appendix for comparability.

[i] Revised.

Occupational

Workers' Compensation Claims Costs, 2012-2013 (cont.)

Average total incurred costs per claim by nature of injury, 2012-2013

$78,091

$54,344

$46,575

$42,388 $36,908

All claims average
$37,738

$34,417 $32,036 $30,680 $29,782 $29,492

- Indemnity
- Medical
- All claims average

Sprain/strain
Lacerate/puncture/rupture
Contusion/concussion
Carpal tunnel

2-2013

All claims average
$37,738

$33,279 $31,788 $28,398

$26,357 $24,964 $22,384 $22,124

- Indemnity
- Medical
- All claims a

per back
Knee
Face
Ankle
Foot/toes
Multiple trunk/abdomen
Hand/fingers/wrist

NATIONAL SAFETY COUNC

Contractor Fatal Occupational Injuries – pg. 72

In 2014, the number of contractor fatalities have increased for the second consecutive year, now totaling 792 and representing 17.0% of all work-related fatalities. The Bureau of Labor Statistics defines contractor as a worker employed by one firm (or who is self-employed), but working at the behest of another firm that exercises overall responsibility for the operations at the site where the decedent was killed. Looking at the percent of fatalities occurring to contractors shows that nearly 52% of the fatalities occurring in the construction industry were contractor deaths, while over 28% of the fatalities occurring in professional and business services occurred to contractors.

The 2013 fatality data presented in this section are preliminary. All Census of Fatal Occupational Injuries fatal injury rates published by the Bureau of Labor Statistics (BLS) for the years 1992-2007 were employment-based, and measured the risk of fatal injury for those employed during a given period of time, regardless of hours worked.

Starting in 2008, BLS moved to hours-based rates to measure fatal injury risk per standardized length of exposure, which are generally considered more accurate than employment-based rates. Caution should be used when comparing fatality rates prior to 2008.

In addition to unintentional fatal work injuries, 667 homicides and suicides occurred in the workplace in 2013. These intentional injuries are not included in the unintentional-injury data shown here.

The State Data section, which begins on page 171, shows fatal occupational injuries and nonfatal injury and illness incidence rates by state.

Unintentional-injury-related deaths 4,005
Unintentional-injury-related deaths per 100,000 full-time equivalent workers[a] 2.9
Medically consulted injuries 4,710,000
Workers 146,307,000
Costs .... $140.0 billion

Unintentional injuries at work by industry (preliminary), United States, 2014

Industry division	Hours worked[a] (millions)	Deaths[a]		Deaths per 100,000 full-time equivalent workers[a]		Medically consulted injuries[c]
		2014	Change from 2013	2014	Change from 2013	
All industries	272,675	4,005	3%	2.9	0%	4,710,000
Agriculture[b]	4,460	551	15%	24.7	9%	120,000
Mining[b]	2,561	181	17%	14.1	14%	30,000
Construction	18,168	837	5%	9.2	-2%	330,000
Manufacturing	30,830	306	9%	2.0	5%	620,000
Wholesale trade	7,430	161	-10%	4.3	-10%	110,000
Retail trade	28,997	125	-11%	0.9	-10%	520,000
Transportation and warehousing	10,897	669	0%	12.3	-4%	260,000
Utilities	1,957	14	-42%	1.4	-48%	20,000
Information	5,759	30	-12%	1.0	-17%	40,000
Financial activities	18,852	71	42%	0.8	60%	110,000
Professional and business services	31,497	353	-4%	2.2	-8%	240,000
Educational and health services	40,633	116	10%	0.6	20%	850,000
Leisure and hospitality	21,334	137	25%	1.3	30%	380,000
Other services[b]	12,440	128	-6%	2.1	-5%	160,000
Government	36,860	328	-12%	1.8	-10%	920,000

Source: Deaths are preliminary data from the Bureau of Labor Statistics (BLS) Census of Fatal Occupational Injuries. All other figures are National Safety Council estimates based on data from BLS.

[a]Deaths include persons of all ages. Workers and death rates include persons 16 years and older. The rate is calculated as: (number of fatal work injuries x 200,000,000/total hours worked). The base for 100,000 full-time equivalent workers is 200,000,000 hours. Prior to 2008, rates were based on estimated employment – not hours worked.

[b]Agriculture includes forestry, fishing, and hunting. Mining includes oil and gas extraction. "Other services" excludes public administration.

[c]See Technical Appendix for the definition of medically consulted injury.

Occupational unintentional-injury-related deaths and death rates by industry, United States, 2014

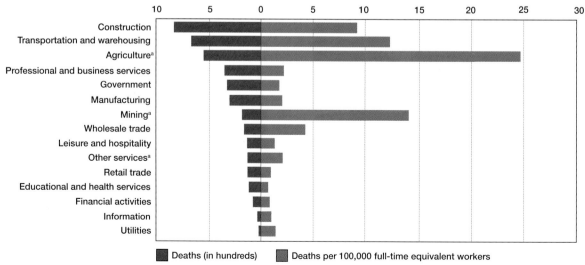

[a]Agriculture includes forestry, fishing, and hunting. Mining includes oil and gas extraction. "Other services" excludes public administration.

Occupational Injuries and Illnesses with Days Away From Work, United States, 2013

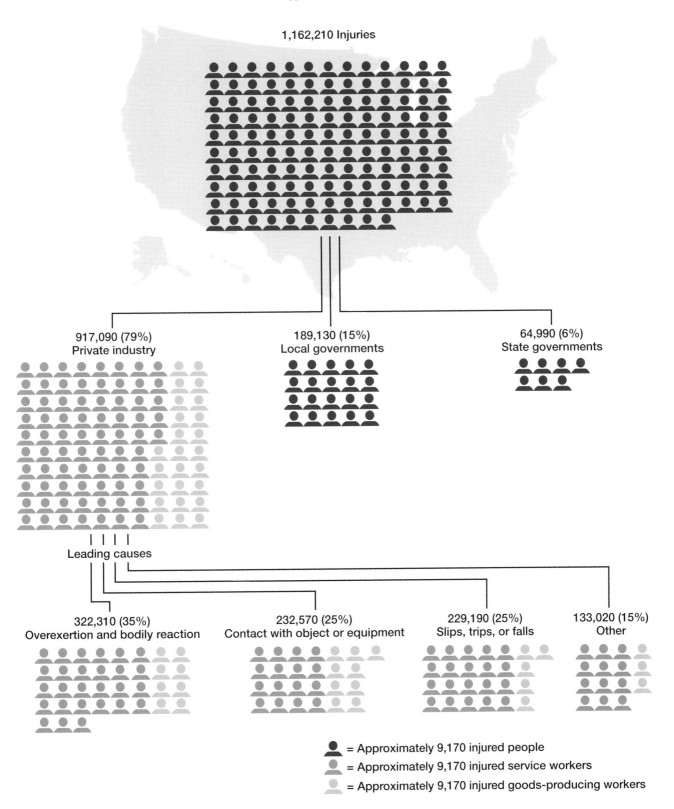

1,162,210 Injuries

917,090 (79%)
Private industry

189,130 (15%)
Local governments

64,990 (6%)
State governments

Leading causes

322,310 (35%)
Overexertion and bodily reaction

232,570 (25%)
Contact with object or equipment

229,190 (25%)
Slips, trips, or falls

133,020 (15%)
Other

= Approximately 9,170 injured people

= Approximately 9,170 injured service workers

= Approximately 9,170 injured goods-producing workers

Unintentional-work-related-injury deaths and death rates, United States, 1992-2014

Year	Deaths	Workers (in thousands)	Hours worked[a] (in millions)	Deaths per 100,000 workers[a]
1992	4,965	119,168		4.2
1993	5,034	120,778		4.2
1994	5,338	124,470		4.3
1995	5,015	126,248		4.0
1996	5,069	127,997		4.0
1997	5,160	130,810		3.9
1998	5,117	132,772		3.9
1999	5,184	134,688		3.8
2000	5,022	136,402		3.7
2001	5,042	136,246		3.7
2002	4,726	137,731		3.4
2003	4,725	138,988		3.4
2004	4,995	140,504		3.6
2005	4,984	142,946		3.5
2006	5,088	145,607		3.5
2007	4,829	147,203		3.3
2008[a]	4,423	146,535	271,958	3.3[a]
2009	3,744	141,102	254,771	2.9
2010	3,896	140,298	255,948	3.0
2011	3,901	140,298	258,293	3.0
2012	3,903	143,709	264,374	3.0
2013[b]	3,899	145,171	268,127	2.9
2014[c]	4,005	146,307	272,663	2.9

Source: Deaths are from the Bureau of Labor Statistics (BLS) Census of Fatal Occupational Injuries (CFOI). Employment is from BLS and is based on the Current Population Survey. All other data are National Safety Council estimates.

Note: Deaths include persons of all ages. Workers and death rates include persons 16 and older. Workers are persons 16 years and older who are gainfully employed, including owners, managers, other paid employees, the self-employed, unpaid family workers, and active-duty resident military personnel. Because of adoption of CFOI, deaths and rates from 1992 to present are not comparable to prior years. See the Technical Appendix for additional information.

[a]Starting in 2008, BLS moved from employment-based rates to hours-based rates to measure fatal injury risk per standardized length of exposure, which are generally considered more accurate than employment-based rates. Caution should be used when comparing with rates prior to 2008.

[b]Revised.

[c]Preliminary. BLS urges caution when using preliminary estimates.

Workers, unintentional-work-related-injury deaths, and death rates, United States, 1992-2014

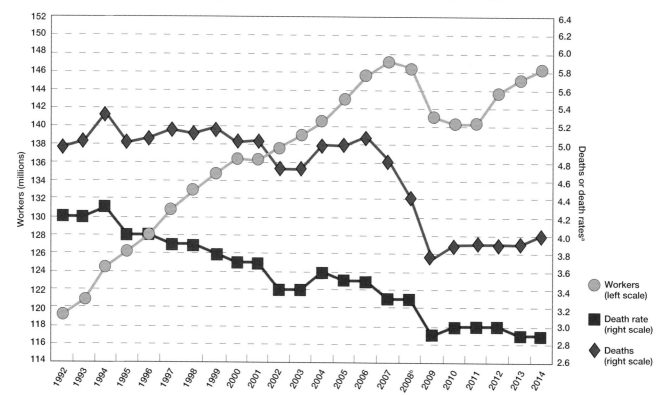

[a]Deaths in thousands; rate per 100,000 workers.

[b]Starting in 2008, the Bureau of Labor Statistics changed from an employment-based rate to an hours-based rate.

Occupational injury-related deaths and death rates, United States, 1994-2002

Year	Total	Homicide and suicide	Unintentional								
			All industries[a]	Agriculture[b]	Mining, quarrying[c]	Construction	Manufacturing	Transportation and public utilities	Trade[d]	Services[e]	Government
Deaths											
1994	6,632	1,294	5,338	814	177	1,000	734	819	492	676	534
1995	6,275	1,260	5,015	769	155	1,021	640	784	461	608	528
1996	6,202	1,133	5,069	762	151	1,025	660	883	451	615	321
1997	6,238	1,078	5,160	799	156	1,075	678	882	451	593	504
1998	6,055	938	5,117	808	143	1,136	631	830	443	634	465
1999	6,054	870	5,184	776	122	1,168	671	918	425	623	451
2000	5,920	898	5,022	693	153	1,114	624	872	447	643	460
2001	5,915	873[f]	5,042	714	169	1,183	546	844	431	636	507
2002	5,534	808	4,726	758	120	1,092	523	843	381	569	437
Deaths per 100,000 workers											
1994	5.3	1.0	4.3	22.8	26.5	14.4	3.7	11.6	1.9	1.7	2.7
1995	4.9	1.0	4.0	21.4	24.8	14.3	3.1	11.0	1.8	1.5	2.7
1996	4.8	0.9	4.0	21.2	26.6	13.7	3.2	12.2	1.7	1.4	1.6
1997	4.8	0.8	3.9	22.5	24.7	13.7	3.3	11.6	1.7	1.3	2.6
1998	4.5	0.7	3.9	22.7	23.1	14.1	3.1	10.8	1.6	1.4	2.4
1999	4.5	0.6	3.8	22.6	21.7	13.8	3.4	11.5	1.5	1.3	2.2
2000	4.3	0.7	3.7	20.1	29.4	12.4	3.1	10.8	1.6	1.4	2.3
2001	4.3	0.6[f]	3.7	22.0	29.9	13.0	2.9	10.4	1.6	1.3	2.5
2002	4.0	0.6	3.4	21.8	23.3	11.9	2.9	10.5	1.4	1.1	2.1

Source: Deaths are from the Bureau of Labor Statistics (BLS) Census of Fatal Occupational Injuries. Rates are National Safety Council estimates based on BLS employment data. Deaths include persons of all ages. Death rates include persons 16 years and older. Industry divisions are based on the Standard Industrial Classification Manual.
[a]*Includes deaths with industry unknown.*
[b]*Agriculture includes forestry, fishing, and agricultural services.*
[c]*Mining includes oil and gas extraction.*
[d]*Trade includes wholesale and retail trade.*
[e]*Services includes finance, insurance, and real estate.*
[f]*Excludes 2,886 homicides of workers on Sept. 11, 2001.*

Occupational injury-related deaths and death rates, United States, 2003-2014

Year	Total	Homicide and suicide	Unintentional															
			All industries[a]	Agriculture, forestry, fishing, and hunting	Mining	Construction	Manufacturing	Wholesale trade	Retail trade	Transportation and warehousing	Utilities	Information	Financial activities	Professional and business services	Educational and health services	Leisure and hospitality	Other services	Government
Deaths																		
2003	5,575	850	4,725	676	141	1,094	379	169	148	735	29	57	82	396	116	142	123	434
2004	5,764	769	4,995	651	151	1,203	421	187	189	779	49	49	68	401	123	144	144	432
2005	5,734	750	4,984	697	154	1,161	357	197	198	831	28	56	66	442	122	114	149	404
2006	5,840	752	5,088	635	190	1,199	423	210	190	803	52	61	82	407	142	136	142	409
2007	5,657	828	4,829	564	180	1,163	364	193	160	819	33	70	69	415	121	138	116	421
2008	5,214	791	4,423	640	173	937	364	157	158	724	37	36	65	351	110	118	130	414
2009	4,551	807	3,744	545	96	793	290	168	137	576	13	28	58	363	101	119	110	347
2010	4,690	794	3,896	603	170	744	284	157	148	595	26	32	65	316	133	142	131	350
2011	4,692	791	3,901	532	148	706	293	173	133	692	34	47	49	374	109	137	122	352
2012	4,628	725	3,903	500	177	775	284	185	149	670	22	31	56	360	106	136	122	327
2013[b]	4,585	686	3,899	479	155	799	280	179	140	670	24	34	50	369	105	110	136	371
2014[c]	4,679	674	4,005	551	181	837	306	161	125	669	14	30	71	353	116	137	128	328
Deaths per 100,000 workers[d]																		
2003	4.0	0.6	3.4	30.0	26.9	11.4	2.3	3.8	0.9	16.0	3.3	1.6	0.9	2.9	0.6	1.3	1.8	2.1
2004	4.1	0.5	3.6	29.7	28.1	11.7	2.6	4.1	1.2	16.7	5.9	1.5	0.7	2.9	0.7	1.3	2.1	2.0
2005	4.0	0.5	3.5	31.7	24.8	10.8	2.2	4.3	1.2	16.7	3.4	1.7	0.7	3.2	0.6	1.0	2.1	1.9
2006	4.0	0.5	3.5	29.1	27.8	10.6	2.6	4.6	1.1	15.7	6.2	1.8	0.8	2.8	0.7	1.2	2.0	1.9
2007	3.8	0.5	3.3	26.9	24.7	10.2	2.2	4.4	1.0	15.6	3.9	2.1	0.7	2.7	0.6	1.2	1.7	1.9
2008[d]	3.8	0.6	3.3	29.4	17.8	9.4	2.3	3.8	1.1	13.6	4.0	1.1	0.7	2.4	0.6	1.1	2.1	2.1
2009	3.6	0.6	2.9	26.3	12.2	9.5	2.1	4.4	1.0	12.1	1.4	1.0	0.6	2.7	0.5	1.2	1.8	1.8
2010	3.7	0.6	3.0	27.9	19.6	9.4	2.0	4.1	1.1	12.4	2.8	1.1	0.7	2.3	0.7	1.4	2.2	1.9
2011	3.6	0.6	3.0	24.1	15.2	8.8	2.0	4.5	1.0	14.2	3.7	1.6	0.6	2.6	0.6	1.4	2.1	1.9
2012	3.5	0.5	3.0	23.1	15.6	9.6	1.9	4.9	1.1	13.2	2.5	1.1	0.6	2.4	0.5	1.3	2.0	1.8
2013[b]	3.4	0.5	2.9	22.6	12.4	9.4	1.9	4.8	1.0	12.8	2.7	1.2	0.5	2.4	0.5	1.0	2.2	2.0
2014[c]	3.4	0.5	2.9	24.7	14.1	9.2	2.0	4.3	0.9	12.3	1.4	1.0	0.8	2.2	0.6	1.3	2.1	1.8

Source: Deaths are from the Bureau of Labor Statistics (BLS) Census of Fatal Occupational Injuries. Rates are National Safety Council estimates based on BLS employment data. Deaths include persons of all ages. Death rates include persons 16 years and older. Industry sectors are based on the North American Industry Classification System.
[a]*Includes deaths with industry unknown.*
[b]*Revised.*
[c]*Preliminary. BLS urges caution when using preliminary estimates.*
[d]*Starting in 2008, BLS moved from employment-based rates to hours-based rates to measure fatal injury risk per standardized length of exposure. Caution should be used when comparing with rates prior to 2008.*

Work Injury Costs

The true cost to the nation, employers, and individuals of work-related deaths and injuries is much greater than the cost of workers' compensation insurance alone. The figures presented below show National Safety Council estimates of the total economic costs of occupational deaths and injuries. Major revisions were made to the National Safety Council cost model for this edition that take advantage of data sources not previously available. Because of the changes made to the cost model, cost estimates provided in this edition are not comparable to previously published estimates. For this reason, **costs should not be compared to prior years.**

TOTAL COST IN 2014 ....$140.0 Billion
Includes wage and productivity losses of $45.7 billion, medical costs of $31.7 billion, and administrative expenses of $44.7 billion. Includes employers' uninsured costs of $11.5 billion, such as the money value of time lost by workers other than those with disabling injuries; who are directly or indirectly involved in injuries; and the cost of time required to investigate injuries, write up injury reports, etc. Also includes damage to motor vehicles in work-related injuries of $3.5 billion and fire losses of $2.9 billion.

COST PER WORKER **$1,000**
Includes the value of goods or services each worker must produce to offset the cost of work injuries. It is *not* the average cost of a work-related injury.

COST PER DEATH $1,000,000

COST PER MEDICALLY CONSULTED INJURY $29,000
Includes estimates of wage losses, medical expenses, administrative expenses, and employer costs; excludes property damage costs except to motor vehicles.

Time Lost Due to Work-Related Injuries

	Days lost
TOTAL TIME LOST IN 2014	**99,000,000**
Due to injuries in 2014	**65,000,000**

Includes primarily the actual time lost during the year from disabling injuries, except it does not include time lost on the day of the injury or time required for further medical treatment or check-up following the injured person's return to work.

Fatalities are included at an average loss of 150 days per case, and permanent impairments are included at actual days lost plus an allowance for lost efficiency resulting from the impairment.

Not included is time lost by people with nondisabling injuries or other people directly or indirectly involved in the incidents.

	Days lost
Due to injuries in prior years	**34,000,000**

Represents productive time lost in 2014 due to permanently disabling injuries that occurred in prior years.

TIME LOST IN FUTURE YEARS	**Days lost**
FROM 2014 INJURIES	**50,000,000**

Includes time lost in future years due to on-the-job deaths and permanently disabling injuries that occurred in 2014.

Nine out of 10 deaths and about 75% of the medically consulted injuries[a] suffered by workers in 2014 occurred off the job. While over 14 times the number of deaths occur off the job compared to on the job (14.5 to 1), over three times as many medically consulted injuries occur off the job (3.1 to 1).

Production time lost due to off-the-job injuries totaled about 270,000,000 days in 2014, compared with 65,000,000 days lost by workers injured on the job.

Production time lost in future years due to off-the-job injuries in 2014 will total an estimated 570,000,000 days, over 11 times the 50,000,000 days lost in future years from 2014's on-the-job injuries.

Off-the-job injuries to workers cost the nation at least $339.4 billion in 2014 compared with $140.0 billion for on-the-job injuries.

Workers' on- and off-the-job deaths and injuries, United States, 2014

| | Deaths | | Medically consulted injuries[a] | |
Place	Number	Rate[b]	Number	Rate[b]
On and off the job	**62,008**	**0.014**	**19,100,000**	**4.4**
On the job	4,008	0.003	4,700,000	3.0
Off the job	58,000	0.021	14,400,000	5.1
Motor vehicle	18,100	0.062	2,100,000	7.2
Public non-motor vehicle	9,800	0.022	3,500,000	7.7
Home	30,100	0.015	8,800,000	4.3

Source: National Safety Council estimates. Procedures for allocating time spent on and off the job were revised for the 1990 edition. Rate basis changed to 200,000 hours for the 1998 edition. Death and injury rates are not comparable to rate estimates prior to the 1998 edition.
[a] Medically consulted injuries are not comparable to estimates provided in earlier editions that used the definition of disabling injury. Please see the Technical Appendix for more information on medically consulted injuries.
[b] Per 200,000 hours exposure by place.

Workers' on- and off-the-job deaths and injuries, United States, 2014

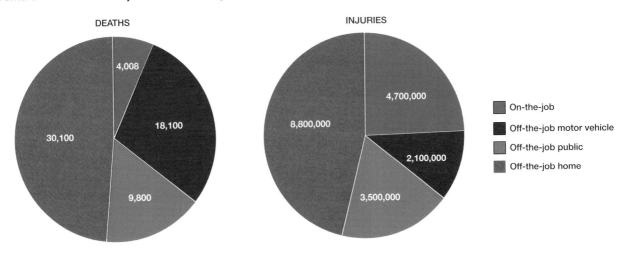

Workers' off-the-job fatalities by event, 2014

Workers' Compensation Cases

According to the National Academy of Social Insurance, an estimated $63.6 billion, including benefits under deductible provisions, was paid out under workers' compensation in 2013 (the latest year for which data were available) – an increase of 8.2% from 2009. Of this total, $32.0 billion was for income benefits and $31.5 billion was for medical and hospitalization costs. Private carriers paid about $35.3 billion of the total workers' compensation benefits in 2013. In 2013,

approximately 129.6 million workers were covered by workers' compensation – an increase of 3.8% from 2009.

The table below shows the trend in the number of compensated or reported cases in each reporting state. Due to the differences in population, industries, and coverage of compensation laws, comparisons among states should not be made.

Workers' compensation cases, 2012-2014

State	Deaths[a]			Cases[a]			2013 compensation paid ($000)
	2014	2013	2012	2014	2013	2012	
Alabama[b]	19	16	32	13,290	13,471	14,809	639,311
California	446	619	658	588,867	584,499	591,438	12,100,181
Colorado[b]	—	73	88	—	27,243	26,757	858,947
Delaware	—	14	10	—	13,478	15,814	240,313
Florida[c]	98	109	116	53,318	56,494	57,500	3,131,293
Georgia	96	98	107	39,212	33,729	36,515	1,566,186
Idaho	33	20	32	34,042	32,119	30,935	251,846
Indiana	90	90	90	56,004	57,279	59,292	674,206
Iowa[b]	48	49	50	16,703	17,035	17,114	668,646
Kansas	50	51	33	52,782	55,269	57,542	387,384
Louisiana[c, d]	78[e]	37[f]	47	9,419[e]	9,912[f]	11,172	870,086
Maryland[g]	58	56	50	24,113	23,241	22,909	944,612
Minnesota[h]	—	55	57	—	98,500	95,850	1,064,684
Mississippi[i]	68	62	67	11,071	10,834	11,313	332,790
Missouri	80	101	83	101,548	103,030	105,643	873,946
Montana	25	27	30	26,115	25,416	25,386	247,003
Nebraska	50	35	50	40,285	40,411	42,552	305,001
New Hampshire	13	18	20	39,425	38,998	39,954	214,560
New Mexico	49	35	34	43,855	44,085	46,758	267,330
North Dakota[g]	47	47	37	26,395	25,835	24,647	193,975
Oregon[i]	31	30	30	19,742	18,633	18,643	668,686
Rhode Island	4	4	2	18,549	19,184	18,935	162,356
South Carolina[i]	55	62	82	65,300	62,213	61,788	878,428
South Dakota	13	6	11	22,433	22,160	22,824	94,015
Tennessee	100	97	100	101,763	98,892	101,950	808,055
Vermont	11	7	12	17,048	16,534	16,688	141,511
Virginia	83	49	71	134,751	133,193	143,271	953,165
Washington[i]	49	43	48	122,423	120,133	120,399	2,331,783
West Virginia	18	23	17	33,996	35,193	34,381	436,017
Wisconsin[j]	—	96[k]	114	31,672	31,759	31,943	1,126,058
Wyoming	12	26	35	13,050	12,981	12,274	191,807

Source: Deaths and Cases–State workers' compensation authorities for calendar or fiscal year. States not listed did not respond to the survey. Compensation paid–Sengupta, I. & Baldwin, M. L. (2015 August). Workers' compensation: benefits, coverage, and costs, 2013. Washington, DC: National Academy of Social Insurance. Note: Dash (—) indicates data not available.

Definitions

Reported case: A reported case may or may not be work-related and may not receive compensation.
Compensated case: A case determined to be work-related and for which compensation was paid.

[a] Reported cases involving medical and indemnity benefits, unless otherwise noted.
[b] Reported cases involving indemnity benefits only.
[c] Lost-time only cases involving medical and indemnity benefits.
[d] Includes reported and closed or compensated cases.
[e] Adopted mandatory International Association of Industrial Accident Boards and Commissions (IAIABC) Electronic Data Interchange (EDI) First Report of Injury (FROI).
[f] Adopted voluntary International Association of Industrial Accident Boards and Commissions (IAIABC) Electronic Data Interchange (EDI) First Report of Injury (FROI).
[g] Includes all claims filed and cases involving medical and indemnity benefits.
[h] Number of paid cases by year, projected to full maturity.
[i] Closed or compensated cases only.
[j] Includes all claims reported.
[k] Preliminary.

The most disabling workplace injuries and illnesses in 2012 amounted to $59.6 billion in direct workers' compensation costs, according to the 2014 Liberty Mutual Workplace Safety Index (WSI). The WSI combines information from Liberty Mutual, the Bureau of Labor Statistics, and the National Academy of Social Insurance to identify the top causes of serious workplace injuries—those that cause an employee to miss six or more days of work. The 2013 WSI began a new series that reflected a significant change in the Bureau of Labor Statistics' injury event coding and the results of it and later series are not directly comparable to those of prior series.

The top 10 causes of serious workplace injuries produced about 84% of the direct workers' compensation costs of disabling work-

place injuries in 2012. Overexertion injuries involving an outside source were the largest contributor to the overall burden, accounting for $15.1 billion, or over 25%, of the total cost. "Fall on the same level" ($9.19 billion) and "struck by object or equipment" ($5.3 billion) were the next most costly injury causes. The combined cost of all falls was slightly less than the cost for the "overexertion" category, indicating that total falls were comparable to "overexertion" in terms of impact on the overall cost burden.

Source: 2014 Liberty Mutual Workplace Safety Index, accessed September 16, 2015 from www.libertymutualgroup.com/researchinstitute.

Workers' compensation costs for the top 10 causes of disabling workplace injuries, United States, 2012

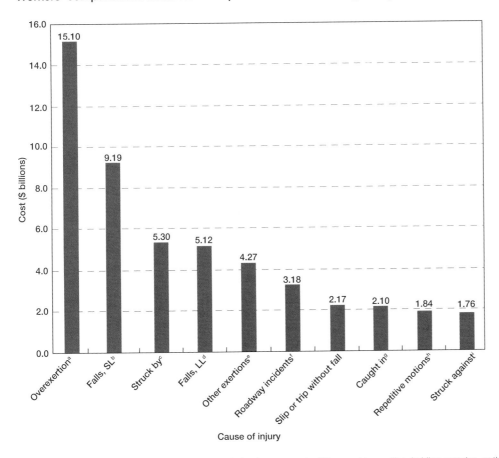

ᵃOverexertion involving an outside source; includes injuries from excessive lifting, pushing, pulling, holding, carrying, or throwing.
ᵇFalls on same level.
ᶜStruck by object—such as a tool falling on a worker from above.
ᵈFalls to lower level.
ᵉOther exertions or bodily reactions; includes injuries from bending, crawling, reaching, twisting, climbing, stepping, kneeling, sitting, standing, or walking (and no longer includes slipping or tripping without falling).
ᶠRoadway incidents involving motorized land vehicle.
ᵍCaught in or compressed by equipment or objects.
ʰRepetitive motions involving micro-tasks.
ⁱStruck against object or equipment—such as a worker walking into a door.

Workers' Compensation Claims Costs, 2012-2013

■ *Head injuries are the most costly workers' compensation claims.*

The data in the graphs on this and the next page are from the National Council on Compensation Insurance's (NCCI) Workers Compensation Statistical Plan (WCSP) database.[a] WCSP reflects claims experience on workers' compensation insurance policies issued in states in which NCCI collects such data. The aggregate unit statistical data were valued 30 months after the inception date of the policy (as of the second report). The average cost for all claims combined in 2012-2013 was $37,738.

NCCI data that appeared in *Injury Facts* prior to the 2011 edition were sourced to NCCI's Detailed Claim Information file, which was a stratified random sample of lost-time claims in 42 states. Workers' compensation estimates provided in this edition are not comparable to estimates provided in editions prior to 2011.

Cause of injury. The most costly lost-time workers' compensation claims by cause of injury, according to NCCI data, are for those resulting from motor vehicle crashes. These injuries averaged $72,379 per workers' compensation claim filed in 2012 and 2013. The only other causes with above-average costs were burns ($45,726) and falls or slips ($44,271).

Nature of injury. The most costly lost-time workers' compensation claims by nature of injury are for those resulting from amputation. These injuries averaged $78,091 per workers' compensation claim filed in 2012 and 2013. The next highest costs were for injuries resulting in fracture, crush, or dislocation ($54,344); other trauma ($46,575); and burns ($42,388).

Part of body. The most costly lost-time workers' compensation claims are for those involving the head or central nervous system. These injuries averaged $78,183 per claim filed in 2012 and 2013. The next highest costs were for injuries involving multiple body parts ($61,814) and the neck ($58,491). Injuries to the hip, thigh, and pelvis; leg; arm or shoulders; and lower back also had above-average costs.

Average total incurred costs per claim by cause of injury, 2012-2013

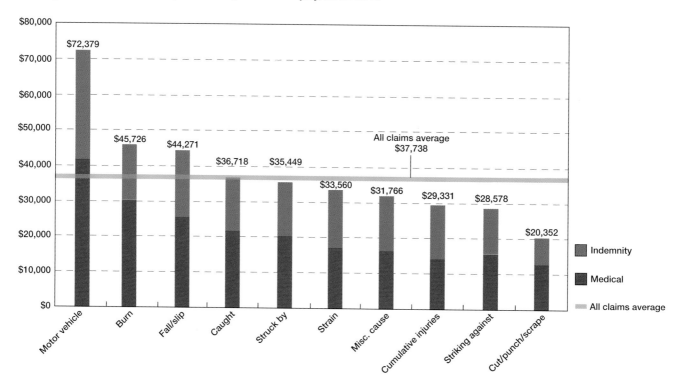

[a] The National Council on Compensation Insurance makes no representations or warranties of any kind nor assumes any responsibility for the accuracy of the underlying data or any third-party use of the data on this and the following page.

Workers' Compensation Claims Costs, 2012-2013 (cont.)

Average total incurred costs per claim by nature of injury, 2012-2013

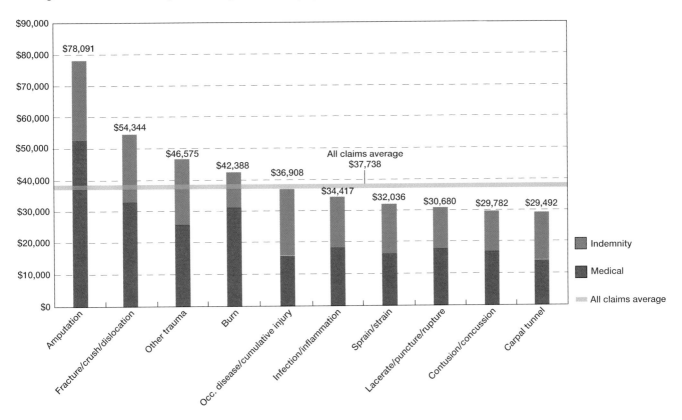

Average total incurred costs per claim by part of body, 2012-2013

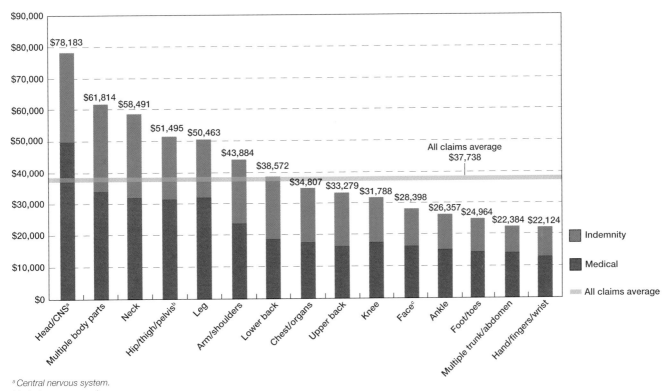

[a] Central nervous system.
[b] Includes sacrum and coccyx.
[c] Includes teeth, mouth, and eyes.

Forklifts

Beginning with 2011, occupational injury data from the Bureau of Labor Statistics are based on the revised Occupational Injury and Illness Classification System (OIICS) 2.01 and are not comparable to the data for prior years in the tables below. The preliminary total of fatal occupational injuries in private industry with a forklift as the primary source of injury numbered 57 in 2014, a 19% decrease from 2013. There was a preliminary total of an additional 32 fatal occupational injuries with a forklift as the secondary source of injury in 2014, up 52% from 2013. Forklift fatalities are most prevalent in the trade, transportation, and utilities; manufacturing; and construction industries.

The rate of nonfatal forklift injuries involving days away from work was 0.7 per 10,000 full-time workers in 2013, down from 0.8 in 2012. Trade, transportation, and utilities had the highest rate of nonfatal forklift injuries, followed by manufacturing and natural resources and mining.

Number of fatal occupational injuries with a forklift as the source of injury, private industry, United States, 2011-2014

Industry division	Year[a]							
	2011		2012		2013		2014[b]	
	Forklift as primary[c] source	Forklift as secondary[d] source	Forklift as primary[c] source	Forklift as secondary[d] source	Forklift as primary[c] source	Forklift as secondary[d] source	Forklift as primary[c] source	Forklift as secondary[d] source
All Industries	66	24	67	27	69	20	57	32
Natural resources and mining[e]	8	—	6	4	5	4	5	3
Construction	11	4	9	5	9	1	7	4
Manufacturing	16	3	18	8	17	4	14	6
Trade, transportation, and utilities	24	9	28	10	27	8	23	17
Information	—	—	—	—	—	—	—	—
Financial activities	—	3	—	—	—	—	—	—
Professional and business services	6	3	—	—	5	—	3	1
Education and health services	—	—	—	—	—	—	—	—
Leisure and hospitality	—	—	—	—	—	—	1	—
Other services[e]	—	—	3	—	5	—	—	—

Source: Bureau of Labor Statistics (BLS) Occupational Injuries and Illnesses and Fatal Injuries Profiles, accessed September 28, 2015. Available at http://www.bls. gov/iif/#data. Data may not add to totals because of rounding or exclusion of data that do not meet publication guidelines. Dashes (–) indicate no data reported or data that do not meet publication guidelines.
[a]Data for 2011-2014 are based on the revised BLS Occupational Injury and Illness Classification System (OIICS) 2.01 and not comparable to data for prior years.
[b]Data for 2014 are preliminary.
[c]The primary source of a fatal occupational injury is the object, substance, person, bodily motion, or exposure that most directly led to, produced, or inflicted the injury or illness.
[d]The secondary source of a fatal occupational injury is the object, substance, person, or exposure other than the source (if any) that most actively generated the source or contributed to the injury or illness.
[e]"Natural resources" includes agriculture, forestry, fishing, and hunting and excludes farms with fewer than 11 employees. "Mining" includes oil and gas extraction. "Other services" excludes public administration.

Incidence rates[a] of nonfatal occupational injuries and illnesses involving days away from work[b] with a forklift as the source of injury or illness, private industry, United States, 2007-2013

Industry division	All sources rate[a]	Forklift injury rate[a]						
	2013	2007	2008	2009	2010	2011[c]	2012[c]	2013[c]
All industries	99.9	1.2	1.1	0.9	0.8	0.7	0.8	0.7
Natural resources and mining[d]	150.4	1.5	1.2	0.6	1.1	0.9	2.5	1.3
Construction	154.7	0.8	0.9	0.8	0.7	0.6	0.8	0.6
Manufacturing	100.9	2.3	2.0	1.5	1.9	1.5	1.6	1.6
Trade, transportation, and utilities	127.7	2.7	2.6	2.3	2	1.6	1.9	1.7
Information	64.7	0.3	0.5	0.2	0.2	0.1	0.1	0.2
Financial activities	40.6	0.0[e]	0.0[e]	0.2	0.0[e]	0.0[e]	0.0[e]	0.1
Professional and business services	49.0	0.4	0.3	0.4	0.3	0.2	0.2	0.2
Education and health services	117.0	0.0[e]	0.1	0.1	0.0[e]	0.0[e]	0.0[e]	0.0[e]
Leisure and hospitality	104.5	0.1	0.1	0.0[e]	0.0[e]	0.0[e]	0.0[e]	0.0[e]
Other services[d]	79.0	0.1	0.2	0.1	0.3	0.2	0.2	1.1

Source: Bureau of Labor Statistics (BLS) Occupational Injuries and Illnesses and Fatal Injuries Profiles, accessed September 28, 2015. Available at http://www.bls. gov/iif/#data.
Dashes (—) indicate no data reported or data that do not meet publication guidelines.
[a]Incidence rates represent the number of injuries and illnesses per 10,000 full-time workers and were calculated as: (N/EH) x 20,000,000, where N = number of injuries and illnesses, EH = total hours worked by all employees during the calendar year, and 20,000,000 = base for 10,000 full-time equivalent workers (working 40 hours per week, 50 weeks per year).
[b]Days away from work include those that result in days away from work with or without restricted work activity.
[c]Data for 2011–2013 are based on the revised BLS Occupational Injury and Illness Classification System (OIICS) 2.01 and not comparable to data for prior years.
[d]"Natural resources" includes agriculture, forestry, fishing, and hunting and excludes farms with fewer than 11 employees. "Mining" includes oil and gas extraction. "Other services" excludes public administration.
[e]Rounded to zero.

Workplace Falls

Following highway crashes, falls to a lower level is the second leading unintentional fatal workplace event and the sixth leading event resulting in cases with days away from work. In 2013, 595 workers died while an additional 47,120 were injured. The 2013 fatality count represents about a 4% increase from 2012, while the nonfatal injuries count remained relatively stable. From 2004, fall-to-a-lower-level fatalities have decreased more than 19%, while nonfatal cases with days away from work have decreased by 41%.

Fatal falls to a lower level typically involve injuries to the head or multiple body parts, while nonfatal injuries most often involve the lower extremities, multiple body parts, upper extremities, or trunk. The most common nonfatal injuries include sprains, strains, or tears, followed by fractures. Falls to a lower level result in dramatically more days away from work than typical injury events. Fall-to-a-lower-level cases result in a median of 21 days away from work compared with eight days across all injury events. In fact, more than 42% of the fall-to-a-lower-level cases involving days away from work result in 31 or more lost workdays. Falls to a lower level resulting in days away from work most often occur on floors, walkways, or ground surfaces (35%), closely followed by ladders (32%). New employees

are disproportionably represented, with 30% of nonfatal injuries involving workers with less than one year of service.

As shown on the accompanying pie chart, fully 11% of fatal falls to a lower level occur from heights of less than six feet. Overall about half of fall-to-a-lower-level deaths occur at heights of 20 feet or less while 16% occur at heights of 30 feet or greater.

Fall to a lower level deaths by height of fall, United States, 2013

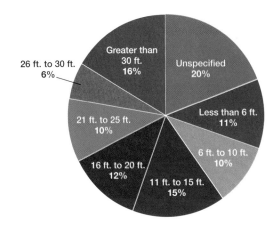

By far, construction is the industry most at risk from falls to a lower level. In 2013, 291 workers in the construction industry died as a result of falls to a lower level, representing 49% of all fall-to-a-lower-level fatalities. The fall-to-a-lower-level fatality rate in the construction industry is 3.2 per 100,000 workers, more than seven times the general industry rate of 0.44. Falls to a lower level also represent the single most dangerous injury event within the construction industry, representing 33% of all construction fatalities. In 2014 the construction industry also experiences the most nonfatal cases involving days away from work, representing 20% of all nonfatal fall-to-a-lower-level cases with 9,560.

Compared to falls to a lower level, falls on the same level tend to result in less severe but more frequent injuries. In 2013, there were 141,060 fall-on-the-same-level cases involving days away from work and 110 fatalities. In 2014, the rate for cases involving days away from work was 16.6 per 10,000 workers compared with 5.3 for falls to a lower level. Transportation and warehousing has the highest fall-on-the-same-level rate with 30.4 per 10,000 workers, followed by education and health services (25.5) and leisure and hospitality (22.6).

The following two pages provide injury profiles for both falls to a lower level and falls on the same level.

Workplace falls to a lower level, United States, 2004-2013

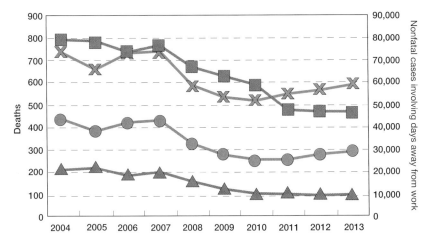

Source: This research was conducted with restricted access to Bureau of Labor Statistics (BLS) data. The views expressed here do not necessarily reflect the views of BLS.

"Fall to lower level" applies to instances in which the injury was produced by impact between the injured person and another surface of lower elevation – the motion producing the contact being that of the person – under the following circumstances:
- The motion of the person and the force of impact were generated by gravity.

- The point of contact with the source of injury was lower than the surface supporting the person at the inception of the fall.

Fall to lower level ranks second behind highway crashes in number of workplace fatalities, and is the sixth leading event resulting in cases involving days away from work.

Fall-to-lower-level nonfatal occupational injuries and illnesses involving days away from work[a] and fatal occupational injuries by selected worker and case characteristics, United States, 2013

Characteristic	Private industry[b,c] nonfatal cases	All industries fatalities
Total	**47,120**	**595**
Sex		
Men	34,290	584
Women	12,810	11
Age		
Younger than 16	—	—
16 to 19	660	—
20 to 24	3,420	27
25 to 34	8,950	75
35 to 44	10,290	110
45 to 54	11,560	152
55 to 64	9,470	140
65 and older	2,310	87
Occupation		
Management, business, and financial	2,020	32
Professional and related	2,270	6
Service	7,340	98
Sales and related	3,800	11
Office and administrative support	2,360	6
Farming, fishing, and forestry	1,590	7
Construction and extractive	8,760	288
Installation, maintenance, and repair	6,010	66
Production	2,950	30
Transportation and material moving	9,970	49
Military occupations	—	—
Race or ethnic origin[d]		
White, non-Hispanic	20,210	379
Black, non-Hispanic	2,300	35
Hispanic	8,720	163
Other, multiple, and not reported	15,890	18
Nature of injury or illness		
Fractures	11,590	9
Sprains or strains tears	12,440	—
Amputations	—	—
Cuts, lacerations, or punctures	1,710	—
Bruises or contusions	5,470	—
Chemical burns and corrosions	—	—
Heat (thermal) burns	—	—
Multiple traumatic injuries	3,370	233
Soreness or pain	8,810	—
Carpal tunnel syndrome	—	—
Tendonitis	—	—
All other	3,720	347

Characteristic	Private industry[b,c] nonfatal cases	All industries fatalities
Part of body affected		
Head	2,470	245
Eye	40	—
Neck	380	16
Trunk	9,670	63
Back	6,150	11
Upper extremities	8,400	—
Shoulder	3,080	—
Arm	1,780	—
Wrist	1,950	—
Hand	1,020	—
Lower extremities	14,570	7
Knee	4,760	—
Ankle	4,450	—
Foot or toe	2,080	—
Body systems	80	24
Multiple	11,030	240
All other	520	—
Industry		
Agriculture, Forestry, Fishing, and Hunting	1,960	25
Mining	470	18
Construction	9,560	291
Manufacturing	4,370	31
Wholesale Trade	3,390	19
Retail Trade	5,810	16
Transportation and Warehousing	4,890	24
Utilities	310	—
Information	920	9
Financial Activities	1,930	15
Professional and Business Services	4,190	85
Education and Health Services	4,400	—
Leisure and Hospitality	3,230	13
Other Services	1,690	20
Government	N/A	26

Source: This research was conducted with restricted access to Bureau of Labor Statistics (BLS) data. The views expressed here do not necessarily reflect the views of BLS.
Note: Because of rounding and data exclusion of nonclassifiable responses, data may not sum to the totals. Dashes (—) indicate data that do not meet publication guidelines. "N/A" means not applicable.
[a]Days away from work include those that result in days away from work with or without restricted work activity or job transfer.
[b]Excludes farms with fewer than 11 employees.

[c]Data for mining operators in coal, metal, and nonmetal mining and for employees in railroad transportation are provided to BLS by the Mine Safety and Health Administration (MSHA), U.S. Department of Labor; and the Federal Railroad Administration (FRA), U.S. Department of Transportation. Independent mining contractors are excluded from the coal, metal, and nonmetal mining industries. MSHA and FRA data do not reflect the changes in OSHA recordkeeping requirements in 2002.
[d]In the fatalities column, non-Hispanic categories include cases with Hispanic origin not reported.

"Fall on same level" applies to instances in which the injury was produced by impact between the injured person and another surface without elevation – the motion producing the contact being that of the person – under the following circumstances:

- The motion of the person was generated by gravity following the employee's loss of equilibrium (the person was unable to maintain an upright position).

- The point of contact with the source of injury was at the same level or above the surface supporting the person at the inception of the fall.

Fall on same level ranks second behind overexertion in the number of nonfatal injuries involving days away from work, but generally is not one of the top 10 events resulting in fatalities.

Fall-on-same-level nonfatal occupational injuries and illnesses involving days away from work[a] and fatal occupational injuries by selected worker and case characteristics, United States, 2013

Characteristic	Private industry[b,c] nonfatal cases	All industries fatalities
Total	**141,060**	**110**
Sex		
Men	61,480	83
Women	79,520	27
Age		
Younger than 16	30	—
16 to 19	3,210	—
20 to 24	8,610	—
25 to 34	20,510	8
35 to 44	23,240	11
45 to 54	37,260	22
55 to 64	34,540	32
65 and older	11,410	36
Occupation		
Management, business, and financial	7,830	12
Professional and related	16,670	—
Service	41,690	38
Sales and related	11,010	12
Office and administrative support	14,210	11
Farming, fishing, and forestry	1,890	—
Construction and extractive	8,040	10
Installation, maintenance, and repair	6,970	—
Production	10,920	8
Transportation and material moving	21,420	12
Military occupations	—	—
Race or ethnic origin[d]		
White, non-Hispanic	58,540	87
Black, non-Hispanic	11,300	10
Hispanic	16,400	13
Other, multiple, and not reported	54,820	—
Nature of injury or illness		
Fractures	24,210	12
Sprains or strains tears	38,930	—
Amputations	20	—
Cuts, lacerations, or punctures	4,150	—
Bruises or contusions	21,680	—
Chemical burns and corrosions	—	—
Heat (thermal) burns	130	—
Multiple injuries	8,210	10
Soreness or pain	30,680	—
Carpal tunnel syndrome	—	—
Tendonitis	40	—
All other	13,010	80

Characteristic	Private industry[b,c] nonfatal cases	All industries fatalities
Part of body affected		
Head	9,420	58
Eye	190	—
Neck	1,030	6
Trunk	24,190	20
Back	15,420	—
Upper extremities	32,940	—
Shoulder	9,330	—
Arm	8,030	—
Wrist	8,700	—
Hand	4,270	—
Lower extremities	44,380	12
Knee	22,120	—
Ankle	11,360	—
Foot or toe	2,710	—
Body systems	380	—
Multiple	27,640	11
All other	1,060	—
Industry		
Agriculture, Forestry, Fishing, and Hunting	2,310	6
Mining	780	—
Construction	8,560	6
Manufacturing	12,730	10
Wholesale Trade	6,430	—
Retail Trade	19,680	15
Transportation and Warehousing	11,460	7
Utilities	490	—
Information	2,640	—
Financial Activities	5,530	—
Professional and Business Services	11,500	6
Education and Health Services	36,210	10
Leisure and Hospitality	20,030	10
Other Services	2,710	8
Government	N/A	26

Source: This research was conducted with restricted access to Bureau of Labor Statistics (BLS) data. The views expressed here do not necessarily reflect the views of BLS.
Note: Because of rounding and data exclusion of nonclassifiable responses, data may not sum to the totals. Dashes (—) indicate data that do not meet publication guidelines. "N/A" means not applicable.
[a]Days away from work include those that result in days away from work with or without restricted work activity or job transfer.
[b]Excludes farms with fewer than 11 employees.

[c]Data for mining operators in coal, metal, and nonmetal mining and for employees in railroad transportation are provided to BLS by the Mine Safety and Health Administration (MSHA), U.S. Department of Labor; and the Federal Railroad Administration (FRA), U.S. Department of Transportation. Independent mining contractors are excluded from the coal, metal, and nonmetal mining industries. MSHA and FRA data do not reflect the changes in OSHA recordkeeping requirements in 2002.
[d]In the fatalities column, non-Hispanic categories include cases with Hispanic origin not reported.

Contractor Fatal Occupational Injuries

In 2014, the number of contractor fatalities have increased for the second consecutive year now totaling 792, representing 17.0% of all work related fatalities. The Bureau of Labor Statistics defines contractor as a worker employed by one firm (or who is self-employed), but working at the behest of another firm that exercises overall responsibility for the operations at the site where the decedent was killed. Looking at the percent of fatalities occurring to contractors shows that nearly 52% of the fatalities occurring in the construction industry were contractor deaths, while over 28% of the fatalities occurring in professional and business services occurred to contractors.

Contractor fatal occupational injuries by selected worker and case characteristics, United States, 2012-2014

Characteristic	2012	2013	2014	2014-percent of contractor fatalities in subgroup
Total	715	749	797	17.0%
Sex				
Men	701	733	780	18.1%
Women	14	16	17	4.7%
Age				
Younger than 16	1	0	1	12.5%
16 to 19	10	6	4	7.4%
20 to 24	54	45	61	21.1%
25 to 34	139	146	150	20.2%
35 to 44	162	159	157	18.7%
45 to 54	180	196	203	18.0%
55 to 64	119	139	160	16.6%
65 and older	50	58	59	9.0%
Employee status				
Wage and salary workers[a]	584	634	648	17.8%
Self-employed[b]	131	115	149	14.2%
Race or ethnic origin[c]				
White, non-Hispanic	441	447	495	15.6%
Black, non-Hispanic	64	64	63	13.8%
Hispanic or Latino	191	214	211	26.7%
Other, multiple, and not reported	19	24	28	10.8%
Event or exposure				
Violence and other injuries by persons or animals	32	40	35	4.7%
Transportation incidents	152	149	170	9.0%
Fire or explosion	29	28	26	19.0%
Falls, slip, trip	229	242	288	36.3%
Exposure to harmful substances or environments	95	92	104	26.7%
Contact with objects and equipment	178	196	174	24.6%
Industry[d]				
Agriculture, Forestry, Fishing, and Hunting	20	24	26	4.6%
Mining[e]	—	—	1	0.6%
Construction	388	403	453	51.8%
Manufacturing	16	15	18	5.3%
Wholesale Trade	16	12	15	8.4%
Retail Trade	5	4	5	1.9%
Transportation and Warehousing	49	55	62	8.4%
Utilities	—	—	—	—
Information	—	8	—	—
Financial Activities	4	6	5	4.4%
Professional and Business Services	132	134	120	28.7%
Education and Health Services	3	—	4	2.8%
Leisure and Hospitality	19	19	16	7.7%
Other Services	19	25	23	13.2%
Government[f]	—	—	4	0.9%
Federal government, contractor	—	—	—	—
State government, contractor	—	—	—	—
Local government, contractor	1	—	—	—

Source: National Safety Council tabulations of Bureau of Labor Statistics (BLS) data.
Note: Because of rounding and data exclusion of nonclassifiable responses, data may not sum to the totals.
Dashes (—) indicate no data reporter or data that do not meet BLS publication criteria.
[a]May include volunteers and workers receiving other types of compensation.
[b]Includes self-employed workers, owners of unincorporated businesses and farms, paid and unpaid family workers, and may include some owners of incorporated businesses or members of partnerships.
[c]Persons identified as Hispanic or Latino may be of any race. The racial categories shown exclude data for Hispanic and Latinos.
[d]Industry is the industry of the contractor's firm not necessarily the industry of the firm contracting the decedent.
[e]Includes fatal injuries at all establishments categorized as Mining, including establishments not goverened by the Mine Safety and Health Administraion rules and reporting, such as those in Oil and Gas Extraction.
[f]Includes fatal injuries to workers employed by governmental organizations regardless of industry.

Occupational Health

■ *More than 28,000 new cases of skin diseases or disorders were diagnosed in 2014.*

Approximately 189,400 occupational illnesses were recognized or diagnosed by employers in 2014, according to the Bureau of Labor Statistics (BLS). The all-industry illness data published by BLS now includes data for state and local governments in addition to the private sector. The overall incidence rate of occupational illness for all industries was 17.5 per 10,000 full-time workers. The highest overall incidence rate for all illnesses was for manufacturing – 35.0 cases per 10,000 full-time workers – double the all industries rate.

Workers in agriculture, forestry, fishing, and hunting had the highest incidence rates for skin diseases or disorders and poisoning. Educational and health services had the highest rate for respiratory conditions, while manufacturing had the highest rates for hearing loss and "all other occupational illnesses."

State and local government, manufacturing, and education and health services accounted for over 67% of all new illness cases in 2014. Skin diseases or disorders were the most common illness with 28,600 new cases, followed by hearing loss with 20,900, respiratory conditions with 17,700, and poisonings with 2,400.

The table below shows the number of occupational illnesses and the incidence rate per 10,000 full-time workers as measured by the 2014 BLS survey. To convert these to incidence rates per 100 full-time workers, which are comparable to other published BLS rates, divide the rates in the table by 100. The BLS survey records illnesses only for the year in which they are recognized or diagnosed as work-related. Because only recognized cases are included, the figures underestimate the incidence of occupational illness.

Nonfatal occupational illness incidence rates and number of illnesses by type of illness and industry sector, 2014

Industry sector	All illnesses	Skin diseases or disorders	Respiratory conditions	Poisoning	Hearing loss	All other occupational illnesses
Incidence rate per 10,000 full-time workers						
All industries, including state and local government[a]	**17.5**	**2.6**	**1.6**	**0.2**	**1.9**	**11.1**
Private industry[a]	**15.3**	**2.3**	**1.3**	**0.2**	**1.9**	**9.6**
Goods producing[a]	26.0	3.3	1.2	0.2	7.2	14.2
Agriculture, forestry, fishing, and hunting[a]	31.1	9.7	2.3	0.7	1.2	17.2
Mining[b,c]	9.3	1.1	2.2	(d)	2.0	3.7
Construction	8.2	2.0	0.7	0.1	0.3	5.1
Manufacturing	35.0	3.6	1.2	0.1	11.2	18.9
Service providing	12.5	2.1	1.3	0.2	0.6	8.4
Wholesale trade	6.2	1.3	0.6	(d)	0.6	3.6
Retail trade	9.7	1.4	(d)	0.1	0.1	6.6
Transportation and warehousing	18.4	1.0	1.2	0.2	4.5	11.4
Utilities	23.2	5.0	0.7	0.5	9.9	7.1
Information	8.4	0.5	0.2	(d)	1.1	6.6
Finance, insurance, and real estate	5.4	0.6	0.7	(d)	(d)	4.0
Professional and business services	7.9	1.5	0.6	0.2	0.4	5.2
Educational and health services	25.2	4.0	2.7	0.1	0.1	18.4
Leisure, entertainment, and hospitality	10.8	3.2	1.3	(d)	0.1	5.8
Other services	7.5	1.1	1.1	0.2	0.5	4.6
State and local government[a]	**31.8**	**4.7**	**3.9**	**0.6**	**1.8**	**20.7**
Number of Illnesses (in thousands)						
All industries, including state and local government[a]	**189.4**	**28.6**	**17.7**	**2.4**	**20.9**	**119.9**
Private industry[a]	**143.7**	**21.8**	**12.1**	**1.5**	**18.2**	**90.1**
Goods producing[a]	51.2	6.6	2.4	0.3	14.1	27.9
Agriculture, forestry, fishing, and hunting[a]	3.0	0.9	0.2	0.1	0.1	1.6
Mining[b,c]	0.8	0.1	0.2	(d)	0.2	0.3
Construction	4.6	1.1	0.4	0.1	0.2	2.8
Manufacturing	42.8	4.4	1.5	0.2	13.7	23.0
Service providing	92.5	15.2	9.8	1.2	4.1	62.2
Wholesale trade	3.4	0.7	0.3	(d)	0.3	2.0
Retail trade	11.2	1.6	(d)	0.1	0.1	7.6
Transportation and warehousing	7.7	0.4	0.5	0.1	1.9	4.8
Utilities	1.3	0.3	(d)	(d)	0.5	0.4
Information	2.1	0.1	(d)	(d)	0.3	1.7
Finance, insurance, and real estate	3.8	0.4	0.5	(d)	(d)	2.9
Professional and business services	11.6	2.1	0.9	0.3	0.6	7.6
Educational and health services	38.9	6.1	4.1	0.2	0.1	28.3
Leisure, entertainment, and hospitality	10.1	3.0	1.2	(d)	0.1	5.4
Other services	2.3	0.3	0.3	0.1	0.2	1.4
State and local government[a]	**45.7**	**6.8**	**5.6**	**0.9**	**2.7**	**29.8**

Source: Bureau of Labor Statistics. Components may not add to totals due to rounding.
[a]*Excludes farms with fewer than 11 employees.*
[b]*Data for mining do not reflect the changes OSHA made to its recordkeeping requirements effective Jan. 1, 2002; therefore, estimates for this industry are not comparable with estimates for other industries.*
[c]*Mining includes quarrying and oil and gas extraction.*
[d]*Data do not meet publication guidelines/too small to be displayed.*

According to the Bureau of Labor Statistics, sprains, strains, or tears were the most common type of injury involving days away from work in 2013, accounting for 36% of the total 917,090 injuries in private industry. Soreness or pain was the second most common type of injury, followed by cuts, lacerations, or punctures. Overall, the education and health services, retail trade, and manufacturing industry sectors had the greatest number of injuries, combining to make up 46% of the total.

Number of nonfatal occupational injuries and illnesses involving days away from work[a] by nature of injury and industry sector, private industry, United States, 2013

Nature of injury	Private sector[b,c,d]	Education and health services	Retail trade	Manufacturing	Leisure and hospitality	Transportation and warehousing[d]	Construction	Professional and business services	Wholesale trade	All other sectors[b,d,e]
Total[c]	917,090	177,640	128,800	120,110	94,730	87,190	82,040	69,710	57,190	99,680
Fractures	77,990	10,580	9,810	11,480	6,620	6,370	11,150	6,190	5,380	10,410
Sprains, strains, or tears	327,060	79,680	49,480	37,000	27,040	38,990	21,420	20,650	20,130	32,670
Amputations	6,160	110	570	2,000	260	210	1,380	450	580	600
Cuts, lacerations, or punctures	88,250	6,640	14,830	14,900	15,130	3,950	11,470	7,160	5,030	9,140
Cuts or lacerations	*71,150*	*4,650*	*12,280*	*12,950*	*14,490*	*2,930*	*8,560*	*4,220*	*4,060*	*7,010*
Punctures (except gunshot wounds)	*17,100*	*1,980*	*2,550*	*1,950*	*640*	*1,020*	*2,910*	*2,940*	*970*	*2,140*
Bruises or contusions	72,710	16,140	12,500	8,750	7,900	8,390	3,970	4,700	4,090	6,270
Chemical burns and corrosions	2,790	220	260	680	230	110	240	380	350	320
Heat (thermal) burns	13,780	1,310	1,100	2,130	6,500	410	660	230	570	870
Multiple traumatic injuries	23,700	5,340	3,020	2,940	1,940	2,520	1,700	2,090	1,380	2,770
With sprains and other injuries	*10,070*	*2,890*	*1,420*	*1,010*	*780*	*970*	*400*	*1,090*	*600*	*910*
With fractures and other injuries	*5,300*	*920*	*400*	*970*	*540*	*530*	*670*	*410*	*340*	*520*
Soreness or pain	153,970	35,400	18,640	14,800	16,380	14,080	15,030	13,450	9,230	16,960
Carpal tunnel syndrome	6,440	510	530	2,480	350	300	200	620	320	1,130
Tendonitis	2,290	370	300	580	170	170	150	80	200	270
All other	141,950	21,330	17,770	22,360	12,200	11,690	14,670	13,700	9,930	18,300

Source: Bureau of Labor Statistics Occupational Injuries/Illnesses and Fatal Injuries Profiles, accessed September 14, 2015 from http://data.bls.gov/gqt/InitialPage.
[a]*Days-away-from-work cases include those that result in days away from work with or without job transfer or restriction.*
[b]*Excludes farms with fewer than 11 employees.*
[c]*Data may not sum to row and column totals because of rounding and exclusion of nonclassifiable responses.*
[d]*Data for transportation and mining do not reflect the changes OSHA made to its recordkeeping requirements effective Jan. 1, 2002; therefore, estimates for these industries are not comparable with estimates for other industries.*
[e]*Includes agriculture, forestry, fishing, and hunting; financial activities; information; mining (including oil and gas extraction); other services (except public administration); and utilities.*

Percent of injuries involving days away from work by nature of injury, private industry, United States, 2013

According to the Bureau of Labor Statistics, the back was the body part most frequently affected in injuries involving days away from work in 2013, accounting for 19% of the total 917,090 injuries in private industry. Hand injuries were the second most common, followed by injuries to multiple body parts. Overall, the education and health services, retail trade, and manufacturing industry sectors had the highest number of injuries, combining to make up 46% of the total.

Number of nonfatal occupational injuries and illnesses involving days away from work[a] by part of body affected and industry sector, private industry, United States, 2013

Part of body affected	Private sector[b,c,d]	Industry sector								
		Education and health services	Retail trade	Manufacturing	Leisure and hospitality	Transportation and warehousing[d]	Construction	Professional and business services	Wholesale trade	All other sectors[b,d,e]
Total[c]	**917,090**	**177,640**	**128,800**	**120,110**	**94,730**	**87,190**	**82,040**	**69,710**	**57,190**	**99,680**
Head	69,680	11,520	10,770	10,010	6,630	5,330	5,730	5,820	4,180	9,690
Eye	*22,120*	*2,000*	*2,730*	*5,100*	*2,060*	*1,480*	*2,300*	*1,670*	*1,170*	*3,610*
Neck	13,430	3,480	2,000	1,250	680	1,610	1,510	1,040	510	1,350
Trunk	226,640	52,950	33,750	25,620	18,240	22,240	19,470	14,420	16,790	23,160
Back	*170,450*	*43,590*	*25,730*	*17,660*	*13,790*	*16,460*	*13,320*	*10,480*	*12,330*	*17,090*
Upper extremities	286,320	43,360	39,000	51,690	35,780	24,070	26,720	21,110	16,550	28,040
Shoulder	*68,500*	*13,700*	*9,960*	*9,820*	*5,400*	*9,090*	*5,330*	*4,580*	*3,920*	*6,700*
Arm	*43,580*	*6,770*	*6,110*	*6,830*	*4,710*	*4,170*	*4,650*	*2,890*	*2,520*	*4,930*
Wrist	*37,500*	*7,370*	*4,750*	*7,210*	*4,110*	*3,100*	*2,250*	*3,230*	*1,930*	*3,550*
Hand	*121,500*	*12,040*	*16,600*	*25,670*	*19,570*	*6,200*	*13,780*	*8,670*	*7,430*	*11,540*
Lower extremities	202,280	35,450	28,550	22,120	21,870	22,740	19,730	15,700	12,800	23,320
Knee	*77,490*	*15,060*	*10,750*	*7,840*	*8,150*	*8,490*	*7,260*	*6,310*	*4,120*	*9,510*
Ankle	*45,620*	*9,290*	*5,660*	*4,690*	*5,560*	*4,770*	*3,380*	*3,660*	*3,290*	*5,320*
Foot	*43,570*	*5,650*	*7,980*	*5,360*	*4,040*	*4,540*	*5,390*	*2,860*	*2,940*	*4,810*
Body systems	18,570	3,810	3,030	1,450	1,810	1,240	1,820	1,980	1,110	2,320
Multiple parts	89,870	25,370	10,390	7,250	8,330	9,090	6,670	7,990	4,570	10,210
All other	10,290	1,710	1,310	720	1,380	870	380	1,650	690	1,580

Source: Bureau of Labor Statistics Occupational Injuries/Illnesses and Fatal Injuries Profiles, accessed September 14, 2015 from http://data.bls.gov/gqt/InitialPage.
[a]Days-away-from-work cases include those that result in days away from work with or without job transfer or restriction.
[b]Excludes farms with fewer than 11 employees.
[c]Data may not sum to row and column totals because of rounding and exclusion of nonclassifiable responses.
[d]Data for transportation and mining do not reflect the changes OSHA made to its recordkeeping requirements effective Jan. 1, 2002; therefore, estimates for these industries are not comparable with estimates for other industries.
[e]Includes agriculture, forestry, fishing, and hunting; financial activities; information; mining (including oil and gas extraction); other services (except public administration); and utilities.

Percent of injuries involving days away from work by part of body affected, private industry, United States, 2013

Safety professionals in business and industry often want to compare, or benchmark, the occupational injury and illness incidence rates of their establishments with the national average rates compiled by the Bureau of Labor Statistics (BLS) through its annual Survey of Occupational Injuries and Illnesses.[a] The incidence rates published on the following pages are for 2014 and were compiled under the revised Occupational Safety and Health Administration (OSHA) recordkeeping requirements that went into effect in 2002.

Step 1

The first step in benchmarking is to calculate the incidence rates for the establishment. The basic formula for computing incidence rates is *(N x 200,000)/EH*, or the number of cases *(N)* multiplied by 200,000 then divided by the number of hours worked *(EH)* by all employees during the time period, where *200,000* is the base for 100 full-time workers (working 40 hours per week, 50 weeks per year). Because BLS rates are based on reports from entire establishments, both the OSHA 300 log and the number of hours worked should cover the whole establishment being benchmarked. The hours worked and the log also should cover the same time period (e.g., a month, quarter, or full year). The following rates may be calculated.

Total cases – The incidence rate of total OSHA recordable cases per 200,000 hours worked. For this rate, *N* is the total number of cases on the OSHA 300 log.

Cases with days away from work or job transfer or restriction – The incidence rate of cases with days away from work, job transfer, or restriction. *N* is the count of cases with a check in column H or column I of the OSHA 300 log.

Cases with days away from work – The incidence rate of cases with days away from work. *N* is the count of cases with a check in column H of the OSHA 300 log.

Cases with job transfer or restriction – The incidence rate of cases with job transfer or restriction, but no days away from work. *N* is the count of cases with a check in column I of the OSHA 300 log.

Other recordable cases – The incidence rate of recordable cases without days away from work or job transfer or restriction. *N* is the count of cases with a check in column J of the OSHA 300 log.

In the flow chart on the opposite page, post the number of cases to each box in the top row and the number of employee hours worked in its box. Then use the formula to calculate the rates and write them in the last row of boxes in Step 1.

An alternative approach is to use the Incidence Rate Calculator and Comparison Tool available on BLS's website at *http://data.bls.gov/iirc*. This tool will calculate your rate and provide a report comparing your rate to your industry.

Step 2

After computing one or more of the rates, the next step is to determine the North American Industry Classification System (NAICS) code for the establishment.[b] (NAICS replaced the Standard Industrial Classification [SIC] code beginning in 2003.) This code is used to find the appropriate BLS rate for comparison. NAICS codes can be found at *www.census.gov/eos/www/naics*. The website also contains a crosswalk between NAICS and SIC codes. Otherwise, call a regional BLS office for assistance.

Write the establishment's NAICS code in the box in Step 2 of the flow chart.

Step 3

Once the NAICS code is known, the national average incidence rates may be found by (a) consulting the table of rates on pages 80-82, (b) visiting BLS's website, or (c) by calling a regional BLS office. Note that some tables on the website provide incidence rates by size of establishment and rate quartiles within each NAICS code. These rates may be useful for a more precise comparison. Note that the incidence rates for 2001 and earlier years were compiled under the old OSHA recordkeeping requirements in effect at that time. Caution must be used in comparing rates computed for 2002 and later years with earlier years – keeping in mind the differences in recordkeeping requirements.

In the flow chart on the opposite page, post the rates from the BLS survey to the boxes in Step 3. Now compare these with the rates calculated in Step 1.

An alternative way of benchmarking is to compare the current incidence rates for an establishment to its own prior historical rates to determine if the rates are improving and if progress is satisfactory (using criteria set by the organization).

[a]*Bureau of Labor Statistics. (1997)*. BLS Handbook of Methods. *Washington, DC: U.S. Government Printing Office (Or at* www.bls.gov/opub/hom/home.htm).
[b]*Executive Office of the President, Office of Management and Budget. (2002)*. North American Industry Classification System, United States, 2002. *Springfield, VA: National Technical Information Service.*

Step 1: Compute establishment incidence rates

Total cases	DAFW, transfer, or restriction cases	DAFW cases	Transfer or restriction cases	Other cases

Cases (*N*)   X 200,000

Incidence rate =

EH

Employee-hours worked

Total cases incidence rate	DAFW, transfer, or restriction cases incidence rate	DAFW cases incidence rate	Transfer or restriction cases incidence rate	Other cases incidence rate

Step 2: Determine North American Industry Classification System (NAICS) code

NAICS code = _____ _____ _____ _____

Step 3: Compare to the Bureau of Labor Statistics incidence rate averages for the industry (NAICS code)

Total cases incidence rate	DAFW, transfer, or restriction cases incidence rate	DAFW cases incidence rate	Transfer or restriction cases incidence rate	Other cases incidence rate

See page 76 for detailed instructions.
DAFW = Days away from work.

OCCUPATIONAL

Trends in Occupational Incidence Rates

■ *Total recordable incidence rate continues steady decrease in 2014.*

Two of the five private-sector occupational injury and illness incidence rates published by the Bureau of Labor Statistics (BLS) for 2014 decreased from 2013, while the remaining three incidence rates were unchanged. The incidence rate for total recordable cases was 3.2 per 100 full-time workers in 2014, down 3% from the 2013 rate of 3.3. The incidence rate for other recordable cases was 1.5 in 2014, down over 6% from 2013. The incidence rates for cases with days away from work, job transfer, or restriction; cases with days away from work; and cases with job transfer or restriction, were all unchanged from 2013.

There have been several changes that affect comparability of incidence rates from year to year. The North American Industry Classification System replaced the Standard Industrial Classification system beginning with the 2003 survey of occupational injuries and illnesses. Revisions to the Occupational Safety and Health Administration's occupational injury and illness recordkeeping requirements went into effect in 2002. Beginning with 1992, BLS revised its annual survey to include only nonfatal cases and stopped publishing the incidence rate of lost workdays.

Occupational injury and illness incidence rates, private industry, United States, 1991-2014

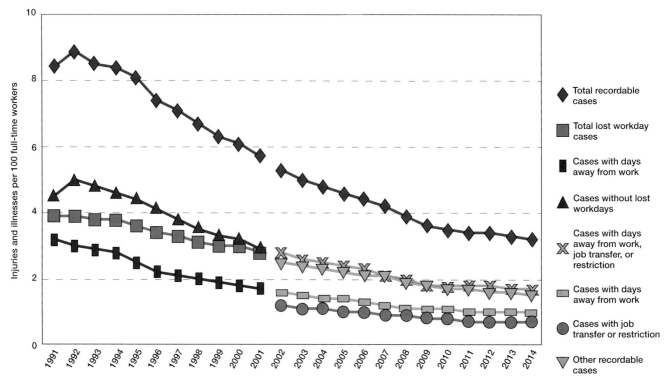

Source: Bureau of Labor Statistics.
Note: Beginning in 1992, all rates are for nonfatal cases only. Changes in OSHA recordkeeping requirements in 2002 affect comparison with earlier years.

The tables below and on pages 80-82 present the results of the 2013 Survey of Occupational Injuries and Illnesses conducted by the Bureau of Labor Statistics (BLS). The survey collects data on injuries and illnesses (from the OSHA 300 log) and employee-hours worked from a nationwide sample of about 230,000 private-industry establishments, as well as state and local governments. The survey excludes private households, the self-employed, and farms with fewer than 11 employees. The incidence rates give the number of cases per 100 full-time workers per year using 200,000 employee-hours as the equivalent. Definitions of the terms are given in the Glossary on page 207.

Beginning with 1992 data, BLS revised its annual survey to include only nonfatal cases and stopped publishing incidence rates of lost workdays. Beginning with 2003 data, BLS adopted the North American Industry Classification System for publication of the incidence rates by industry.

Bureau of Labor Statistics estimates of nonfatal occupational injury and illness incidence rates and number of injuries and illnesses by industry sector, 2014

Industry sector[a]	Total recordable cases	Cases with days away from work, job transfer, or restriction			
		Total	Cases with days away from work	Cases with job transfer or restriction	Other recordable cases
Incidence rate per 100 full-time workers[c]					
All industries, including state and local government[d]	**3.4**	**1.8**	**1.1**	**0.7**	**1.6**
Private sector[d]	**3.2**	**1.7**	**1.0**	**0.7**	**1.5**
Goods producing[d]	3.8	2.2	1.1	1.0	1.7
Agriculture, forestry, fishing, and hunting[d]	5.5	3.3	1.8	1.5	2.2
Mining[e]	2.0	1.3	0.8	0.4	0.7
Construction	3.6	2.0	1.3	0.6	1.6
Manufacturing	4.0	2.2	1.0	1.2	1.7
Service providing	3.0	1.6	0.9	0.6	1.4
Wholesale trade	2.9	1.9	1.1	0.9	1.0
Retail trade	3.6	2.0	1.0	1.0	1.6
Transportation and warehousing	4.8	3.4	2.3	1.2	1.4
Utilities	2.4	1.3	0.7	0.6	1.2
Information	1.4	0.8	0.6	0.2	0.6
Financial, insurance, and real estate	1.2	0.5	0.4	0.2	0.7
Professional and business services	1.5	0.8	0.5	0.3	0.7
Education and health services	4.2	2.0	1.1	0.8	2.2
Leisure, entertainment, and hospitality	3.6	1.5	1.0	0.6	2.1
Other services	2.5	1.2	0.9	0.4	1.2
State and local government[d]	**5.0**	**2.3**	**1.7**	**0.6**	**2.7**
Number of injuries and illnesses (in thousands)					
All industries, including state and local government[d]	**3,675.8**	**1,909.6**	**1,157.4**	**752.1**	**1,766.2**
Private sector[d]	**2,953.5**	**1,580.0**	**916.4**	**663.6**	**1,373.5**
Goods producing[d]	754.5	427.2	225.2	202.0	327.3
Agriculture, forestry, fishing, and hunting[d]	52.4	31.2	17.0	14.2	21.2
Mining[e]	17.9	11.4	7.7	3.7	6.4
Construction	200.9	110.0	74.5	35.6	90.9
Manufacturing	483.3	274.5	126.0	148.5	208.8
Service providing	2,199.0	1,152.8	691.3	461.6	1,046.2
Wholesale trade	163.1	107.9	59.2	48.6	55.3
Retail trade	416.1	233.6	120.6	112.9	182.5
Transportation and warehousing	201.5	144.4	95.0	49.3	57.2
Utilities	13.4	6.9	3.8	3.2	6.5
Information	35.3	20.8	15.7	5.0	14.5
Financial, insurance, and real estate	85.9	38.9	26.4	12.5	47.0
Professional and business services	220.3	115.3	77.7	37.6	105.0
Education and health services	651.0	304.6	175.9	128.7	346.4
Leisure, entertainment, and hospitality	337.5	142.9	90.9	52.0	194.6
Other services	74.8	37.6	25.9	11.6	37.2
State and local government[d]	**722.3**	**329.5**	**241.0**	**88.6**	**392.8**

Source: Bureau of Labor Statistics.
[a]Industry sector and two- and three-digit NAICS code totals on pages 80-82 include data for industries not shown separately.
[b]North American Industry Classification System–United States, 2007, for industries shown on pages 80-82.
[c]Incidence rate =

$$\text{Incidence rate} = \frac{\text{Number of injuries and illnesses} \times 200,000}{\text{Total hours worked by all employees during period covered}}$$

where 200,000 is the base for 100 full-time workers (working 40 hours per week, 50 weeks per year). The "Total recordable cases" rate is based on the number of cases with check marks in columns (G), (H), (I), and (J) of the OSHA 300 log. The "Cases with days away from work, job transfer, or restriction – total" rate is based on columns (H) and (I). The "Cases with days away from work" rate is based on column (H). The "Cases with job transfer or restriction" rate is based on column (I). The "Other recordable cases" rate is based on column (J).
[d]Excludes farms with fewer than 11 employees.
[e]These data do not reflect the changes the Occupational Safety and Health Administration made to its recordkeeping requirements effective January 1, 2002; therefore, estimates for these industries are not comparable to estimates in other industries.
[f]Data do not meet publication guidelines/too small to be displayed.

Occupational Injuries and Illnesses (cont.)

Bureau of Labor Statistics estimates of nonfatal occupational injury and illness incidence rates for selected industries, 2014

Industry[a]	NAICS code[b]	Incidence rates[c]				
		Total recordable cases	Cases with days away from work, job transfer, or restriction			Other recordable cases
			Total	Cases with days away from work	Cases with job transfer or restriction	
All industries, including state and local government[d]		**3.4**	**1.8**	**1.1**	**0.7**	**1.6**
Private sector[d]		**3.2**	**1.7**	**1.0**	**0.7**	**1.5**
Goods producing[d]		**3.8**	**2.2**	**1.1**	**1.0**	**1.7**
Natural resources and mining[d,e]		**3.8**	**2.3**	**1.3**	**1.0**	**1.5**
Agriculture, forestry, fishing, and hunting[d]	11	5.5	3.3	1.8	1.5	2.2
Crop production[d]	111	5.5	3.3	1.6	1.7	2.3
Animal production and aquaculture[d]	112	7.1	4.4	2.5	1.9	2.7
Forestry and logging	113	5.1	2.1	1.9	0.2	2.9
Support activities for agriculture and forestry	115	4.5	2.7	1.4	1.3	1.8
Mining[e]	21	2.0	1.3	0.8	0.4	0.7
Oil and gas extraction	211	(f)	0.8	0.6	0.2	0.5
Mining (except oil and gas)[e]	212	2.8	1.9	1.4	0.5	0.9
Coal mining[e]	2121	3.8	2.5	2.3	0.2	1.3
Metal ore mining[e]	2122	2.2	1.5	0.9	0.6	0.6
Nonmetallic mineral mining and quarrying[e]	2123	2.2	1.5	0.9	0.6	0.7
Support activities for mining	213	1.8	1.1	0.7	0.5	0.7
Construction		**3.6**	**2.0**	**1.3**	**0.6**	**1.6**
Construction of buildings	236	3.3	1.9	1.3	0.6	1.4
Residential building construction	2361	4.1	2.6	2.0	(f)	1.6
Nonresidential building construction	2362	2.7	1.4	0.8	0.6	1.3
Heavy and civil engineering construction	237	3.0	1.7	1.1	0.7	1.3
Utility system construction	2371	2.6	1.5	1.0	0.5	1.1
Land subdivision	2372	2.1	1.1	1.0	0.1	1.0
Highway, street, and bridge construction	2373	3.8	2.3	1.2	1.0	1.5
Other heavy and civil engineering construction	2379	3.1	1.6	1.2	0.4	1.5
Specialty trade contractors	238	3.8	2.0	1.4	0.6	1.8
Foundation, structure, and building exterior contractors	2381	4.6	2.7	1.7	0.9	2.0
Building equipment contractors	2382	3.6	1.8	1.2	0.6	1.8
Building finishing contractors	2383	4.2	2.4	1.8	0.6	1.8
Other specialty trade contractors	2389	3.2	1.7	1.2	0.4	1.5
Manufacturing		**4.0**	**2.2**	**1.0**	**1.2**	**1.7**
Food manufacturing	311	5.1	3.3	1.3	2.0	1.8
Animal food manufacturing	3111	5.1	3.4	1.6	1.8	1.7
Grain and oilseed milling	3112	3.6	2.1	1.0	1.1	1.5
Sugar and confectionery product manufacturing	3113	4.8	2.8	1.3	1.5	2.0
Fruit and vegetable preserving and specialty food manufacturing	3114	4.7	2.9	1.3	1.6	1.9
Dairy product manufacturing	3115	5.2	3.5	1.6	1.9	1.7
Animal slaughtering and processing	3116	5.5	3.7	1.0	2.7	1.8
Seafood product preparation and packaging	3117	6.3	3.9	2.5	1.4	2.4
Bakeries and tortilla manufacturing	3118	4.9	3.3	1.6	1.7	1.6
Other food manufacturing	3119	5.1	2.8	1.4	1.5	2.2
Beverage and tobacco product manufacturing	312	6.0	4.0	1.6	2.3	2.0
Beverage manufacturing	3121	6.2	4.1	1.7	2.4	2.1
Tobacco manufacturing	3122	3.4	2.0	1.2	0.8	1.4
Textile mills	313	3.2	1.7	0.7	1.0	1.5
Fiber, yarn, and thread mills	3131	2.8	1.6	0.7	0.9	1.3
Fabric mills	3132	3.5	1.7	0.8	1.0	1.7
Textile and fabric finishing and fabric coating mills	3133	3.0	1.7	0.7	1.0	1.2
Textile product mills	314	3.5	2.1	1.0	1.1	1.4
Textile furnishings mills	3141	3.0	1.8	0.7	1.1	1.2
Other textile product mills	3149	3.9	2.4	1.2	1.1	1.5
Apparel manufacturing	315	1.5	0.8	0.4	0.5	0.7
Apparel knitting mills	3151	2.1	1.3	0.5	0.8	0.8
Cut and sew apparel manufacturing	3152	1.3	0.7	0.4	0.4	0.6
Apparel accessories and other apparel manufacturing	3159	3.1	1.4	0.4	1.0	1.7
Leather and allied product manufacturing	316	3.9	2.2	1.0	1.1	1.7
Footwear manufacturing	3162	5.1	2.8	1.7	1.1	2.3
Other leather and allied product manufacturing	3169	2.2	0.9	0.3	0.7	1.3
Wood product manufacturing	321	6.8	3.8	1.9	1.8	3.0
Sawmills and wood preservation	3211	6.5	3.6	1.9	1.7	2.9
Veneer, plywood, and engineered wood product manufacturing	3212	6.0	3.3	1.7	1.7	2.6
Other wood product manufacturing	3219	7.2	4.0	2.0	1.9	3.2
Paper manufacturing	322	2.9	1.7	0.9	0.9	1.1
Pulp, paper, and paperboard mills	3221	2.1	1.1	0.6	0.5	1.0
Converted paper product manufacturing	3222	3.2	2.0	1.0	1.0	1.2
Printing and related support activities	323	2.5	1.5	0.8	0.7	1.0
Petroleum and coal products manufacturing	324	1.7	0.8	0.5	0.3	0.9
Chemical manufacturing	325	2.3	1.4	0.7	0.7	0.9
Basic chemical manufacturing	3251	2.1	1.3	0.6	0.7	0.8
Resin, synthetic rubber, and artificial and synthetic fibers and filaments manufacturing	3252	2.4	1.4	0.5	0.8	1.0
Pesticide, fertilizer, and other agricultural chemical manufacturing	3253	3.4	1.9	1.1	0.8	1.5
Pharmaceutical and medicine manufacturing	3254	2.0	1.2	0.6	0.6	0.8
Paint, coating, and adhesive manufacturing	3255	3.1	1.7	0.8	1.0	1.3
Soap, cleaning compound, and toilet preparation manufacturing	3256	2.3	1.5	0.9	0.6	0.7
Other chemical product and preparation manufacturing	3259	2.7	1.6	0.8	0.7	1.1

See source and footnotes on page 79.

Bureau of Labor Statistics estimates of nonfatal occupational injury and illness incidence rates for selected industries, 2014 (cont.)

Industry[a]	NAICS code[b]	Total recordable cases	Incidence rates[c]			Other recordable cases
			Cases with days away from work, job transfer, or restriction			
			Total	Cases with days away from work	Cases with job transfer or restriction	
Plastics and rubber products manufacturing	326	4.6	2.7	1.3	1.5	1.9
Plastics product manufacturing	3261	4.7	2.7	1.3	1.4	2.0
Rubber product manufacturing	3262	4.4	2.8	1.1	1.7	1.6
Nonmetallic mineral product manufacturing	327	5.1	3.2	1.7	1.5	2.0
Clay product and refractory manufacturing	3271	5.0	2.7	1.6	1.1	2.2
Glass and glass product manufacturing	3272	4.8	2.6	1.2	1.4	2.2
Cement and concrete product manufacturing	3273	6.1	4.1	2.2	1.9	2.0
Lime and gypsum product manufacturing	3274	3.9	0.9	0.4	0.5	3.0
Other nonmetallic mineral product manufacturing	3279	3.6	2.3	1.2	1.1	1.3
Primary metal manufacturing	331	5.2	2.9	1.2	1.6	2.3
Iron and steel mills and ferroalloy manufacturing	3311	2.7	1.5	0.6	0.9	1.2
Steel product manufacturing from purchased steel	3312	5.3	2.7	1.1	1.6	2.6
Alumina and aluminum production and processing	3313	4.0	2.1	0.9	1.2	1.8
Nonferrous metal (except aluminum) production and processing	3314	4.6	2.7	1.5	1.3	1.8
Foundries	3315	7.8	4.4	1.8	2.6	3.5
Fabricated metal product manufacturing	332	4.8	2.4	1.3	1.2	2.4
Forging and stamping	3321	5.5	2.7	1.3	1.4	2.8
Cutlery and hand tool manufacturing	3322	4.1	1.9	0.9	1.0	2.2
Architectural and structural metals manufacturing	3323	5.9	2.8	1.5	1.3	3.1
Boiler, tank, and shipping container manufacturing	3324	4.6	2.3	1.2	1.1	2.3
Hardware manufacturing	3325	5.0	2.3	1.0	1.3	2.7
Spring and wire product manufacturing	3326	5.5	2.9	1.3	1.6	2.6
Machine shops; turned product; and screw, nut, and bolt manufacturing	3327	4.3	2.1	1.2	0.9	2.2
Coating, engraving, heat treating, and allied activities	3328	5.0	2.9	1.5	1.4	2.1
Other fabricated metal product manufacturing	3329	3.7	1.9	0.9	1.0	1.8
Machinery manufacturing	333	3.8	1.9	0.9	1.0	1.9
Agriculture, construction, and mining machinery manufacturing	3331	4.1	2.1	1.0	1.1	2.0
Industrial machinery manufacturing	3332	3.5	1.7	0.8	0.8	1.9
Commercial and service machinery manufacturing	3333	3.1	1.5	0.7	0.8	1.6
Ventilation, heating, air conditioning, and commercial refrigeration equipment manufacturing	3334	4.1	2.1	0.8	1.3	2.1
Metalworking machinery manufacturing	3335	4.0	1.6	0.8	0.8	2.4
Engine, turbine, and power transmission equipment manufacturing	3336	3.3	1.9	0.8	1.1	1.4
Other general purpose machinery manufacturing	3339	3.8	2.0	1.0	1.0	1.8
Computer and electronic product manufacturing	334	1.3	0.7	0.4	0.3	0.6
Computer and peripheral equipment manufacturing	3341	0.6	0.3	0.2	0.1	0.3
Communications equipment manufacturing	3342	0.8	0.4	0.2	0.2	0.4
Audio and video equipment manufacturing	3343	1.5	1.0	0.6	0.4	0.5
Semiconductor and other electronic component manufacturing	3344	1.6	0.8	0.4	0.4	0.8
Navigational, measuring, electromedical, and control instruments manufacturing	3345	1.4	0.8	0.4	0.3	0.6
Manufacturing and reproducing magnetic and optical media	3346	1.3	1.0	0.5	0.4	0.3
Electrical equipment, appliance, and component manufacturing	335	3.0	1.8	0.8	1.0	1.3
Electric lighting equipment manufacturing	3351	3.3	1.9	0.8	1.1	1.4
Household appliance manufacturing	3352	3.7	2.2	0.9	1.3	1.6
Electrical equipment manufacturing	3353	2.7	1.5	0.7	0.8	1.2
Other electrical equipment and component manufacturing	3359	3.0	1.9	0.8	1.1	1.1
Transportation equipment manufacturing	336	4.7	2.6	1.0	1.6	2.1
Motor vehicle manufacturing	3361	6.9	3.7	1.6	2.2	3.1
Motor vehicle body and trailer manufacturing	3362	8.3	4.0	1.7	2.3	4.3
Motor vehicle parts manufacturing	3363	4.6	2.6	0.9	1.6	2.1
Aerospace product and parts manufacturing	3364	2.8	1.7	0.6	1.2	1.0
Ship and boat building	3366	6.5	4.0	2.0	2.0	2.5
Other transportation equipment manufacturing	3369	2.4	1.2	0.6	0.6	1.2
Furniture and related product manufacturing	337	4.8	2.6	1.2	1.4	2.2
Household and institutional furniture and kitchen cabinet manufacturing	3371	4.5	2.5	1.1	1.4	2.0
Office furniture (including fixtures) manufacturing	3372	5.6	2.8	1.4	1.4	2.7
Other furniture-related product manufacturing	3379	4.2	2.8	1.0	1.7	1.4
Miscellaneous manufacturing	339	2.5	1.4	0.7	0.7	1.1
Medical equipment and supplies manufacturing	3391	2.1	1.1	0.5	0.6	1.0
Other miscellaneous manufacturing	3399	3.0	1.7	0.9	0.8	1.3
Service providing		**3.0**	**1.6**	**0.9**	**0.6**	**1.4**
Trade, transportation, and utilities		**3.6**	**2.2**	**1.3**	**1.0**	**1.4**
Wholesale trade	42	2.9	1.9	1.1	0.9	1.0
Merchant wholesalers, durable goods	423	2.6	1.6	0.9	0.7	1.0
Merchant wholesalers, nondurable goods	424	3.9	2.8	1.5	1.3	1.1
Retail trade	44-45	3.6	2.0	1.0	1.0	1.6
Motor vehicle and parts dealers	441	3.4	1.7	1.0	0.7	1.7
Furniture and home furnishings stores	442	3.9	2.3	1.5	0.8	1.6
Electronics and appliance stores	443	1.4	0.8	0.6	0.2	0.6

See source and footnotes on page 79.

Occupational Injuries and Illnesses (cont.)

Bureau of Labor Statistics estimates of nonfatal occupational injury and illness incidence rates for selected industries, 2014 (cont.)

Industry[a]	NAICS code[b]	Total recordable cases	Cases with days away from work, job transfer, or restriction			Other recordable cases
			Total	Cases with days away from work	Cases with job transfer or restriction	
Building material and garden equipment and supplies dealers	444	5.0	3.4	1.6	1.8	1.6
Food and beverage stores	445	4.4	2.6	1.4	1.2	1.7
Health and personal care stores	446	2.1	0.9	0.6	0.3	1.3
Gasoline stations	447	2.3	1.1	0.6	0.5	1.2
Clothing and clothing accessories stores	448	2.0	0.7	0.4	0.3	1.4
Sporting goods, hobby, book, and music stores	451	2.6	1.1	0.6	0.5	1.4
General merchandise stores	452	4.8	2.8	1.2	1.6	2.0
Miscellaneous store retailers	453	3.4	1.7	1.0	0.7	1.7
Nonstore retailers	454	1.8	1.2	0.6	0.5	0.7
Transportation and warehousing	48-49	4.8	3.4	2.3	1.2	1.4
Air transportation	481	7.5	6.1	4.5	1.6	1.3
Rail transportation	482	2.0	1.5	1.3	0.1	0.5
Water transportation	483	2.3	1.4	0.9	0.6	0.9
Truck transportation	484	4.5	3.2	2.3	0.9	1.3
Transit and ground passenger transportation	485	4.6	3.2	2.4	0.8	1.4
Pipeline transportation	486	1.8	0.8	0.6	0.2	0.9
Scenic and sightseeing transportation	487	3.2	2.4	1.9	0.6	0.8
Support activities for transportation	488	3.6	2.2	1.5	0.8	1.4
Couriers and messengers	492	7.1	5.2	3.1	2.2	1.8
Warehousing and storage	493	5.2	3.7	1.7	1.9	1.5
Utilities	22	2.4	1.3	0.7	0.6	1.2
Electric power generation, transmission, and distribution	2211	2.1	1.0	0.6	0.4	1.1
Natural gas distribution	2212	2.6	1.6	0.8	0.8	1.0
Water, sewage, and other systems	2213	5.3	2.7	1.4	1.3	2.6
Information		**1.4**	**0.8**	**0.6**	**0.2**	**0.6**
Publishing industries (except Internet)	511	1.0	0.4	0.3	0.1	0.6
Motion picture and sound recording industries	512	1.6	0.6	0.4	0.2	1.0
Broadcasting (except Internet)	515	1.4	0.6	0.4	0.2	0.7
Telecommunications	517	2.2	1.6	1.3	0.3	0.6
Other information services	519	0.4	0.2	(f)	(f)	0.2
Finance, insurance, and real estate		**1.2**	**0.5**	**0.4**	**0.2**	**0.7**
Finance and insurance	52	0.7	0.2	0.2	(f)	0.4
Monetary authorities	521	1.0	0.5	0.3	0.2	0.5
Credit intermediation and related activities	522	0.8	0.3	0.2	0.1	0.5
Securities, commodity contracts, and other financial investments and related activities	523	0.2	0.1	0.1	(f)	0.1
Insurance carriers and related activities	524	0.6	0.2	0.2	(f)	0.4
Real estate and rental and leasing	53	2.9	1.5	0.9	0.6	1.4
Real estate	531	2.5	1.3	0.9	0.4	1.2
Rental and leasing services	532	4.0	1.9	0.9	1.0	2.1
Lessors of nonfinancial intangible assets (except copyrighted works)	533	1.0	0.2	0.1	(f)	0.8
Professional and business services		**1.5**	**0.8**	**0.5**	**0.3**	**0.7**
Professional, scientific, and technical services	54	0.9	0.4	0.3	0.1	0.6
Management of companies and enterprises	55	1.0	0.5	0.3	0.2	0.5
Administrative and support and waste management and remediation services	56	2.6	1.6	1.1	0.5	1.1
Administrative and support services	561	2.4	1.4	1.0	0.4	1.0
Waste management and remediation services	562	5.1	3.4	2.2	1.2	1.7
Educational and health services		**4.2**	**2.0**	**1.1**	**0.8**	**2.2**
Educational services	61	2.1	0.9	0.6	0.2	1.2
Health care and social assistance	62	4.5	2.1	1.2	0.9	2.4
Ambulatory health care services	621	2.4	0.9	0.6	0.3	1.5
Hospitals	622	6.2	2.5	1.5	1.0	3.7
Nursing and residential care facilities	623	7.1	4.3	2.0	2.3	2.8
Social assistance	624	3.5	1.8	1.3	0.6	1.6
Leisure, entertainment, and hospitality		**3.6**	**1.5**	**1.0**	**0.6**	**2.1**
Arts, entertainment, and recreation	71	4.2	2.1	1.2	0.9	2.1
Accommodation and food services	72	3.5	1.4	0.9	0.5	2.1
Accommodation	721	4.9	2.7	1.4	1.2	2.3
Food services and drinking places	722	3.2	1.2	0.8	0.3	2.0
Other services, except public administration		**2.5**	**1.2**	**0.9**	**0.4**	**1.2**
Repair and maintenance	811	3.0	1.4	1.0	0.4	1.6
Personal and laundry services	812	2.2	1.4	0.9	0.5	0.8
Religious, grantmaking, civic, professional, and similar organizations	813	2.0	0.9	0.6	0.2	1.1
State and local government[d]		**5.0**	**2.3**	**1.7**	**0.6**	**2.7**
State government[d]		**4.1**	**2.1**	**1.7**	**0.4**	**2.0**
Local government[d]		**5.4**	**2.3**	**1.7**	**0.7**	**3.0**

See source and footnotes on page 79.

Bureau of Labor Statistics estimates of nonfatal occupational injury and illness incidence rates[a] for selected industries, 2014

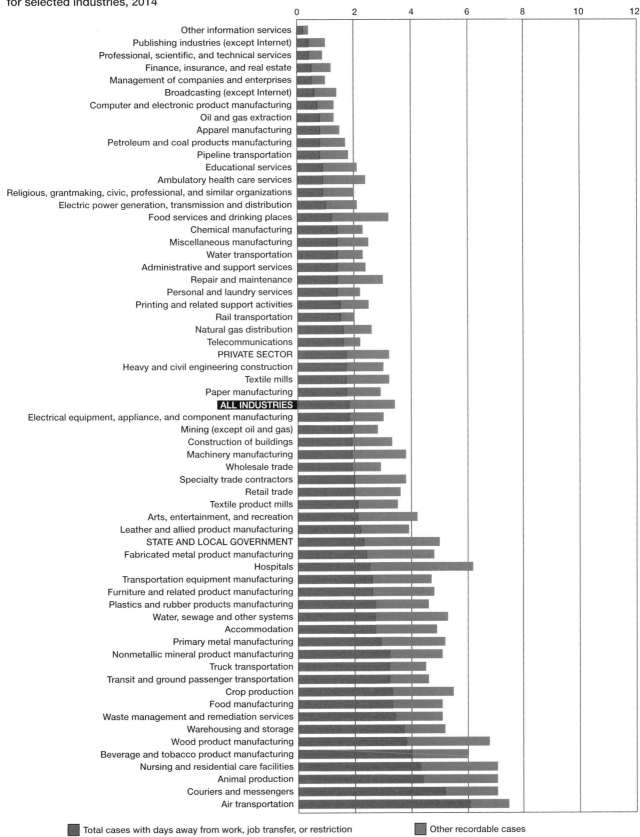

Total cases with days away from work, job transfer, or restriction ■ Other recordable cases

Note: Industries are shown at the two-, three-, or four-digit NAICS level.
[a]*Total cases with days away from work, job transfer, or restriction plus other recordable cases equals total recordable cases per 200,000 hours worked.*

Causes of Work-Related Deaths and Injuries

Roadway incidents involving motorized land vehicles are the leading cause of work-related deaths, followed by falls, slips, or trips and contact with objects and equipment. For nonfatal cases with days away from work, events involving overexertion and bodily reaction are the leading cause, followed by contact with objects and equipment and falls, slips, or trips.

Work-related deaths and injuries by event or exposure, United States, 2013

Event or exposure	Deaths[a]	Cases with days away from work[b]
Total, all events or exposures	**4,585**	**917,090**
Violence and other injuries by persons or animals	773	38,500
Intentional injury by person	*686*	*14,150*
Homicides (Intentional injury by other person)	404	13,800
Suicides (Self-inflicted injury--intentional)	282	–
Injury by person – unintentional or intent unknown	*52*	*11,830*
Injury by other person – unintentional or intent unknown	17	10,470
Self-inflicted injury – unintentional or intent unknown	35	80
Animal- and insect-related incidents	*35*	*11,980*
Transportation incidents	1,865	44,410
Aircraft incidents	*136*	*680*
Rail vehicle incidents	*41*	*250*
Animal and other nonmotorized vehicle transportation incidents	*8*	*380*
Pedestrian vehicular incidents	*294*	*5,480*
Water vehicle incidents	*60*	*210*
Roadway incidents involving motorized land vehicle	*1,099*	*30,840*
Nonroadway incident involving motorized land vehicles	*227*	*5,900*
Fires and explosions	149	1,470
Fires	*82*	*830*
Explosions	*67*	*510*
Slips, trips, or falls	724	229,190
Fall to lower level	*595*	*47,120*
Fall on same level	*110*	*141,060*
Exposure to harmful substances or environments	335	40,100
Exposure to electricity	*141*	*2,090*
Exposure to temperature extremes	*38*	*16,320*
Exposure to other harmful substances	*124*	*16,630*
Exposure to oxygen deficiency, n.e.c.[c]	*30*	*90*
Contact with objects and equipment	721	232,570
Struck by object or equipment	*509*	*133,860*
Struck against object or equipment	*3*	*51,580*
Caught in or compressed by equipment or objects	*131*	*33,770*
Struck, caught, or crushed in collapsing structure, equipment, or material	*78*	*670*
Overexertion and bodily reaction	15	322,310
Overexertion involving outside sources	*7*	*213,090*
Overexertion involving lifting, lowering	4	107,910
Overexertion in lifting–single episode	3	80,240
Repetitive motions involving microtasks	*–*	*24,420*
Nonclassifiable	–	8,560

Deaths[a] by event or exposure, United States, 2013

Cases with days away from work[b] by event or exposure, United States, 2013

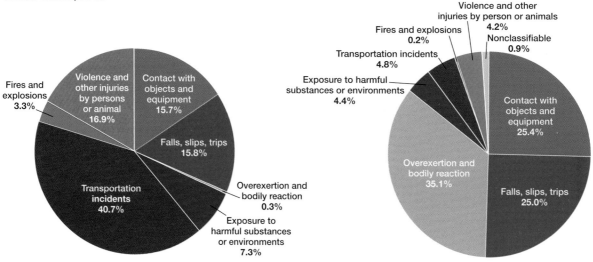

Source: Bureau of Labor Statistics.
[a]Includes deaths among all workers.
[b]Includes cases with days away from work among private-sector wage and salary workers. Excludes government employees, the self-employed, and unpaid family workers.
[c]"n.e.c." means "not elsewhere classified."

The tables on pages 86-101 present data on the characteristics of injured and ill workers and the injuries and illnesses that affected them. These data indicate how many workers died from on-the-job injuries and how many were affected by nonfatal injuries and illnesses. The data may be used to help set priorities for occupational safety and health programs and for benchmarking.

The fatality information covers only deaths due to injuries and comes from the Bureau of Labor Statistics (BLS) Census of Fatal Occupational Injuries. The data are for calendar year 2013 and include wage and salary workers, the self-employed, and unpaid family workers in all types of businesses and industries.

The data on nonfatal cases cover both occupational injuries and illnesses and come from the BLS Survey of Occupational Injuries and Illnesses for 2013. The survey also is used to produce the incidence rates shown on the preceding pages. The estimates on the following pages are the number of cases involving days away from work (with or without days of restricted work activity). The nonfatal cases presented on pages 86-100 do not cover the self-employed; unpaid family workers; or federal, state, or local government employees. Nonfatal cases involving state and local government employees are presented on page 101.

Data are presented for the sex, age, occupation, and race or ethnic origin of the worker and for the nature of the injury or illness, the part of body affected, the source of the injury or illness, and the event or exposure that produced the injury or illness.

The text at the top of each page describes the kind of establishments that are included in the industry sector and gives the total number of workers in the industry in 2013 and the number working in the private sector.

How to benchmark

Incidence rates, percent distributions, or ranks may be used for benchmarking purposes. The results of the calculations described here may be compared to similar rates, percent distributions, and rankings based on data for a company.

For nonfatal incidence rates, multiply the number of cases by 1,000 and then divide by the private-sector employment given in the text at the top of the page. This will give the number of cases with days away from work per 1,000 employees per year. For fatality rates, multiply the number of fatalities by 100,000 then divide by the total employment given at the top of the page. This will give the number of deaths per 100,000 employees per year.

To compute percent distributions, divide the number of cases for each characteristic by the total number of cases found on the first line of the table. Multiply the quotient by 100 and round to one decimal place. Percent distributions may not add to 100% because of unclassifiable cases not shown.

Ranks are determined by arranging the characteristics from largest to smallest within each group and then numbering consecutively starting with one for the largest.

Industry sectors

Page 86 shows nonfatal injury and illness data for the private sector of the economy (excluding government entities) and fatal injury data for all industries (including government). Pages 87-100 present the data for industry sectors based on the North American Industry Classification System. Page 101 presents the fatal injury data for all government and nonfatal cases for state and local government (the BLS survey does not cover federal government entities).

The nonfatal occupational injury and illness data cover only private sector employees and exclude employees in federal, state, and local government entities and the self-employed. The fatal injury data cover all workers in both the private sector and government.

There were 145,172,000 people employed in 2013, of which 123,630,000 worked in the private sector.

Number of nonfatal occupational injuries and illnesses involving days away from work[a] and fatal occupational injuries by selected worker and case characteristics, private industry, United States, 2013

Characteristic	Private industry[b,c] nonfatal cases	All industries fatalities
Total	917,090	4,585
Sex		
Men	562,790	4,265
Women	350,510	319
Age		
Younger than 16	120	5
16 to 19	21,860	66
20 to 24	87,470	279
25 to 34	199,570	777
35 to 44	194,900	853
45 to 54	218,950	1,115
55 to 64	147,190	933
65 and older	32,020	557
Occupation		
Management, business, and financial	30,520	430
Professional and related	81,990	75
Service	222,340	804
Sales and related	62,870	220
Office and administrative support	67,030	76
Farming, fishing, and forestry	15,560	232
Construction and extractive	77,380	845
Installation, maintenance, and repair	81,870	372
Production	104,590	213
Transportation and material moving	170,290	1,259
Military occupations	—	58
Race or ethnic origin[d]		
White, non-Hispanic	363,220	3,124
Black, non-Hispanic	70,500	439
Hispanic	124,330	817
Other, multiple, and not reported	359,040	205
Nature of injury or illness		
Fractures	77,990	30
Sprains, strains, or tears	327,060	14
Amputations	6,160	8
Cuts, lacerations, or punctures	88,250	69
Bruises or contusions	72,710	—
Chemical burns and corrosions	2,790	—
Heat (thermal) burns	13,780	77
Multiple traumatic injuries	23,700	1,754
Soreness or pain	153,970	—
Carpal tunnel syndrome	6,440	—
Tendonitis	2,290	—
All other	141,950	2,626
Part of body affected		
Head	69,680	952
Eye	*22,120*	*—*
Neck	13,430	202
Trunk	226,640	719
Back	*170,450*	*62*
Upper extremities	286,320	12
Shoulder	*68,500*	*7*
Arm	*43,580*	*—*
Wrist	*37,500*	*—*
Hand	*121,500*	*—*
Lower extremities	202,280	58
Knee	*77,490*	*9*
Ankle	*45,620*	*10*
Foot or toe	*43,570*	*6*
Body systems	18,570	623
Multiple	89,870	1,953
All other	10,290	—

Characteristic	Private industry[b,c] nonfatal cases	All industries fatalities
Source of injury or illness		
Chemicals or chemical products	11,580	142
Containers	107,490	63
Furniture or fixtures	41,090	6
Machinery	50,670	356
Parts and materials	76,130	197
Worker motion or position	136,200	8
Health care patient	48,250	—
Floors, walkways, or ground surfaces	143,460	145
Handtools	42,480	25
Ladders	19,980	133
Vehicles	87,480	2,017
All other	152,280	1,493
Event or exposure		
Violence and other injuries by persons or animals	38,500	773
Intentional injury by other person	*13,800*	*101*
Injury by person unintentional or intent unknown	*11,830*	*52*
Transportation incidents	44,410	1,865
Roadway incidents involving motorized land vehicles	*30,840*	*1,099*
Fires or explosions	1,470	149
Falls, slips, or trips	229,190	724
Slips or trips without fall	*35,000*	*6*
Fall on same level	*141,060*	*110*
Fall to lower level	*47,120*	*595*
Exposed to harmful substances or environments	40,100	335
Contact with object or equipment	232,570	721
Struck by object	*133,860*	*509*
Struck against object	*51,580*	*—*
Caught in object, equipment, or material	*33,770*	*131*
Overexertion and bodily reaction	322,310	15
Overexertion in lifting or lowering	*107,910*	*—*
Repetitive motion involving microtasks	*24,420*	*—*
All other	8,560	—

Source: This research was conducted with restricted access to Bureau of Labor Statistics (BLS) data. The views expressed here do not necessarily reflect the views of BLS.

Note: Because of rounding and data exclusion of nonclassifiable responses, data may not sum to the totals. Dashes (—) indicate data that do not meet publication guidelines.

[a]Days away from work include those that result in days away from work with or without restricted work activity or job transfer.

[b]Excludes farms with fewer than 11 employees.

[c]Data for mining operators in coal, metal, and nonmetal mining and for employees in railroad transportation are provided to BLS by the Mine Safety and Health Administration (MSHA), U.S. Department of Labor; and the Federal Railroad Administration (FRA), U.S. Department of Transportation. Independent mining contractors are excluded from the coal, metal, and nonmetal mining industries. MSHA and FRA data do not reflect the changes in OSHA recordkeeping requirements in 2002.

[d]In the fatalities column, non-Hispanic categories include cases with Hispanic origin not reported.

The Agriculture, Forestry, Fishing and Hunting industry sector includes growing crops; raising animals; harvesting timber; harvesting fish and other animals from a farm, ranch, or their natural habitats; and agricultural support services.

Employment in Agriculture, Forestry, Fishing, and Hunting totaled 2,129,000 in 2013, of which 2,076,000 were private sector employees.

Number of nonfatal occupational injuries and illnesses involving days away from work[a] and fatal occupational injuries by selected worker and case characteristics, private industry, United States, Agriculture, Forestry, Fishing, and Hunting, 2013

Characteristic	Nonfatal cases[b]	Fatalities
Total	19,550	500
Sex		
Men	15,880	480
Women	3,660	20
Age		
Younger than 16	20	—
16 to 19	610	16
20 to 24	2,090	16
25 to 34	5,260	58
35 to 44	4,450	62
45 to 54	3,570	83
55 to 64	2,050	114
65 and older	350	147
Occupation		
Management, business, and financial	330	234
Professional and related	250	—
Service	840	6
Sales and related	—	—
Office and administrative support	270	—
Farming, fishing, and forestry	14,170	213
Construction and extractive	70	—
Installation, maintenance, and repair	660	10
Production	660	—
Transportation and material moving	2,280	34
Military occupations	—	—
Race or ethnic origin[c]		
White, non-Hispanic	4,720	403
Black, non-Hispanic	690	12
Hispanic	10,160	70
Other, multiple, and not reported	3,980	15
Nature of injury or illness		
Fractures	1,700	—
Sprains, strains, or tears	5,090	—
Amputations	120	—
Cuts, lacerations, or punctures	2,040	—
Bruises or contusions	1,850	—
Chemical burns and corrosions	130	—
Heat (thermal) burns	150	7
Multiple traumatic injuries	440	156
Soreness or pain	3,840	—
Carpal tunnel syndrome	30	—
Tendonitis	—	—
All other	4,130	329
Part of body affected		
Head	2,010	94
Eye	*1,120*	—
Neck	190	20
Trunk	4,440	129
Back	*3,140*	*8*
Upper extremities	5,390	—
Shoulder	*1,410*	—
Arm	*900*	—
Wrist	*320*	—
Hand	*2,490*	—
Lower extremities	4,830	6
Knee	*1,460*	—
Ankle	*1,240*	—
Foot or toe	*1,200*	—
Body systems	430	86
Multiple	1,610	164
All other	660	—

Characteristic	Nonfatal cases[b]	Fatalities
Source of injury or illness		
Chemicals or chemical products	280	7
Containers	1,980	10
Furniture or fixtures	410	—
Machinery	1,210	66
Parts and materials	1,480	10
Worker motion or position	1,950	—
Health care patient	—	—
Floors, walkways, or ground surfaces	2,400	8
Handtools	930	—
Ladders	1,250	5
Vehicles	2,190	254
All other	5,470	139
Event or exposure		
Violence and other injuries by persons or animals	1,520	45
Intentional injury by other person	*110*	*9*
Injury by person unintentional or intent unknown	*20*	—
Transportation incidents	1,220	237
Roadway incidents involving motorized land vehicles	*720*	*66*
Fires or explosions	20	7
Falls, slips, or trips	5,030	32
Slips or trips without fall	*600*	—
Fall on same level	*2,310*	*6*
Fall to lower level	*1,960*	*25*
Exposed to harmful substances or environments	770	22
Contact with object or equipment	6,410	157
Struck by object	*3,800*	*118*
Struck against object	*1,080*	—
Caught in object, equipment, or material	*960*	*27*
Overexertion and bodily reaction	4,210	—
Overexertion in lifting or lowering	*1,520*	—
Repetitive motion involving microtasks	*210*	—
All other	350	—

Source: This research was conducted with restricted access to Bureau of Labor Statistics (BLS) data. The views expressed here do not necessarily reflect the views of BLS.

Note: Because of rounding and data exclusion of nonclassifiable responses, data may not sum to the totals. Dashes (—) indicate data that do not meet publication guidelines.

[a]Days away from work include those that result in days away from work with or without restricted work activity or job transfer.

[b]Excludes farms with less than 11 employees.

[c]In the fatalities column, non-Hispanic categories include cases with Hispanic origin not reported.

The Mining industry sector includes extraction of naturally occurring mineral solids, such as coal and ores; liquid minerals, such as crude petroleum; and gases, such as natural gas. It also includes quarrying, well operations, beneficiating, other preparation customarily performed at the site, and mining support activities.

Mining employment in 2013 totaled 1,065,000 workers of which 1,062,000 were private sector employees.

Number of nonfatal occupational injuries and illnesses involving days away from work[a] and fatal occupational injuries by selected worker and case characteristics, private industry, United States, Mining, 2013

Characteristic	Nonfatal cases[b]	Fatalities
Total	**7,830**	**155**
Sex		
Men	7,560	152
Women	270	—
Age		
Younger than 16	—	—
16 to 19	80	—
20 to 24	1,300	20
25 to 34	1,940	40
35 to 44	1,770	26
45 to 54	1,420	40
55 to 64	1,100	22
65 and older	120	—
Occupation		
Management, business, and financial	50	—
Professional and related	180	—
Service	40	—
Sales and related	—	—
Office and administrative support	110	—
Farming, fishing, and forestry	—	—
Construction and extractive	3,770	95
Installation, maintenance, and repair	780	10
Production	620	7
Transportation and material moving	2,210	39
Military occupations	—	—
Race or ethnic origin[c]		
White, non-Hispanic	2,290	106
Black, non-Hispanic	100	8
Hispanic	900	39
Other, multiple, and not reported	4,540	—
Nature of injury or illness		
Fractures	1,620	—
Sprains, strains, or tears	2,470	—
Amputations	180	—
Cuts, lacerations, or punctures	630	—
Bruises or contusions	490	—
Chemical burns and corrosions	40	—
Heat (thermal) burns	90	8
Multiple traumatic injuries	200	62
Soreness or pain	640	—
Carpal tunnel syndrome	—	—
Tendonitis	—	—
All other	1,480	82
Part of body affected		
Head	820	25
Eye	130	—
Neck	60	5
Trunk	1,590	32
Back	1,070	—
Upper extremities	2,530	—
Shoulder	470	—
Arm	460	—
Wrist	170	—
Hand	1,380	—
Lower extremities	1,970	—
Knee	910	—
Ankle	350	—
Foot or toe	310	—
Body systems	120	21
Multiple	640	70
All other	80	—

Characteristic	Nonfatal cases[b]	Fatalities
Source of injury or illness		
Chemicals or chemical products	190	13
Containers	400	9
Furniture or fixtures	130	—
Machinery	700	34
Parts and materials	1,540	19
Worker motion or position	540	—
Health care patient	—	—
Floors, walkways, or ground surfaces	1,080	—
Handtools	870	—
Ladders	60	—
Vehicles	740	59
All other	1,580	17
Event or exposure		
Violence and other injuries by persons or animals	—	—
Intentional injury by other person	—	—
Injury by person unintentional or intent unknown	—	—
Transportation incidents	430	58
Roadway incidents involving motorized land vehicles	320	38
Fires or explosions	60	17
Falls, slips, or trips	1,550	20
Slips or trips without fall	210	—
Fall on same level	780	—
Fall to lower level	470	18
Exposed to harmful substances or environments	380	15
Contact with object or equipment	3,270	42
Struck by object	1,720	31
Struck against object	500	—
Caught in object, equipment, or material	1,030	5
Overexertion and bodily reaction	2,070	—
Overexertion in lifting or lowering	660	—
Repetitive motion involving microtasks	—	—
All other	60	—

Source: This research was conducted with restricted access to Bureau of Labor Statistics (BLS) data. The views expressed here do not necessarily reflect the views of BLS.

Note: Because of rounding and data exclusion of nonclassifiable responses, data may not sum to the totals. Dashes (—) indicate data that do not meet publication guidelines.

[a]Days away from work include those that result in days away from work with or without restricted work activity or job transfer.

[b]Data for mining operators in coal, metal, and nonmetal mining are provided to BLS by the Mine Safety and Health Administration (MSHA), Department of Labor. Independent mining contractors are excluded from the coal, metal, and nonmetal mining industries. MSHA data do not reflect the changes in OSHA recordkeeping requirements in 2002.

[c]In the fatalities column, non-Hispanic categories include cases with Hispanic origin not reported.

Construction

The Construction industry sector includes establishments engaged in construction of buildings, heavy construction other than buildings, and specialty trade contractors such as plumbing, electrical, carpentry, etc.

In 2013, employment in the Construction industry totaled 9,271,000 workers, of which 8,864,000 were private sector employees.

Number of nonfatal occupational injuries and illnesses involving days away from work[a] and fatal occupational injuries by selected worker and case characteristics, private industry, United States, Construction, 2013

Characteristic	Nonfatal cases	Fatalities
Total	**82,040**	**828**
Sex		
Men	80,620	819
Women	1,400	9
Age		
Younger than 16	—	—
16 to 19	1,810	5
20 to 24	7,820	55
25 to 34	20,710	160
35 to 44	20,540	171
45 to 54	19,220	217
55 to 64	9,300	162
65 and older	1,360	58
Occupation		
Management, business, and financial	2,000	22
Professional and related	170	7
Service	450	9
Sales and related	390	—
Office and administrative support	270	—
Farming, fishing, and forestry	—	—
Construction and extractive	62,540	632
Installation, maintenance, and repair	11,210	65
Production	2,230	25
Transportation and material moving	2,730	68
Military occupations	—	—
Race or ethnic origin[b]		
White, non-Hispanic	44,210	520
Black, non-Hispanic	2,160	41
Hispanic	15,470	241
Other, multiple, and not reported	20,200	26
Nature of injury or illness		
Fractures	11,150	—
Sprains, strains, or tears	21,420	—
Amputations	1,380	—
Cuts, lacerations, or punctures	11,470	8
Bruises or contusions	3,970	—
Chemical burns and corrosions	240	—
Heat (thermal) burns	660	8
Multiple traumatic injuries	1,700	336
Soreness or pain	15,030	—
Carpal tunnel syndrome	200	—
Tendonitis	150	—
All other	14,670	469
Part of body affected		
Head	5,730	195
Eye	*2,300*	—
Neck	1,510	25
Trunk	19,470	106
Back	*13,320*	*8*
Upper extremities	26,720	—
Shoulder	*5,330*	—
Arm	*4,650*	—
Wrist	*2,250*	—
Hand	*13,780*	—
Lower extremities	19,730	5
Knee	*7,260*	—
Ankle	*3,380*	—
Foot or toe	*5,390*	—
Body systems	1,820	143
Multiple	6,670	354
All other	380	—

Characteristic	Nonfatal cases	Fatalities
Source of injury or illness		
Chemicals or chemical products	1,170	27
Containers	3,100	6
Furniture or fixtures	2,450	—
Machinery	6,290	83
Parts and materials	15,280	77
Worker motion or position	10,830	—
Health care patient	—	—
Floors, walkways, or ground surfaces	9,180	20
Handtools	7,140	11
Ladders	5,900	76
Vehicles	5,560	227
All other	15,140	300
Event or exposure		
Violence and other injuries by persons or animals	680	36
Intentional injury by other person	*70*	*13*
Injury by person unintentional or intent unknown	*90*	*6*
Transportation incidents	3,270	223
Roadway incidents involving motorized land vehicles	*2,190*	*112*
Fires or explosions	130	13
Falls, slips, or trips	21,890	302
Slips or trips without fall	*3,010*	—
Fall on same level	*8,560*	*6*
Fall to lower level	*9,560*	*291*
Exposed to harmful substances or environments	3,400	111
Contact with object or equipment	28,310	140
Struck by object	*17,180*	*84*
Struck against object	*5,420*	—
Caught in object, equipment, or material	*3,640*	*21*
Overexertion and bodily reaction	23,810	—
Overexertion in lifting or lowering	*8,500*	—
Repetitive motion involving microtasks	*780*	—
All other	540	—

Source: This research was conducted with restricted access to Bureau of Labor Statistics (BLS) data. The views expressed here do not necessarily reflect the views of BLS.
Note: Because of rounding and data exclusion of nonclassifiable responses, data may not sum to the totals. Dashes (—) indicate data that do not meet publication guidelines.
[a]*Days away from work include those that result in days away from work with or without restricted work activity or job transfer.*
[b]*In the fatalities column, non-Hispanic categories include cases with Hispanic origin not reported.*

Manufacturing

The Manufacturing industry sector includes establishments engaged in the mechanical or chemical transformation of materials, substances, or components into new products. It includes durable and nondurable goods such as food, textiles, apparel, lumber, wood products, paper and paper products, printing, chemicals and pharmaceuticals, petroleum and coal products, rubber and plastics products, metals and metal products, machinery, electrical equipment, and transportation equipment.

Manufacturing employment in 2013 was 14,869,000 workers, of which 14,763,000 were private sector employees.

Number of nonfatal occupational injuries and illnesses involving days away from work[a] and fatal occupational injuries by selected worker and case characteristics, private industry, United States, Manufacturing, 2013

Characteristic	Nonfatal cases	Fatalities
Total	**120,110**	**312**
Sex		
Men	94,610	289
Women	25,240	23
Age		
Younger than 16	—	—
16 to 19	1,900	—
20 to 24	10,490	21
25 to 34	24,160	45
35 to 44	25,950	62
45 to 54	31,490	79
55 to 64	21,100	77
65 and older	2,910	24
Occupation		
Management, business, and financial	1,610	17
Professional and related	1,490	15
Service	2,320	—
Sales and related	550	10
Office and administrative support	3,990	—
Farming, fishing, and forestry	610	7
Construction and extractive	3,580	17
Installation, maintenance, and repair	8,290	35
Production	77,770	128
Transportation and material moving	19,630	76
Military occupations	—	—
Race or ethnic origin[b]		
White, non-Hispanic	57,660	215
Black, non-Hispanic	9,750	29
Hispanic	19,130	54
Other, multiple, and not reported	33,570	14
Nature of injury or illness		
Fractures	11,480	—
Sprains, strains, or tears	37,000	—
Amputations	2,000	—
Cuts, lacerations, or punctures	14,900	6
Bruises or contusions	8,750	—
Chemical burns and corrosions	680	—
Heat (thermal) burns	2,130	8
Multiple traumatic injuries	2,940	102
Soreness or pain	14,800	—
Carpal tunnel syndrome	2,480	—
Tendonitis	580	—
All other	22,360	189
Part of body affected		
Head	10,010	64
Eye	*5,100*	—
Neck	1,250	19
Trunk	25,620	67
Back	*17,660*	*9*
Upper extremities	51,690	—
Shoulder	*9,820*	—
Arm	*6,830*	—
Wrist	*7,210*	—
Hand	*25,670*	—
Lower extremities	22,120	—
Knee	*7,840*	—
Ankle	*4,690*	—
Foot or toe	*5,360*	—
Body systems	1,450	41
Multiple	7,250	116
All other	720	—

Characteristic	Nonfatal cases	Fatalities
Source of injury or illness		
Chemicals or chemical products	2,340	—
Containers	13,030	14
Furniture or fixtures	3,410	—
Machinery	15,000	79
Parts and materials	20,090	24
Worker motion or position	21,580	—
Health care patient	—	—
Floors, walkways, or ground surfaces	12,940	13
Handtools	8,650	—
Ladders	1,450	—
Vehicles	6,850	97
All other	14,770	75
Event or exposure		
Violence and other injuries by persons or animals	570	36
Intentional injury by other person	*100*	*8*
Injury by person unintentional or intent unknown	*160*	—
Transportation incidents	2,210	91
Roadway incidents involving motorized land vehicles	*760*	*56*
Fires or explosions	380	12
Falls, slips, or trips	21,430	42
Slips or trips without fall	*3,790*	—
Fall on same level	*12,730*	*10*
Fall to lower level	*4,370*	*31*
Exposed to harmful substances or environments	5,940	18
Contact with object or equipment	44,290	110
Struck by object	*21,710*	*54*
Struck against object	*8,210*	—
Caught in object, equipment, or material	*11,560*	*51*
Overexertion and bodily reaction	44,230	—
Overexertion in lifting or lowering	*13,030*	—
Repetitive motion involving microtasks	*8,130*	—
All other	1,060	—

Source: This research was conducted with restricted access to Bureau of Labor Statistics (BLS) data. The views expressed here do not necessarily reflect the views of BLS.

Note: Because of rounding and data exclusion of nonclassifiable responses, data may not sum to the totals. Dashes (—) indicate data that do not meet publication guidelines.

[a]Days away from work include those that result in days away from work with or without restricted work activity or job transfer.

[b]In the fatalities column, non-Hispanic categories include cases with Hispanic origin not reported.

Wholesale Trade

Establishments in Wholesale Trade generally sell merchandise to other businesses. The merchandise includes the outputs of agriculture, mining, manufacturing, and certain information industries, such as publishing.

Wholesale Trade employed 3,647,000 people in 2013, of which 3,631,000 were private sector employees.

Number of nonfatal occupational injuries and illnesses involving days away from work[a] and fatal occupational injuries by selected worker and case characteristics, private industry, United States, Wholesale Trade, 2013

Characteristic	Nonfatal cases	Fatalities
Total	**57,190**	**201**
Sex		
Men	47,670	193
Women	9,500	8
Age		
Younger than 16	—	—
16 to 19	1,660	—
20 to 24	4,170	10
25 to 34	12,360	36
35 to 44	13,340	35
45 to 54	14,280	55
55 to 64	8,660	39
65 and older	1,820	23
Occupation		
Management, business, and financial	2,340	11
Professional and related	630	—
Service	1,150	—
Sales and related	4,320	37
Office and administrative support	5,480	—
Farming, fishing, and forestry	360	9
Construction and extractive	750	6
Installation, maintenance, and repair	7,090	14
Production	6,180	8
Transportation and material moving	28,720	107
Military occupations	—	—
Race or ethnic origin[b]		
White, non-Hispanic	25,040	140
Black, non-Hispanic	4,500	19
Hispanic	9,630	36
Other, multiple, and not reported	18,020	6
Nature of injury or illness		
Fractures	5,380	—
Sprains, strains, or tears	20,130	—
Amputations	580	—
Cuts, lacerations, or punctures	5,030	—
Bruises or contusions	4,090	—
Chemical burns and corrosions	350	—
Heat (thermal) burns	570	—
Multiple traumatic injuries	1,380	92
Soreness or pain	9,230	—
Carpal tunnel syndrome	320	—
Tendonitis	200	—
All other	9,930	99
Part of body affected		
Head	4,180	46
Eye	*1,170*	—
Neck	510	12
Trunk	16,790	30
Back	*12,330*	—
Upper extremities	16,550	—
Shoulder	*3,920*	—
Arm	*2,520*	—
Wrist	*1,930*	—
Hand	*7,430*	—
Lower extremities	12,800	5
Knee	*4,120*	—
Ankle	*3,290*	—
Foot or toe	*2,940*	—
Body systems	1,110	13
Multiple	4,570	95
All other	690	—

Characteristic	Nonfatal cases	Fatalities
Source of injury or illness		
Chemicals or chemical products	950	7
Containers	11,120	—
Furniture or fixtures	1,790	—
Machinery	2,440	8
Parts and materials	6,530	10
Worker motion or position	8,660	—
Health care patient	—	—
Floors, walkways, or ground surfaces	6,760	—
Handtools	2,000	—
Ladders	720	—
Vehicles	10,060	126
All other	6,160	38
Event or exposure		
Violence and other injuries by persons or animals	450	24
Intentional injury by other person	*70*	*5*
Injury by person unintentional or intent unknown	*70*	—
Transportation incidents	4,600	110
Roadway incidents involving motorized land vehicles	*3,360*	*77*
Fires or explosions	370	5
Falls, slips, or trips	12,640	25
Slips or trips without fall	*2,100*	—
Fall on same level	*6,430*	—
Fall to lower level	*3,390*	*19*
Exposed to harmful substances or environments	1,980	8
Contact with object or equipment	15,050	29
Struck by object	*8,650*	*25*
Struck against object	*2,590*	—
Caught in object, equipment, or material	*3,060*	—
Overexertion and bodily reaction	21,480	—
Overexertion in lifting or lowering	*8,640*	—
Repetitive motion involving microtasks	*1,600*	—
All other	650	—

Source: This research was conducted with restricted access to Bureau of Labor Statistics (BLS) data. The views expressed here do not necessarily reflect the views of BLS.

Note: Because of rounding and data exclusion of nonclassifiable responses, data may not sum to the totals. Dashes (—) indicate data that do not meet publication guidelines.

[a]*Days away from work include those that result in days away from work with or without restricted work activity or job transfer.*

[b]*In the fatalities column, non-Hispanic categories include cases with Hispanic origin not reported.*

Establishments in Retail Trade generally sell merchandise in small quantities for personal or household consumption. This sector includes both store and nonstore retailers.

Retail Trade employed 16,007,000 people in 2013, of which 15,912,000 were private sector employees.

Number of nonfatal occupational injuries and illnesses involving days away from work[a] and fatal occupational injuries by selected worker and case characteristics, private industry, United States, Retail Trade, 2013

Characteristic	Nonfatal cases	Fatalities
Total	128,800	263
Sex		
Men	72,080	230
Women	56,670	33
Age		
Younger than 16	20	–
16 to 19	4,440	6
20 to 24	15,920	20
25 to 34	29,010	49
35 to 44	22,730	43
45 to 54	28,120	60
55 to 64	20,950	40
65 and older	6,070	45
Occupation		
Management, business, and financial	3,450	5
Professional and related	1,690	–
Service	11,730	11
Sales and related	47,360	149
Office and administrative support	19,990	7
Farming, fishing, and forestry	90	–
Construction and extractive	1,070	–
Installation, maintenance, and repair	14,280	32
Production	6,060	–
Transportation and material moving	22,580	56
Military occupations	–	–
Race or ethnic origin[b]		
White, non-Hispanic	46,520	176
Black, non-Hispanic	5,690	21
Hispanic	9,500	27
Other, multiple, and not reported	67,090	39
Nature of injury or illness		
Fractures	9,810	–
Sprains, strains, or tears	49,480	–
Amputations	570	–
Cuts, lacerations, or punctures	14,830	11
Bruises or contusions	12,500	–
Chemical burns and corrosions	260	–
Heat (thermal) burns	1,100	6
Multiple traumatic injuries	3,020	47
Soreness or pain	18,640	–
Carpal tunnel syndrome	530	–
Tendonitis	300	–
All other	17,770	198
Part of body affected		
Head	10,770	80
Eye	2,730	–
Neck	2,000	18
Trunk	33,750	65
Back	25,730	6
Upper extremities	39,000	–
Shoulder	9,960	–
Arm	6,110	–
Wrist	4,750	–
Hand	16,600	–
Lower extremities	28,550	–
Knee	10,750	–
Ankle	5,660	–
Foot or toe	7,980	–
Body systems	3,030	25
Multiple	10,390	72
All other	1,310	–

Characteristic	Nonfatal cases	Fatalities
Source of injury or illness		
Chemicals or chemical products	1,020	12
Containers	26,070	–
Furniture or fixtures	8,960	–
Machinery	8,260	–
Parts and materials	10,340	–
Worker motion or position	17,290	–
Health care patient	–	–
Floors, walkways, or ground surfaces	18,950	16
Handtools	6,650	–
Ladders	3,870	8
Vehicles	10,870	77
All other	16,520	141
Event or exposure		
Violence and other injuries by persons or animals	2,680	127
Intentional injury by other person	690	95
Injury by person unintentional or intent unknown	480	–
Transportation incidents	4,140	63
Roadway incidents involving motorized land vehicles	2,710	48
Fires or explosions	110	7
Falls, slips, or trips	29,690	32
Slips or trips without fall	3,660	
Fall on same level	19,680	15
Fall to lower level	5,810	16
Exposed to harmful substances or environments	4,230	14
Contact with object or equipment	37,060	20
Struck by object	24,280	15
Struck against object	8,490	–
Caught in object, equipment, or material	3,080	–
Overexertion and bodily reaction	50,090	–
Overexertion in lifting or lowering	23,660	–
Repetitive motion involving microtasks	3,000	–
All other	780	–

Source: This research was conducted with restricted access to Bureau of Labor Statistics (BLS) data. The views expressed here do not necessarily reflect the views of BLS.

Note: Because of rounding and data exclusion of nonclassifiable responses, data may not sum to the totals. Dashes (–) indicate data that do not meet publication guidelines.

[a]Days away from work include those that result in days away from work with or without restricted work activity or job transfer.

[b]In the fatalities column, non-Hispanic categories include cases with Hispanic origin not reported.

Transportation and Warehousing

This industry sector includes transportation of cargo and passengers, warehousing and storage of goods, scenic and sightseeing transportation, and support activities related to transportation by rail, highway, air, water, or pipeline.

Employment in the Transportation and Warehousing industry sector totaled 6,228,000 in 2013, of which 5,200,000 were private sector employees.

Number of nonfatal occupational injuries and illnesses involving days away from work[a] and fatal occupational injuries by selected worker and case characteristics, private industry, United States, Transportation and Warehousing[b], 2013

Characteristic	Nonfatal cases	Fatalities
Total	**87,190**	**733**
Sex		
Men	66,830	712
Women	17,290	21
Age		
Younger than 16	—	—
16 to 19	960	—
20 to 24	4,670	18
25 to 34	13,730	101
35 to 44	19,890	128
45 to 54	26,210	191
55 to 64	17,230	206
65 and older	3,190	87
Occupation		
Management, business, and financial	940	11
Professional and related	220	—
Service	1,860	—
Sales and related	400	—
Office and administrative support	12,420	9
Farming, fishing, and forestry	50	—
Construction and extractive	920	7
Installation, maintenance, and repair	5,370	21
Production	1,390	—
Transportation and material moving	63,390	678
Military occupations	—	—
Race or ethnic origin[c]		
White, non-Hispanic	24,100	500
Black, non-Hispanic	5,040	111
Hispanic	7,250	83
Other, multiple, and not reported	50,800	39
Nature of injury or illness		
Fractures	6,370	—
Sprains, strains, or tears	38,990	—
Amputations	210	—
Cuts, lacerations, or punctures	3,950	6
Bruises or contusions	8,390	—
Chemical burns and corrosions	110	—
Heat (thermal) burns	410	20
Multiple traumatic injuries	2,520	403
Soreness or pain	14,080	—
Carpal tunnel syndrome	300	—
Tendonitis	170	—
All other	11,690	299
Part of body affected		
Head	5,330	97
Eye	*1,480*	—
Neck	1,610	28
Trunk	22,240	100
Back	*16,460*	*5*
Upper extremities	24,070	—
Shoulder	*9,090*	—
Arm	*4,170*	—
Wrist	*3,100*	—
Hand	*6,200*	—
Lower extremities	22,740	6
Knee	*8,490*	—
Ankle	*4,770*	—
Foot or toe	*4,540*	—
Body systems	1,240	70
Multiple	9,090	431
All other	870	—

Characteristic	Nonfatal cases	Fatalities
Source of injury or illness		
Chemicals or chemical products	670	15
Containers	17,370	7
Furniture or fixtures	1,930	—
Machinery	1,330	7
Parts and materials	7,730	12
Worker motion or position	13,050	—
Health care patient	60	—
Floors, walkways, or ground surfaces	11,890	7
Handtools	1,400	—
Ladders	640	—
Vehicles	21,360	597
All other	9,760	86
Event or exposure		
Violence and other injuries by persons or animals	840	71
Intentional injury by other person	*260*	*36*
Injury by person unintentional or intent unknown	*180*	*7*
Transportation incidents	9,560	538
Roadway incidents involving motorized land vehicles	*6,590*	*400*
Fires or explosions	130	5
Falls, slips, or trips	21,970	35
Slips or trips without fall	*4,140*	—
Fall on same level	*11,460*	*7*
Fall to lower level	*4,890*	*24*
Exposed to harmful substances or environments	2,030	21
Contact with object or equipment	17,760	63
Struck by object	*9,750*	*55*
Struck against object	*4,550*	—
Caught in object, equipment, or material	*2,480*	*6*
Overexertion and bodily reaction	33,850	—
Overexertion in lifting or lowering	*12,030*	—
Repetitive motion involving microtasks	*1,370*	—
All other	1,050	—

Source: This research was conducted with restricted access to Bureau of Labor Statistics (BLS) data. The views expressed here do not necessarily reflect the views of BLS.

Note: Because of rounding and data exclusion of nonclassifiable responses, data may not sum to the totals. Dashes (–) indicate data that do not meet publication guidelines.

[a]*Days away from work include those that result in days away from work with or without restricted work activity or job transfer.*

[b]*Data for employees in railroad transportation are provided to BLS by the Federal Railroad Administration (FRA), U.S. Department of Transportation. FRA data do not reflect the changes in OSHA recordkeeping requirements in 2002.*

[c]*In the fatalities column, non-Hispanic categories include cases with Hispanic origin not reported.*

Utilities

The Utilities sector includes establishments that provide electric power generation, transmission, and distribution; natural gas distribution; steam supply; water treatment and distribution; and sewage collection, treatment, and disposal.

The Utilities sector employed 1,187,000 people in 2013, of which 870,000 were private sector employees.

Number of nonfatal occupational injuries and illnesses involving days away from work[a] and fatal occupational injuries by selected worker and case characteristics, private industry, United States, Utilities, 2013

Characteristic	Nonfatal cases	Fatalities
Total	**3,300**	**24**
Sex		
Men	2,950	24
Women	350	–
Age		
Younger than 16	–	–
16 to 19	–	–
20 to 24	80	–
25 to 34	520	7
35 to 44	820	6
45 to 54	930	7
55 to 64	810	–
65 and older	100	–
Occupation		
Management, business, and financial	70	–
Professional and related	170	–
Service	50	–
Sales and related	50	–
Office and administrative support	390	–
Farming, fishing, and forestry	–	–
Construction and extractive	670	–
Installation, maintenance, and repair	1,450	11
Production	360	–
Transportation and material moving	90	5
Military occupations	–	–
Race or ethnic origin[b]		
White, non-Hispanic	1,340	16
Black, non-Hispanic	190	–
Hispanic	90	–
Other, multiple, and not reported	1,680	–
Nature of injury or illness		
Fractures	290	–
Sprains, strains, or tears	1,380	–
Amputations	–	–
Cuts, lacerations, or punctures	150	–
Bruises or contusions	200	–
Chemical burns and corrosions	–	–
Heat (thermal) burns	50	–
Multiple traumatic injuries	130	5
Soreness or pain	480	–
Carpal tunnel syndrome	20	–
Tendonitis	–	–
All other	580	18
Part of body affected		
Head	190	–
Eye	*60*	–
Neck	60	–
Trunk	700	8
Back	*510*	–
Upper extremities	1,010	–
Shoulder	*320*	–
Arm	*300*	–
Wrist	*110*	–
Hand	*210*	–
Lower extremities	830	–
Knee	*380*	–
Ankle	*230*	–
Foot or toe	*80*	–
Body systems	60	10
Multiple	450	5
All other	–	–

Characteristic	Nonfatal cases	Fatalities
Source of injury or illness		
Chemicals or chemical products	60	–
Containers	110	–
Furniture or fixtures	30	–
Machinery	160	–
Parts and materials	530	7
Worker motion or position	730	–
Health care patient	–	–
Floors, walkways, or ground surfaces	540	–
Handtools	170	–
Ladders	90	–
Vehicles	330	11
All other	550	–
Event or exposure		
Violence and other injuries by persons or animals	90	–
Intentional injury by other person	*30*	–
Injury by person unintentional or intent unknown	–	–
Transportation incidents	200	10
Roadway incidents involving motorized land vehicles	*170*	*8*
Fires or explosions	–	–
Falls, slips, or trips	1,070	–
Slips or trips without fall	*260*	–
Fall on same level	*490*	–
Fall to lower level	*310*	–
Exposed to harmful substances or environments	210	8
Contact with object or equipment	590	–
Struck by object	*350*	–
Struck against object	*130*	–
Caught in object, equipment, or material	*70*	–
Overexertion and bodily reaction	1,120	–
Overexertion in lifting or lowering	*190*	–
Repetitive motion involving microtasks	*70*	–
All other	–	–

Source: This research was conducted with restricted access to Bureau of Labor Statistics (BLS) data. The views expressed here do not necessarily reflect the views of BLS.

Note: Because of rounding and data exclusion of nonclassifiable responses, data may not sum to the totals. Dashes (–) indicate data that do not meet publication guidelines.

[a]*Days away from work include those that result in days away from work with or without restricted work activity or job transfer.*

[b]*In the fatalities column, non-Hispanic categories include cases with Hispanic origin not reported.*

The Information sector includes establishments that produce and distribute information and cultural products, provide the means to transmit or distribute these products as well as data or communications, and process data. Included are both traditional and Internet publishing and broadcasting, motion pictures and sound recordings, telecommunications, Internet service providers, Web search portals, data processing, and information services.

The Information sector employed 2,961,000 people in 2013, of which 2,793,000 were private sector employees.

Number of nonfatal occupational injuries and illnesses involving days away from work[a] and fatal occupational injuries by selected worker and case characteristics, private industry, United States, Information, 2013

Characteristic	Nonfatal cases	Fatalities
Total	**16,090**	**40**
Sex		
Men	11,850	35
Women	4,230	5
Age		
Younger than 16	—	—
16 to 19	200	—
20 to 24	1,030	—
25 to 34	3,040	7
35 to 44	4,540	11
45 to 54	4,110	13
55 to 64	2,600	7
65 and older	400	—
Occupation		
Management, business, and financial	520	—
Professional and related	1,170	—
Service	510	11
Sales and related	1,130	—
Office and administrative support	1,940	—
Farming, fishing, and forestry	—	—
Construction and extractive	110	—
Installation, maintenance, and repair	8,790	17
Production	770	—
Transportation and material moving	1,140	7
Military occupations	—	—
Race or ethnic origin[b]		
White, non-Hispanic	4,550	30
Black, non-Hispanic	590	8
Hispanic	370	—
Other, multiple, and not reported	10,580	—
Nature of injury or illness		
Fractures	1,240	—
Sprains, strains, or tears	6,590	—
Amputations	—	—
Cuts, lacerations, or punctures	840	—
Bruises or contusions	1,220	—
Chemical burns and corrosions	—	—
Heat (thermal) burns	100	—
Multiple traumatic injuries	480	17
Soreness or pain	1,790	—
Carpal tunnel syndrome	280	—
Tendonitis	120	—
All other	3,400	22
Part of body affected		
Head	1,330	10
Eye	*550*	—
Neck	210	—
Trunk	3,930	5
Back	*2,890*	—
Upper extremities	4,020	—
Shoulder	*930*	—
Arm	*740*	—
Wrist	*640*	—
Hand	*1,380*	—
Lower extremities	4,090	—
Knee	*1,880*	—
Ankle	*860*	—
Foot or toe	*740*	—
Body systems	820	5
Multiple	1,480	18
All other	220	—

Characteristic	Nonfatal cases	Fatalities
Source of injury or illness		
Chemicals or chemical products	100	—
Containers	850	—
Furniture or fixtures	320	—
Machinery	810	—
Parts and materials	1,390	—
Worker motion or position	4,350	—
Health care patient	—	—
Floors, walkways, or ground surfaces	2,900	—
Handtools	400	—
Ladders	1,520	5
Vehicles	1,350	19
All other	2,100	12
Event or exposure		
Violence and other injuries by persons or animals	340	7
Intentional injury by other person	*90*	—
Injury by person unintentional or intent unknown	*20*	—
Transportation incidents	840	18
Roadway incidents involving motorized land vehicles	*720*	*14*
Fires or explosions	—	—
Falls, slips, or trips	4,850	10
Slips or trips without fall	*1,150*	—
Fall on same level	*2,640*	—
Fall to lower level	*920*	*9*
Exposed to harmful substances or environments	850	—
Contact with object or equipment	3,220	—
Struck by object	*2,070*	—
Struck against object	*540*	—
Caught in object, equipment, or material	*350*	—
Overexertion and bodily reaction	5,890	—
Overexertion in lifting or lowering	*940*	—
Repetitive motion involving microtasks	*820*	—
All other	110	—

Source: This research was conducted with restricted access to Bureau of Labor Statistics (BLS) data. The views expressed here do not necessarily reflect the views of BLS.
Note: Because of rounding and data exclusion of nonclassifiable responses, data may not sum to the totals. Dashes (–) indicate data that do not meet publication guidelines.
[a]*Days away from work include those that result in days away from work with or without restricted work activity or job transfer.*
[b]*In the fatalities column, non-Hispanic categories include cases with Hispanic origin not reported.*

Financial Activities includes the Finance and Insurance sector and the Real Estate and Rental and Leasing sector. Included are banks and other savings institutions; securities and commodities brokers, dealers, exchanges, and services; insurance carriers, brokers, and agents; real estate operators, developers, agents, and brokers; and establishments that rent and lease goods, such as automobiles, computers, and household and industrial machinery and equipment.

Financial Activities had 9,848,000 workers in 2013, of which 9,612,000 were private sector employees.

Number of nonfatal occupational injuries and illnesses involving days away from work[a] and fatal occupational injuries by selected worker and case characteristics, private industry, United States, Financial Activities, 2013

Characteristic	Nonfatal cases	Fatalities
Total	**29,000**	**87**
Sex		
Men	17,300	75
Women	11,680	12
Age		
Younger than 16	—	—
16 to 19	160	—
20 to 24	1,680	—
25 to 34	5,640	20
35 to 44	6,010	13
45 to 54	8,500	25
55 to 64	5,380	10
65 and older	1,310	15
Occupation		
Management, business, and financial	4,640	28
Professional and related	650	—
Service	5,530	—
Sales and related	2,920	16
Office and administrative support	5,380	9
Farming, fishing, and forestry	—	—
Construction and extractive	590	—
Installation, maintenance, and repair	6,020	14
Production	230	—
Transportation and material moving	2,920	12
Military occupations	—	—
Race or ethnic origin[b]		
White, non-Hispanic	10,920	61
Black, non-Hispanic	2,050	13
Hispanic	4,210	8
Other, multiple, and not reported	11,820	5
Nature of injury or illness		
Fractures	3,030	—
Sprains, strains, or tears	9,500	—
Amputations	250	—
Cuts, lacerations, or punctures	2,380	6
Bruises or contusions	1,330	—
Chemical burns and corrosions	50	—
Heat (thermal) burns	250	—
Multiple traumatic injuries	1,030	31
Soreness or pain	5,650	—
Carpal tunnel syndrome	670	—
Tendonitis	40	—
All other	4,830	47
Part of body affected		
Head	2,060	15
Eye	*380*	—
Neck	400	6
Trunk	7,230	16
Back	*5,330*	—
Upper extremities	7,550	—
Shoulder	*1,390*	—
Arm	*1,360*	—
Wrist	*1,620*	—
Hand	*2,710*	—
Lower extremities	6,570	—
Knee	*2,670*	—
Ankle	*1,680*	—
Foot or toe	*1,420*	—
Body systems	450	6
Multiple	4,380	41
All other	360	—

Characteristic	Nonfatal cases	Fatalities
Source of injury or illness		
Chemicals or chemical products	160	—
Containers	2,490	—
Furniture or fixtures	2,960	—
Machinery	1,450	—
Parts and materials	1,380	—
Worker motion or position	5,130	—
Health care patient	40	—
Floors, walkways, or ground surfaces	6,030	—
Handtools	920	—
Ladders	920	—
Vehicles	2,480	26
All other	5,040	47
Event or exposure		
Violence and other injuries by persons or animals	1,100	37
Intentional injury by other person	*150*	*26*
Injury by person unintentional or intent unknown	*60*	—
Transportation incidents	1,770	24
Roadway incidents involving motorized land vehicles	*1,450*	*16*
Fires or explosions	—	—
Falls, slips, or trips	9,050	15
Slips or trips without fall	*1,220*	—
Fall on same level	*5,530*	—
Fall to lower level	*1,930*	*15*
Exposed to harmful substances or environments	760	—
Contact with object or equipment	5,850	—
Struck by object	*2,900*	—
Struck against object	*1,880*	—
Caught in object, equipment, or material	*360*	—
Overexertion and bodily reaction	10,220	—
Overexertion in lifting or lowering	*3,910*	—
Repetitive motion involving microtasks	*1,620*	—
All other	260	—

Source: This research was conducted with restricted access to Bureau of Labor Statistics (BLS) data. The views expressed here do not necessarily reflect the views of BLS.

Note: Because of rounding and data exclusion of nonclassifiable responses, data may not sum to the totals. Dashes (–) indicate data that do not meet publication guidelines.

[a]Days away from work include those that result in days away from work with or without restricted work activity or job transfer.

[b]In the fatalities column, non-Hispanic categories include cases with Hispanic origin not reported.

The Professional and Business Services sector includes legal, accounting, architectural, engineering, computer, consulting, research, advertising, photographic, translation and interpretation, veterinary, and other professional scientific and technical services. Also included are business management and administrative and support activities and waste management and remediation services.

Professional and Business Services employed 16,792,000 people in 2013, of which 16,337,000 were private sector employees.

Number of nonfatal occupational injuries and illnesses involving days away from work[a] and fatal occupational injuries by selected worker and case characteristics, private industry, United States, Professional and Business Services, 2013

Characteristic	Nonfatal cases	Fatalities
Total	**69,710**	**430**
Sex		
Men	45,270	401
Women	24,380	29
Age		
Younger than 16	—	—
16 to 19	780	8
20 to 24	5,450	30
25 to 34	17,560	66
35 to 44	15,620	103
45 to 54	14,870	107
55 to 64	11,050	75
65 and older	2,670	40
Occupation		
Management, business, and financial	2,950	18
Professional and related	6,960	27
Service	29,330	240
Sales and related	1,730	—
Office and administrative support	6,210	5
Farming, fishing, and forestry	40	—
Construction and extractive	1,840	33
Installation, maintenance, and repair	4,590	18
Production	3,060	14
Transportation and material moving	12,260	73
Military occupations	—	—
Race or ethnic origin[b]		
White, non-Hispanic	27,080	240
Black, non-Hispanic	5,560	52
Hispanic	13,760	125
Other, multiple, and not reported	23,310	13
Nature of injury or illness		
Fractures	6,190	—
Sprains, strains, or tears	20,650	—
Amputations	450	—
Cuts, lacerations, or punctures	7,160	5
Bruises or contusions	4,700	—
Chemical burns and corrosions	380	—
Heat (thermal) burns	230	—
Multiple traumatic injuries	2,090	153
Soreness or pain	13,450	—
Carpal tunnel syndrome	620	—
Tendonitis	80	—
All other	13,700	268
Part of body affected		
Head	5,820	92
Eye	1,670	—
Neck	1,040	12
Trunk	14,420	73
Back	10,480	6
Upper extremities	21,110	—
Shoulder	4,580	—
Arm	2,890	—
Wrist	3,230	—
Hand	8,670	—
Lower extremities	15,700	—
Knee	6,310	—
Ankle	3,660	—
Foot or toe	2,860	—
Body systems	1,980	80
Multiple	7,990	169
All other	1,650	—

Characteristic	Nonfatal cases	Fatalities
Source of injury or illness		
Chemicals or chemical products	1,220	13
Containers	6,870	—
Furniture or fixtures	3,200	—
Machinery	2,500	38
Parts and materials	3,850	13
Worker motion or position	11,170	—
Health care patient	360	—
Floors, walkways, or ground surfaces	11,560	6
Handtools	2,940	9
Ladders	1,610	12
Vehicles	8,800	153
All other	15,630	184
Event or exposure		
Violence and other injuries by persons or animals	4,460	65
Intentional injury by other person	500	32
Injury by person unintentional or intent unknown	490	—
Transportation incidents	6,320	143
Roadway incidents involving motorized land vehicles	5,050	78
Fires or explosions	40	—
Falls, slips, or trips	19,300	91
Slips or trips without fall	3,350	—
Fall on same level	11,500	6
Fall to lower level	4,190	85
Exposed to harmful substances or environments	2,720	50
Contact with object or equipment	14,970	76
Struck by object	7,290	63
Struck against object	4,290	—
Caught in object, equipment, or material	2,200	10
Overexertion and bodily reaction	20,220	—
Overexertion in lifting or lowering	5,930	—
Repetitive motion involving microtasks	1,970	—
All other	1,670	—

Source: This research was conducted with restricted access to Bureau of Labor Statistics (BLS) data. The views expressed here do not necessarily reflect the views of BLS.

Note: Because of rounding and data exclusion of nonclassifiable responses, data may not sum to the totals. Dashes (–) indicate data that do not meet publication guidelines.

[a]Days away from work include those that result in days away from work with or without restricted work activity.

[b]In the fatalities column, non-Hispanic categories include cases with Hispanic origin not reported.

Educational Services includes instruction and training through schools, colleges, universities, and training centers. Health Services includes ambulatory health care facilities, hospitals, nursing and residential care facilities, and social assistance for individuals, families, and communities.

Educational and Health Services employed 32,535,000 people in 2013, of which 22,303,000 were private sector employees.

Number of nonfatal occupational injuries and illnesses involving days away from work[a] and fatal occupational injuries by selected worker and case characteristics, private industry, United States, Educational and Health Services, 2013

Characteristic	Nonfatal cases	Fatalities
Total	**177,640**	**135**
Sex		
Men	35,480	81
Women	141,990	53
Age		
Younger than 16	–	–
16 to 19	1,940	–
20 to 24	14,890	5
25 to 34	35,880	25
35 to 44	37,440	26
45 to 54	44,170	27
55 to 64	33,300	32
65 and older	7,420	19
Occupation		
Management, business, and financial	6,820	8
Professional and related	61,710	–
Service	91,550	94
Sales and related	710	–
Office and administrative support	7,960	–
Farming, fishing, and forestry	90	–
Construction and extractive	760	–
Installation, maintenance, and repair	3,500	–
Production	1,440	–
Transportation and material moving	2,720	20
Military occupations	–	–
Race or ethnic origin[b]		
White, non-Hispanic	73,080	105
Black, non-Hispanic	25,380	13
Hispanic	13,680	13
Other, multiple, and not reported	65,500	–
Nature of injury or illness		
Fractures	10,580	–
Sprains, strains, or tears	79,680	–
Amputations	110	–
Cuts, lacerations, or punctures	6,640	–
Bruises or contusions	16,140	–
Chemical burns and corrosions	220	–
Heat (thermal) burns	1,310	–
Multiple traumatic injuries	5,340	54
Soreness or pain	35,400	–
Carpal tunnel syndrome	510	–
Tendonitis	370	–
All other	21,330	74
Part of body affected		
Head	11,520	26
Eye	2,000	–
Neck	3,480	10
Trunk	52,950	17
Back	43,590	–
Upper extremities	43,360	–
Shoulder	13,700	–
Arm	6,770	–
Wrist	7,370	–
Hand	12,040	–
Lower extremities	35,450	–
Knee	15,060	–
Ankle	9,290	–
Foot or toe	5,650	–
Body systems	3,810	19
Multiple	25,370	60
All other	1,710	–

Characteristic	Nonfatal cases	Fatalities
Source of injury or illness		
Chemicals or chemical products	1,990	8
Containers	9,240	–
Furniture or fixtures	8,890	–
Machinery	3,540	–
Parts and materials	2,020	–
Worker motion or position	21,810	–
Health care patient	47,740	–
Floors, walkways, or ground surfaces	36,430	11
Handtools	2,070	–
Ladders	600	–
Vehicles	9,700	70
All other	33,610	38
Event or exposure		
Violence and other injuries by persons or animals	22,590	35
Intentional injury by other person	*10,900*	*14*
Injury by person unintentional or intent unknown	*9,130*	*5*
Transportation incidents	6,390	69
Roadway incidents involving motorized land vehicles	*5,440*	*29*
Fires or explosions	50	–
Falls, slips, or trips	47,740	13
Slips or trips without fall	*6,800*	–
Fall on same level	*36,210*	*10*
Fall to lower level	*4,400*	–
Exposed to harmful substances or environments	6,670	11
Contact with object or equipment	21,870	–
Struck by object	*11,720*	–
Struck against object	*6,940*	–
Caught in object, equipment, or material	*2,290*	–
Overexertion and bodily reaction	71,630	–
Overexertion in lifting or lowering	*18,490*	–
Repetitive motion involving microtasks	*2,700*	–
All other	690	–

Source: This research was conducted with restricted access to Bureau of Labor Statistics (BLS) data. The views expressed here do not necessarily reflect the views of the BLS.

Note: Because of rounding and data exclusion of nonclassifiable responses, data may not sum to the totals. Dashes (–) indicate data that do not meet publication guidelines.

[a]*Days away from work include those that result in days away from work with or without restricted work activity.*

[b]*In the fatalities column, non-Hispanic categories include cases with Hispanic origin not reported.*

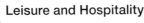

Leisure and Hospitality

The Leisure sector includes establishments that provide arts, entertainment, and recreation experiences such as theatre, dance, music, and spectator sports, museums, zoos, amusement and theme parks, casinos, golf courses, ski areas, marinas, and fitness and sports centers. The Hospitality sector includes hotels and other traveler accommodations, food services, and drinking places.

The Leisure and Hospitality sector employed 13,555,000 people in 2013, of which 13,112,000 were private sector employees.

Number of nonfatal occupational injuries and illnesses involving days away from work[a] and fatal occupational injuries by selected worker and case characteristics, private industry, United States, Leisure and Hospitality, 2013

Characteristic	Nonfatal cases	Fatalities
Total	**94,730**	**207**
Sex		
Men	48,390	182
Women	46,240	25
Age		
Younger than 16	60	—
16 to 19	6,520	6
20 to 24	15,530	24
25 to 34	25,180	47
35 to 44	16,320	34
45 to 54	16,080	45
55 to 64	10,200	29
65 and older	3,160	22
Occupation		
Management, business, and financial	3,280	47
Professional and related	5,520	—
Service	71,520	126
Sales and related	2,650	—
Office and administrative support	1,710	—
Farming, fishing, and forestry	130	—
Construction and extractive	380	—
Installation, maintenance, and repair	3,670	12
Production	1,580	—
Transportation and material moving	4,140	16
Military occupations	—	—
Race or ethnic origin[b]		
White, non-Hispanic	30,690	123
Black, non-Hispanic	6,850	29
Hispanic	16,780	37
Other, multiple, and not reported	40,410	18
Nature of injury or illness		
Fractures	6,620	—
Sprains, strains, or tears	27,040	—
Amputations	260	—
Cuts, lacerations, or punctures	15,130	12
Bruises or contusions	7,900	—
Chemical burns and corrosions	230	—
Heat (thermal) burns	6,500	5
Multiple traumatic injuries	1,940	40
Soreness or pain	16,380	—
Carpal tunnel syndrome	350	—
Tendonitis	170	—
All other	12,200	150
Part of body affected		
Head	6,630	56
Eye	*2,060*	—
Neck	680	18
Trunk	18,240	43
Back	*13,790*	*5*
Upper extremities	35,780	—
Shoulder	*5,400*	—
Arm	*4,710*	—
Wrist	*4,110*	—
Hand	*19,570*	—
Lower extremities	21,870	—
Knee	*8,150*	—
Ankle	*5,560*	—
Foot or toe	*4,040*	—
Body systems	1,810	24
Multiple	8,330	60
All other	1,380	—

Characteristic	Nonfatal cases	Fatalities
Source of injury or illness		
Chemicals or chemical products	1,190	10
Containers	13,160	—
Furniture or fixtures	5,920	—
Machinery	5,560	9
Parts and materials	1,780	7
Worker motion or position	14,580	—
Health care patient	20	—
Floors, walkways, or ground surfaces	19,440	11
Handtools	7,360	—
Ladders	820	—
Vehicles	4,460	40
All other	20,440	127
Event or exposure		
Violence and other injuries by persons or animals	2,380	107
Intentional injury by other person	*770*	*75*
Injury by person unintentional or intent unknown	*1,020*	*7*
Transportation incidents	2,180	46
Roadway incidents involving motorized land vehicles	*1,010*	*17*
Fires or explosions	80	—
Falls, slips, or trips	27,120	24
Slips or trips without fall	*3,410*	—
Fall on same level	*20,030*	*10*
Fall to lower level	*3,230*	*13*
Exposed to harmful substances or environments	9,360	14
Contact with object or equipment	27,090	13
Struck by object	*18,050*	*7*
Struck against object	*5,520*	—
Caught in object, equipment, or material	*2,390*	—
Overexertion and bodily reaction	25,390	—
Overexertion in lifting or lowering	*8,120*	—
Repetitive motion involving microtasks	*1,600*	—
All other	1,140	—

Source: This research was conducted with restricted access to Bureau of Labor Statistics (BLS) data. The views expressed here do not necessarily reflect the views of the BLS.

Note: Because of rounding and data exclusion of nonclassifiable responses, data may not sum to the totals. Dashes (–) indicate data that do not meet publication guidelines.

[a]Days away from work include those that result in days away from work with or without restricted work activity or job transfer.

[b]In the fatalities column, non-Hispanic categories include cases with Hispanic origin not reported.

The Other Services sector includes repair and maintenance of equipment and machinery and personal and household goods; personal care and laundry services; and religious, grant making, civic, professional, and similar organizations.

The Other Services sector employed 7,127,000 people in 2013, of which 7,095,000 were private sector employees.

Number of nonfatal occupational injuries and illnesses involving days away from work[a] and fatal occupational injuries by selected worker and case characteristics, private industry, United States, Other Services (except Public Administration), 2013

Characteristic	Nonfatal cases	Fatalities
Total	**23,920**	**186**
Sex		
Men	16,310	168
Women	7,610	18
Age		
Younger than 16	—	—
16 to 19	770	—
20 to 24	2,360	6
25 to 34	4,580	33
35 to 44	5,470	34
45 to 54	5,970	49
55 to 64	3,470	32
65 and older	1,110	28
Occupation		
Management, business, and financial	1,510	10
Professional and related	1,140	—
Service	5,460	47
Sales and related	610	—
Office and administrative support	920	—
Farming, fishing, and forestry	30	—
Construction and extractive	330	8
Installation, maintenance, and repair	6,190	82
Production	2,220	12
Transportation and material moving	5,470	23
Military occupations	—	—
Race or ethnic origin[b]		
White, non-Hispanic	11,020	121
Black, non-Hispanic	1,940	25
Hispanic	3,390	35
Other, multiple, and not reported	7,570	5
Nature of injury or illness		
Fractures	2,520	—
Sprains, strains, or tears	7,630	—
Amputations	40	—
Cuts, lacerations, or punctures	3,100	—
Bruises or contusions	1,170	—
Chemical burns and corrosions	70	—
Heat (thermal) burns	240	—
Multiple traumatic injuries	500	61
Soreness or pain	4,550	—
Carpal tunnel syndrome	140	—
Tendonitis	80	—
All other	3,880	117
Part of body affected		
Head	3,290	36
Eye	*1,380*	—
Neck	420	7
Trunk	5,270	36
Back	*4,140*	—
Upper extremities	7,560	—
Shoulder	*2,160*	—
Arm	*1,140*	—
Wrist	*700*	—
Hand	*3,360*	—
Lower extremities	5,030	—
Knee	*2,210*	—
Ankle	*970*	—
Foot or toe	*1,060*	—
Body systems	450	28
Multiple	1,650	76
All other	260	—

Characteristic	Nonfatal cases	Fatalities
Source of injury or illness		
Chemicals or chemical products	230	12
Containers	1,710	—
Furniture or fixtures	690	—
Machinery	1,440	11
Parts and materials	2,190	7
Worker motion or position	4,540	—
Health care patient	30	—
Floors, walkways, or ground surfaces	3,350	10
Handtools	980	—
Ladders	540	7
Vehicles	2,730	71
All other	5,490	62
Event or exposure		
Violence and other injuries by persons or animals	790	51
Intentional injury by other person	*60*	*31*
Injury by person unintentional or intent unknown	*120*	—
Transportation incidents	1,290	49
Roadway incidents involving motorized land vehicles	*360*	*26*
Fires or explosions	80	11
Falls, slips, or trips	5,860	28
Slips or trips without fall	*1,280*	—
Fall on same level	*2,710*	*8*
Fall to lower level	*1,690*	*20*
Exposed to harmful substances or environments	790	16
Contact with object or equipment	6,840	29
Struck by object	*4,410*	*26*
Struck against object	*1,460*	—
Caught in object, equipment, or material	*290*	—
Overexertion and bodily reaction	8,090	—
Overexertion in lifting or lowering	*2,290*	—
Repetitive motion involving microtasks	*530*	—
All other	190	—

Source: This research was conducted with restricted access to Bureau of Labor Statistics (BLS) data. The views expressed here do not necessarily reflect the views of the BLS.

Note: Because of rounding and data exclusion of nonclassifiable responses, data may not sum to the totals. Dashes (–) indicate data that do not meet publication guidelines.

[a]Days away from work include those that result in days away from work with or without restricted work activity or job transfer.

[b]In the fatalities column, non-Hispanic categories include cases with Hispanic origin not reported.

Government includes public employees at all levels from federal (civilian and military) to state, county, and municipal.

Total government employment was 21,542,000 in 2013, of which 16,790,000 were state and local government employees.

Number of nonfatal occupational injuries and illnesses involving days away from work[a] and fatal occupational injuries by selected worker and case characteristics, United States, Government, 2013

Characteristic	State and local government nonfatal cases[b]	All government fatalities
Total	**245,120**	**484**
Sex		
Men	142,300	424
Women	102,490	60
Age		
Younger than 16	50	—
16 to 19	1,340	8
20 to 24	6,270	48
25 to 34	42,140	83
35 to 44	59,520	99
45 to 54	74,930	117
55 to 64	47,440	86
65 and older	8,650	43
Occupation		
Management, business, and financial	5,420	16
Professional and related	50,040	15
Service	122,520	248
Sales and related	760	—
Office and administrative support	10,870	32
Farming, fishing, and forestry	430	—
Construction and extractive	13,350	34
Installation, maintenance, and repair	13,200	28
Production	5,260	5
Transportation and material moving	22,430	45
Military occupations	—	58
Race or ethnic origin[c]		
White, non-Hispanic	90,970	368
Black, non-Hispanic	18,730	54
Hispanic	14,090	45
Other, multiple, and not reported	121,330	17
Nature of injury or illness		
Fractures	13,770	10
Sprains, strains, or tears	99,880	—
Amputations	320	—
Cuts, lacerations, or punctures	10,430	—
Bruises or contusions	22,250	—
Chemical burns and corrosions	260	—
Heat (thermal) burns	2,110	6
Multiple traumatic injuries	8,910	195
Soreness or pain	48,650	—
Carpal tunnel syndrome	1,190	—
Tendonitis	420	—
All other	36,910	265
Part of body affected		
Head	17,260	118
Eye	3,170	—
Neck	4,430	21
Trunk	54,190	54
Back	41,630	6
Upper extremities	59,230	—
Shoulder	18,190	—
Arm	8,940	—
Wrist	7,580	—
Hand	18,320	—
Lower extremities	60,940	17
Knee	26,430	—
Ankle	13,960	—
Foot or toe	9,020	—
Body systems	6,860	52
Multiple	39,310	222
All other	2,900	—

Characteristic	State and local government nonfatal cases[b]	All government fatalities
Source of injury or illness		
Chemicals or chemical products	2,130	9
Containers	14,800	—
Furniture or fixtures	9,620	—
Machinery	5,500	12
Parts and materials	9,860	6
Worker motion or position	41,160	—
Health care patient	16,810	—
Floors, walkways, or ground surfaces	46,150	33
Handtools	6,640	—
Ladders	2,510	7
Vehicles	23,200	190
All other	66,740	221
Event or exposure		
Violence and other injuries by persons or animals	37,110	128
Intentional injury by other person	15,860	56
Injury by person unintentional or intent unknown	18,280	13
Transportation incidents	14,970	186
Roadway incidents involving motorized land vehicles	12,740	114
Fires or explosions	310	59
Falls, slips, or trips	66,940	54
Slips or trips without fall	11,590	—
Fall on same level	44,170	26
Fall to lower level	9,900	26
Exposed to harmful substances or environments	10,450	22
Contact with object or equipment	35,810	31
Struck by object	19,530	21
Struck against object	10,930	—
Caught in object, equipment, or material	3,100	—
Overexertion and bodily reaction	77,780	—
Overexertion in lifting or lowering	21,310	—
Repetitive motion involving microtasks	4,630	—
All other	1,740	—

Source: This research was conducted with restricted access to Bureau of Labor Statistics (BLS) data. The views expressed here do not necessarily reflect the views of BLS.

Note: Because of rounding and data exclusion of nonclassifiable responses, data may not sum to the totals. Dashes (–) indicate data that do not meet publication guidelines.

[a]*Days away from work include those that result in days away from work with or without restricted work activity.*

[b]*Data for government entities is only collected for state and local governments in the BLS National Survey of Occupational Injuries and Illnesses.*

[c]*In the fatalities column, non-Hispanic categories include cases with Hispanic origin not reported.*

Motor Vehicle

Motor Vehicle, 2014

Travel, deaths, and death rates, United States, 1925-2014

1970   1975   1980   1985   1990   1995   2000   2005   2010

- Deaths (x 1,000)
- Deaths per 100,000 population
- Deaths per 100,000,000 vehicle miles
- Vehicle miles (x 100 billion)

NATIONAL SAFETY COUN

Marijuana - pg. 127

Twenty-three states and the District of Columbia now allow some form of legal marijuana use, either for medical reasons or recreationally. An additional five states have decriminalized marijuana but do not allow either medical or recreational use. Results from the National Highway Traffic Safety Administration's (NHTSA) 2013-2014 National Roadside Survey of Alcohol and Drug Use by Drivers found that the prevalence of THC among drivers on weekend nights increased 48% since 2007, from 8.6% of drivers to 12.6%. However, many states have not yet updated their impaired driving laws to address the growing prevalence of marijuana use and driving.

National Safety Council

Motor Vehicle, 2014

Between 1912 and 2013, motor-vehicle deaths per 10,000 registered vehicles decreased 96%, from 33 to 1.37. In 1912, 3,100 fatalities occurred when the number of registered vehicles totaled only 950,000. In 2014, 35,398 fatalities occurred, but registrations soared to 258 million. While mileage data were not available in 1912, the 2014 mileage death rate of 1.16 per 100,000,000 vehicle miles was down 2% from the revised 2013 rate of 1.18.

Beginning with the 2011 edition of *Injury Facts*, the concept of medically consulted injury was adopted to replace disabling injury as the measure of nonfatal injuries. A medically consulted injury is an injury serious enough that a medical professional was consulted. Medically consulted injuries reported in this edition are not comparable to previous disabling injury estimates. A refinement of the medically consulted injury estimate was also made this year. This refinement makes comparison of medically consulted injuries to previous years inappropriate. Please see the Technical Appendix for a detailed description of this change. Medically consulted injuries in motor-vehicle incidents totaled 4,100,000 in 2014, and total motor vehicle costs were estimated at $379.4 billion. Costs include wage and productivity losses, medical expenses, administrative expenses,

motor-vehicle property damage, and employer costs. Major revisions were made to the National Safety Council (NSC) cost model for this edition that take advantage of data sources not previously available. Because of the changes made to the cost model, cost estimates provided in this edition are not comparable to previously published estimates.

Motor-vehicle deaths increased less than 0.5% from 2013 to 2014 following a decrease of 3% from 2012 to 2013. Miles traveled was up 2%, the number of registered vehicles increased 1%, and the population increased 1%. As a result, the mileage rate was down 2% while the vehicle and population death rates were each down 1% from 2013 to 2014.

Compared to 2005, 2014 motor-vehicle deaths decreased by about 22%. Mileage, registration, and population death rates also were sharply lower in 2014 compared with 2005 (see chart on next page).

The National Safety Council avoids using the word "accident." To some people, the word "accident" may imply a sense of inevitability. In contrast, the safety practice continually strives to decrease and ultimately prevent all unintentional injuries. NSC uses the terms "collision" and "crashes" in place of the word "accident."

Deaths	35,398
Medically consulted injuries	4,100,000
Cost	$379.4 billion
Motor-vehicle mileage	3,041 billion
Registered vehicles in the United States	257,800,000
Licensed drivers in the United States	212,800,000
Death rate per 100,000,000 vehicle miles	1.16
Death rate per 10,000 registered vehicles	1.37
Death rate per 100,000 population	11.10

Motor-vehicle crash outcomes, United States, 2014

Severity	Deaths or injuries	Crashes	Drivers (vehicles) involved
Fatal (within 1 year)	35,398	32,500	48,300
Medically consulted injury	4,100,000	2,800,000	5,300,000
Property damage (including unreported) and nondisabling injury		9,500,000	16,700,000
Total		**12,300,000**	**22,000,000**
Fatal (within 30 days)	32,675	29,989	44,583
Injury (disabling and nondisabling)	2,300,000	1,675,000	3,011,000
Police-reported property damage		4,392,000	7,718,000
Total		**6,100,000**	**10,774,000**

Source: National Highway Traffic Safety Administration for deaths, injuries, and total crashes in bottom half of table. All other figures are National Safety Council estimates.

Travel, deaths, and death rates, United States, 1925-2014

Deaths Due to Motor-Vehicle Crashes, 2014

Type of crash and age of victim

All motor-vehicle crashes

Includes deaths involving mechanically or electrically powered highway-transport vehicles in motion (except those on rails), both on and off the highway or street.

	Total	Change from 2013	Death rate[a]
Deaths	35,398	+0.1%	11.1
Nonfatal injuries[b]	4,100,000		

Age	0-4	5-14	15-24	25-44	45-64	65-74	75+
Death Rate[b]	2.4	2.0	15.3	12.5	12.0	11.9	18.6
Deaths	473	829	6,709	10,518	10,024	3,153	3,692

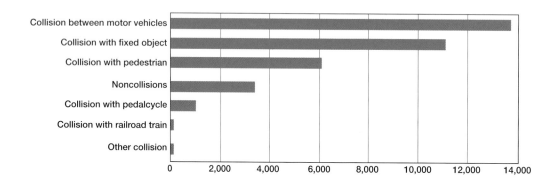

Collision between motor vehicles
Collision with fixed object
Collision with pedestrian
Noncollisions
Collision with pedalcycle
Collision with railroad train
Other collision

Collision between motor vehicles

Includes deaths from collisions of two or more motor vehicles. Motorized bicycles and scooters, trolley buses, and farm tractors or road machinery traveling on highways are motor vehicles.

	Total	Change from 2013	Death rate[a]
Deaths	13,900	+2%	4.4
Nonfatal injuries[b]	3,150,000		

Age	0-4	5-14	15-24	25-44	45-64	65-74	75+
Death Rate[b]	0.8	0.8	5.4	4.6	4.6	5.3	10.1
Deaths	155	343	2,361	3,837	3,797	1,404	2,003

Collision with fixed object

Includes deaths from collisions in which the first harmful event is the striking of a fixed object such as a guardrail, abutment, impact attenuator, etc.

	Total	Change from 2013	Death rate[a]
Deaths	10,700	-3%	3.4
Nonfatal injuries[b]	520,000		

Age	0-4	5-14	15-24	25-44	45-64	65-74	75+
Death Rate[b]	0.5	0.3	6.2	4.3	3.1	2.9	3.8
Deaths	90	144	2,711	3,655	2,592	757	751

Collision with pedestrian

Includes all deaths of people struck by motor vehicles, either on or off a street or highway, regardless of the circumstances of the incident.

	Total	Change from 2013	Death rate[a]
Deaths	6,300	+5%	2.0
Nonfatal injuries[b]	145,000		

See footnotes on page 107.

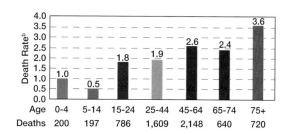

Age	0-4	5-14	15-24	25-44	45-64	65-74	75+
Death Rate[b]	1.0	0.5	1.8	1.9	2.6	2.4	3.6
Deaths	200	197	786	1,609	2,148	640	720

Type of crash and age of victim

Noncollisions

Includes deaths from noncollisions in which the first injury or damage-producing event was an overturn, jackknife, or other type of noncollision.

	Total	Change from 2013	Death rate[a]
Deaths	3,300	-3%	1.0
Nonfatal injuries[b]	150,000		

Age	0-4	5-14	15-24	25-44	45-64	65-74	75+
Deaths	23	86	716	1,150	981	215	129

Collision with pedalcycle

Includes deaths of pedalcyclists and motor-vehicle occupants from collisions between pedalcycles and motor vehicles on streets, highways, private driveways, parking lots, etc.

	Total	Change from 2013	Death rate[a]
Deaths	1,000	0%	0.3
Nonfatal injuries[b]	120,000		

Age	0-4	5-14	15-24	25-44	45-64	65-74	75+
Deaths	3	53	102	212	439	121	70

Collision with railroad train

Includes deaths from collisions of motor vehicles (moving or stalled) and railroad vehicles at public or private grade crossings. In other types of incidents, classification requires motor vehicle to be in motion.

	Total	Change from 2013	Death rate[a]
Deaths	144	+6%	(d)
Nonfatal injuries[b]	1,000		

Age	0-4	5-14	15-24	25-44	45-64	65-74	75+
Deaths	2	4	24	41	47	11	15

Other collision

Includes deaths from motor-vehicle collisions not specified in other categories above. Most of the deaths arose from collisions involving animals or animal-drawn vehicles.

	Total	Change from 2013	Death rate[a]
Deaths	100	0%	(d)
Nonfatal injuries[b]	14,000		

Note: Procedures and benchmarks for estimating deaths by type of incident and age were changed in 1990. Estimates for 1987 and later years are not comparable to earlier years. The noncollision and fixed-object categories were most affected by the changes.

[a] *Deaths per 100,000 population.*

[b] *Nonfatal injury is defined as medically consulted injuries and is not comparable to estimates provided in earlier editions that used the definition of disabling injury. A refinement of the medically consulted injury estimate was also made this year. This refinement makes comparison of medically consulted injuries to previous years inappropriate. Please see the Technical Appendix for more information regarding medically consulted injuries.*

[c] *Deaths per 100,000 population in each age group.*

[d] *Death rate was less than 0.05.*

Motor-vehicle crashes were the leading cause of death for people in the 1 to 24 age group in 2013. Motor-vehicle crashes also were the leading cause of unintentional-injury-related death for people for each single year of age from 3 to 25 and from ages 63 to 67. This is a summary of the most important issues that affect traffic safety.

Occupant protection. Safety belt use was at 87% overall in 2014, statistically unchanged from the record high set in 2013. Forty-nine states and the District of Columbia have mandatory safety belt use laws in effect, with laws in 35 of the states and the District of Columbia allowing standard (primary) enforcement. In 2014, safety belt use was significantly higher in states with standard (primary) enforcement (90%) than in states with secondary enforcement or no safety belt use law (79%). Nearly half (48%) of the passenger vehicle occupants killed in 2014 were unrestrained. Reported helmet use rates for fatally injured motorcyclists in 2014 were 60% for operators and 52% for passengers, compared with the corresponding helmet use rates of 60% and 49%, respectively, in 2013. Safety belts saved an estimated 12,584 lives in 2013 among passenger vehicle occupants older than 4. Child passenger restraints saved an additional 263 lives, while air bags saved approximately 2,388 lives.

Alcohol. From 2013 to 2014, traffic fatalities in alcohol-impaired crashes as a percentage of total traffic fatalities decreased by less than 1% to 30.5%. Overall, 9,967 people were killed in alcohol-impaired crashes in 2014, a decrease of 1% from the 10,076 in 2013. Males continue to comprise the majority – 82% in 2014 – of all drivers involved in fatal crashes with a BAC of 0.08 g/dL or higher.

Speeding. Excessive speed was a factor in 28% of all traffic fatalities in 2014, killing an average of 25 people per day for a total of 9,262 speeding-related fatalities. Alcohol involvement is highly prevalent among drivers in speeding-related crashes. Thirty-eight percent of fatalities involving young drivers (ages 15-19) are speeding-related, compared with 27% of fatalities involving drivers older than 19. It has been estimated that speeding-related crashes cost the nation nearly $52 billion annually.

Distracted driving. Over the last two years the prevalence of drivers using hand-held or hands-free cell phones at any given daylight moment has decreased from 9% of drivers in 2012 to 7.82% in 2014. The percentage of drivers likely to be on either hand-held or hands-free cell phones decreased from 11% in 2007 and 2008 down to 9% starting in 2009 and continuing through 2012. The corresponding hand-held cell phone use estimate has also dropped from 5.2% of drivers in 2012 to 4.3% of drivers in 2014. The drop in hand-held cell phone use was across all driver age groups, but most pronounced among younger drivers. The percent of young drivers, 16 to 24 years of age, using hand-held cell phones has decreased 44% from 10.4% in 2005 down to 5.85% in 2014. A very different trend is apparent regarding the prevalence of drivers observed manipulating hand-held electronic devices. The percent of drivers manipulating hand-held electronic devices has increased 1,000% from 0.2% in 2005 to 2.2% in

2014. Among other activities, this observation would include text messaging as well as manipulating devices such as MP3 players. This increase has been driven by younger drivers and middle aged drivers.

Large trucks. In 2014, 3,903 fatalities resulted from traffic crashes involving a large truck (gross vehicle weight rating greater than 10,000 pounds), a 1.5% decrease from 3,964 in 2013. The majority of these deaths (73%) were occupants of vehicles other than the large truck. Fatalities among non-occupants in large truck crashes decreased 11% from 2013 to 2014, while fatalities among truck occupants declined about 5% and fatalities among other vehicle occupants increased less than 1%. Large trucks are more likely to be involved in a multiple-vehicle fatal crash than passenger vehicles – 79% versus 35%, respectively, in 2014.

Motorcycles. Fatalities among motorcycle riders and passengers remained relatively stable between 2005 and 2014, increasing 0.2% from 4,576 to 4,586. However, nonfatal injuries have increased from 87,000 to 92,000 over the same period. The number of motorcycle fatalities decreased 2% from 2013 to 2014, while injuries increased by 4%. The latest available mileage data show that motorcycle travel has increased nearly 32% from 2004 to 2013, increasing from 10.1 billion miles to 20.4 billion over this period. As a result, the death rate has declined 42% from 2004 to 2013, going from 39.79 to 22.92 deaths per 100 million miles traveled. In 2013, speeding was a factor in 34% of motorcycle crashes compared with 21% for fatal passenger car crashes.

Young drivers. There were 4,272 fatalities in crashes involving young drivers ages 15-20 in 2013, a 1% decrease from 2013 and the tenth consecutive yearly decline. Motor-vehicle crashes, however, remain the number one cause of death for U.S. teens and increased for the first time in 12 years in 2014 to 2,282 from 2,176 in 2013. The young driver fatality rate per miles driven is still more than three times higher than for all drivers of passenger vehicles. With the advent of state graduated driver licensing programs, fatal crash risk among young drivers have decreased substantially since 1995. The fatal crash rate per 100,000,000 miles driven for 16 year old drivers decreased from 13.4 per 100 million miles driven in 1995-96 down to 9.1 in 2008.

Pedestrians. About 6,300 pedestrian deaths and 145,000 medically consulted injuries due to motor-vehicle incidents occurred in 2014. Over half (54%) of pedestrian deaths and injuries involve no improper action or circumstance. About 6% of the deaths and injuries result from pedestrians failure to obey traffic signs, signals, or officers; 3% result from improper crossing of the roadway or intersection; and a further 3% involve pedestrians who were not visible due to dark clothing, no lighting, etc. Pedestrians younger than 5 and those in age groups beginning at age 16 and older are more likely to exhibit no improper action prior to the incident, while those in age groups from 5 to 15 are more likely to exhibit some other action or circumstance. Pedestrians under age 10 were more likely to be killed or injured due to their darting or running into the roadway than other age groups.

The National Safety Council cost estimate procedures were extensively updated for this edition of *Injury Facts®* and are not comparable to estimates provided in previous editions. Two methods commonly are used to measure the costs of motor-vehicle crashes. One is the economic cost framework and the other is the comprehensive cost framework.

Economic costs may be used by a community or state to estimate the economic impact of motor-vehicle crashes that occurred within its jurisdiction in a given time period. It is a measure of the productivity lost and expenses incurred because of the crashes. Economic costs, however, should not be used for a cost-benefit analysis because they do not reflect what society is willing to pay to prevent a statistical fatality or injury.

There are five economic cost components: (1) wage and productivity losses, which include wages, fringe benefits, household production, and travel delay; (2) medical expenses, including emergency service costs; (3) administrative expenses, which include the administrative cost of private and public insurance plus police and legal costs; (4) motor-vehicle damage, including the value of damage to property; and (5) uninsured employer costs for crashes involving workers.

The information below shows the average economic costs in 2014 per death (not per fatal crash), per injury (not per injury crash), and per property damage crash.

Economic costs, 2014

Death	$1,500,000
Disabling injury	$88,500
Evident injury	$25,600
Possible injury	$21,000
No Injury observed	$11,300
Property damage only	$4,200

Comprehensive costs include not only the economic cost components, but also a measure of the value of lost quality of life associated with the deaths and injuries – that is, what society is willing to pay to prevent them. The values of lost quality of life were obtained through empirical studies of what people actually pay to reduce their safety and health risks, such as through the purchase of air bags or smoke detectors. Comprehensive costs should be used for a cost-benefit analysis, but because the lost quality of life represents only a dollar equivalence of intangible qualities, they do not represent real economic losses and should not be used to determine the economic impact of past crashes.

The information below shows the average comprehensive costs in 2014 on a per-person basis.

Comprehensive costs, 2014

Death	$9,900,000
Disabling injury	$1,100,000
Evident injury	$298,000
Possible injury	$138,000
No Injury observed	$46,000
Property damage only	$8,400

Note: The National Safety Council's cost-estimating procedures were extensively revised for the 1993 edition, for the 2005-2006 edition, and again for this 2016 edition. The costs are not comparable to those of prior years.

State Laws

No state has passed a total ban on cell phone use while driving, although 14 states and the District of Columbia have bans on handheld devices. Mandatory breath alcohol ignition interlock device laws are in effect in 26 states and four California counties for first-time DUI convictions. Mandatory safety belt use laws are in effect in 49 states and the District of Columbia, of which 21 states and the District of Columbia have primary enforcement for all seating positions. Graduated Driver Licensing is in effect in some form in all states and the District of Columbia, yet relatively few have optimum laws. Please see pages 124-125 for further details regarding young driver issues.

State laws

State	Distracted driving laws			Alcohol law	Mandatory safety belt use law		Graduated Driver Licensing laws				
	Total cell phone ban	Total text messaging ban	Additional novice driver restrictions^c	Mandatory alcohol ignition interlock device^e	Enforcement	Seating positions covered by law	Minimum instructional permit period^k	Minimum hours of supervised driving^l	No passengers younger than 20	10 p.m. or earlier nighttime driving restriction	Unrestricted license minimum age^m
Alabama	no	yes	cell phone^b	yes	primary	front	6 mo.	none	no	no	17 yrs.
Alaska	no	yes	no	yes	primary	all	6 mo.	40/10	no	no	16 yrs., 6 mo.
Arizona	no	no	no	yes	secondary	front^j	6 mo.	none	no	no	16 yrs., 6 mo.
Arkansas	no	yes	cell phone^b	yes	primary	front	6 mo.	none	no	no	18 yrs.
California	no^a	yes^d	cell phone^b	yes^h	primary	all	6 mo.	50/10	yes	no	17 yrs.
Colorado	no	yes	cell phone	yes	secondary	front	12 mo.	50/10	yes	no	17 yrs.
Connecticut	no^a	yes	cell phone	yes	primary	front	4 mo.	40/–	yes	no	18 yrs.
Delaware	no^a	yes	cell phone	yes	primary	all	6 mo.	50/10	no	yes	17 yrs.
District of Columbia	no^a	yes	cell phone	no	primary	all	6 mo.	40/10	yes	no	18 yrs.
Florida	no	yes^b	no	yes^f, g	primary	front^j	12 mo.	50/10	no	no	18 yrs.
Georgia	no	yes	cell phone	yes^g	primary	front^j	12 mo.	40/6	yes	no	18 yrs.
Hawaii	no^a	yes	cell phone	yes	primary	all	6 mo.	50/10	no	no	17 yrs.
Idaho	no	yes	no	yes^g	secondary	all	6 mo.	50/10	no	yes	16 yrs.
Illinois	no^a	yes	cell phone	yes	primary	all	9 mo.	50/10	no	no	18 yrs.
Indiana	no	yes	cell phone	no	primary	all	6 mo.	50/10	yes	yes	18 yrs.
Iowa	no	yes^b	cell phone	yes^f, g	primary	front	12 mo.	20/2	no	no	17 yrs.
Kansas	no	yes	cell phone	yes	primary	front^j	12 mo.	50/10	no	yes	16 yrs., 6 mo.
Kentucky	no	yes	cell phone	yes^f, g	primary	all	6 mo.	60/10	no	no	17 yrs.
Louisiana	no	yes	cell phone	yes	primary	all	6 mo.	50/15	no	no	17 yrs.
Maine	no	yes	cell phone	yes	primary	all	6 mo.	70/10	yes	no	16 yrs., 9 mo.
Maryland	no^a	yes	cell phone	yes^f, g	primary	all	9 mo.	60/10	no	no	18 yrs.
Massachusetts	no	yes	cell phone	yes^g	secondary	all	6 mo.	40/–	no	no	18 yrs.
Michigan	no	yes	cell phone^d	yes^f, g	primary	front	6 mo.	50/10	no	yes	17 yrs.
Minnesota	no	yes	cell phone	yes^f, g	primary	all	6 mo.	40/15	no	no	17 yrs.
Mississippi	no	yes	no	yes	primary	front	12 mo.	none	no	no	16 yrs., 6 mo.
Missouri	no	no	texting	yes	secondary	front	6 mo.	40/10	no	no	17 yrs., 11 mo.
Montana	no	no	no	no	secondary	all	6 mo.	50/10	no	no	16 yrs.
Nebraska	no	yes^b	cell phone^b	yes	secondary	front	6 mo.	none	no	no	17 yrs.
Nevada	no^a	yes	no	yes^f	secondary	all	6 mo.	50/10	no	yes	18 yrs.
New Hampshire	no^a	yes	cell phone	yes	no law	no law	none	40/10	no	no	18 yrs.
New Jersey	no^a	yes	cell phone	yes^f, g	primary	all	6 mo.	none	no	no	18 yrs.
New Mexico	no	yes	cell phone	yes	primary	all	6 mo.	50/10	no	no	16 yrs., 6 mo.
New York	no^a	yes	no	yes	primary	front	6 mo.	50/15	no	yes	17 yrs.
North Carolina	no	yes	cell phone	yes^f, g	primary	all	12 mo.	72/16	no	yes	16 yrs., 6 mo.
North Dakota	no	yes	cell phone	no	secondary	front	6 mo.	none	no	yes	16 yrs.
Ohio	no	yes^b	cell phone	yes^g	secondary	front^j	6 mo.	50/10	no	no	18 yrs.
Oklahoma	no	yes	handheld and texting	yes^f, g	primary	front	6 mo.	50/10	no	yes	16 yrs., 6 mo.
Oregon	no^a	yes	cell phone	yes	primary	all	6 mo.	50/–	yes	no	17 yrs.
Pennsylvania	no	yes	no	yes^g	secondary	front^j	6 mo.	65/10	no	no	17 yrs.
Rhode Island	no	yes	cell phone	yes^f, g	primary	all	6 mo.	50/10	no	no	17 yrs., 6 mo.
South Carolina	no	yes	no	yes^f, g	primary	all	6 mo.	40/10	no	yes	16 yrs., 6 mo.
South Dakota	no	yes	cell phone^b	no	secondary	front	3 mo.	none	no	yes	16 yrs.
Tennessee	no	yes	cell phone	yes	primary	front	6 mo.	50/10	no	no	17 yrs.
Texas	no	no	cell phone and texting	yes	primary	all	6 mo.	30/10	no	no	18 yrs.
Utah	no	yes	cell phone	yes	primary	all	6 mo.	40/10	yes	no	17 yrs.
Vermont	no^a	yes	cell phone	yes	secondary	all	12 mo.	40/10	yes	no	16 yrs., 6 mo.
Virginia	no	yes	cell phone^b	yes	secondary	front	9 mo.	45/15	no	no	18 yrs.
Washington	no^a	yes	cell phone	yes	primary	all	6 mo.	50/10	yes	no	17 yrs.
West Virginia	no^a	yes	cell phone	yes	primary	front^j	6 mo.	none	yes	yes	17 yrs.
Wisconsin	no	yes	cell phone	yes^f, g	primary	all	6 mo.	30/10	no	no	16 yrs., 9 mo.
Wyoming	no	yes	no	yes^f, g	secondary	all	10 days	50/10	no	no	16 yrs., 6 mo.

Source: Insurance Institute for Highway Safety data retrieved from www.iihs.org on September 26, 2014.

^a Statewide handheld ban (effective 7/1/15 for New Hampshire).
^b Secondary enforcement.
^c Restrictions specific to novice drivers in addition to any other all-driver ban.
^d Integrated voice-operated systems excepted.
^e Instruments designed to prevent drivers from starting their cars when breath-alcohol content is at or above a set point. Mandatory in New Hampshire effective 1/1/16.
^f Mandatory with a conviction for a BAC of at least .15 versus the lower limit of .08 found in other mandatory states.
^g Mandatory with repeat convictions or upon reinstatement.
^h Mandatory for all offenders in four counties.
^i Mandatory as a condition of suspending the jail sentence for a high-BAC first-time offender.
^j Required for certain ages at all seating positions.
^k Minimum instructional periods often include time spent in driver education classes.
^l Figures shown as follows: Total hours/nighttime hours. For example, 25/5 means 25 hours of supervised driving, 5 of which must be at night. When states (Alabama, Arizona, Connecticut, Nebraska, Oregon, South Dakota, and West Virginia) have lower requirements if driver education is taken, the lower requirement is reflected in the table. Pennsylvania additionally requires 5 of the total hours of supervised driving to be during inclement weather.
^m Minimum age to obtain unrestricted license provided driver is crash and violation free. Alcohol restrictions still apply at least until age 21.

Seat belt use was at 87% overall in 2014, unchanged from the record high set in 2013. No significant increases in seat belt use from 2013 to 2014 were identified. Three significant decreases in seat belt use include: occupants traveling in moderately dense traffic (86% to 84%), occupants traveling in light fog (94% to 81%), and among occupants traveling during weekday rush hours (87% to 86%). Overall, seat belt use has shown an increasing trend since 1995 that has been accompanied by a steady decline in the percentage of unrestrained passenger vehicle occupant fatalities during the daytime (see graph below). These results are from the National Occupant Protection Use Survey (NOPUS) that is conducted annually by the National Highway Traffic Safety Administration. NOPUS includes the observation of drivers and right-front passengers of passenger vehicles with no commercial or governmental markings.

In 2014, seat belt use was significantly higher for drivers (87%) than right-front passengers (85%); for occupants in states with primary enforcement laws (90%) than those with secondary enforcement laws or no safety belt use law (79%); and for occupants traveling on expressways (90%) rather than on surface streets (84%). By vehicle type, safety belt use was significantly higher in vans and SUVs (89%) and in passenger cars (88%) than in pickup trucks (77%).

Safety belt use by state in 2014 ranged from 68.9% in South Dakota to 97.8% in Oregon. Nineteen states and the District of Columbia achieved use rates of 90% or higher, including Oregon, Georgia, California, Alabama, Minnesota, Washington, Illinois, Nevada, Hawaii, Michigan, Iowa, Maryland, New Mexico, Delaware, Texas, New York, North Carolina, Indiana, and South Carolina. Jurisdictions with stronger safety belt laws continue to exhibit generally higher use rates than those with weaker laws.

Results from the 2013 NOPUS Controlled Intersection Study show that safety belt use among black occupants increased significantly from 77% in 2012 to 81% in 2013. Belt use among drivers age 16 to 24 with passengers all from the same age group showed a significant increase from 76% to 85% over the same time period. In 2013, females occupants (89%) had higher use rates than male occupants (85%), members of other races (93%) had higher use rates than whites (87%) and blacks (81%), drivers with at least one passenger (90%) had higher use rates than drivers with no passengers (87%), and drivers age 16 to 24 with at least one passenger not age 16-24 (87%) had higher use rates than drivers age 16 to 24 with no passengers (84%) or passengers all age 16-24 (85%). Occupants age 25 to 69 had the highest use rates among all age groups, while occupants age 16 to 24 had the lowest use rates (83%). Drivers with passengers all under 8 years of age (90%), with passengers all age 8 and older (90%), and with a mixture of passengers from both groups (91%) had higher use rates than did drivers with no passengers (87%).

Child restraint use. Restraint use for child passengers younger than 8 was 89% in 2013, down a significant 2% from the 91% use rate observed in 2012. From 2012 to 2013, significant decreases in belt use were observed for child passengers driven by a belted driver (93% to 91%), a male driver (92% to 87%), and drivers age 16 to 24 (92% to 84%). Other significant reductions in belt use from 2012 to 2013 among child passengers included children in the rear seat (92% to 90%), child passengers on expressways (93% to 89%), traveling in slow traffic (92% to 85%), in pickup trucks (91% to 76%), in the South (88% to 81%), and traveling during weekends (92% to 88%).

Safety belt use by the driver strongly influences the restraint status of child passengers. When the driver was belted, a significantly high 91% of child passengers younger than 8 were restrained in 2013, compared to a significantly low 68% of children when the driver was unbelted. However, as noted above, belt use by children driven by a belted driver dropped by a significant two percentage points from 2012 to 2013.

Children ages 4-7 should be restrained in a front-facing safety seat or booster seat, depending on the child's height and weight. The results from the 2013 National Survey of the Use of Booster Seats showed a non-significant decline in booster seat use among 4- to 7-year-old from 47% in 2011 to 46% in 2013, although restraint use for all children under 13 remained the same at 91% in 2013. The results also indicate that premature graduation continues to be a problem, but some improvements in the use of appropriate restraint types were noted from 2011 to 2013.

Source: Pickrell, T.M., & Liu, C. (2015, January). Occupant Restraint Use in 2013–Results from the National Occupant Protection Use Survey Controlled Intersection Study (DOT HS 812 080). *Washington, DC: National Highway Traffic Safety Administration.*

Chen, Y.Y. (2015, June). Seat belt use in 2014–use rates in the States and Territories. Traffic Safety Facts Crash Stats (DOT HS 812 149). *Washington, DC: National Highway Traffic Safety Administration.*

Pickrell, T.M., & Choi, E. (2014, June). The 2013 National Survey of the Use of Booster Seats (DOT HS 812 037). *Washington, DC: National Highway Traffic Safety Administration.*

Pickrell, T.M., & Choi, E.-H.. (2015, February). Seat belt use in 2014–overall results. Traffic Safety Facts Research Note (DOT HS 812 113). *Washington, DC: National Highway Traffic Safety Administration.*

Sivinski, R. (2010, July). Booster Seat Effectiveness Estimates Based on CDS and State Data (DOT HS 811 338). *Washington, DC: National Highway Traffic Safety Administration.*

Traffic Safety Facts Research Note *(DOT HS 811 875). Washington, DC: National Highway Traffic Safety Administration.*

Safety belt use rate and daytime percent of unrestrained passenger vehicle occupant fatalities, United States, 2000-2014

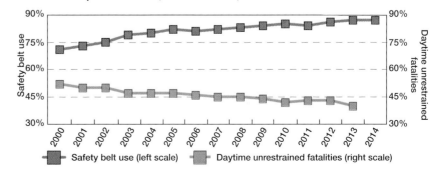

Safety belt use (left scale)   Daytime unrestrained fatalities (right scale)

Occupant Protection

Safety belts

- When used properly, lap/shoulder safety belts reduce the risk of fatal injury to front-seat passenger car occupants by 45% and reduce the risk of moderate-to-critical injury by 50%.
- For light-truck occupants, safety belts reduce the risk of fatal injury by 60% and moderate-to-critical injury by 65%.
- Forty-nine states and the District of Columbia have mandatory safety belt use laws in effect, the only exception being New Hampshire. Fourteen of the states with safety belt use laws in effect in 2014 specified secondary enforcement (i.e., police officers are permitted to write a citation only after a vehicle is stopped for some other traffic infraction). Thirty-five states and the District of Columbia had laws that allowed primary enforcement, enabling officers to stop vehicles and write citations whenever they observe violations of the safety belt law. (See page 110 for additional information on state laws.)

- Safety belts saved an estimated 12,584 lives in 2013 among passenger vehicle occupants older than 4. An additional 2,800 lives could have been saved in 2013 if all passenger vehicle occupants older than 4 wore safety belts. From 1975 through 2013, an estimated 317,645 lives were saved by safety belts (see table on following page).
- A total of 21,022 occupants of passenger vehicles (cars, pickup trucks, vans, and SUVs) were killed in motor vehicle traffic crashes in 2014, 64% of the total traffic fatalities reported for the year. Of those for whom restraint use was known, 9,385 (49%) were unrestrained. The table below shows the number of driver and passenger fatalities in crashes by vehicle type and restraint use in 2014.

Drivers and passengers killed, by vehicle type and restraint use, 2014

Type of passenger vehicle	Restrained Number	Restrained %	Unrestrained Number	Unrestrained %	Unknown Number	Unknown %	Total Number	Total %	Known restrained (%)	Known unrestrained (%)
Drivers killed										
Passenger car	4,652	54	3,383	39	655	8	8,690	100	58	42
Pickup trucks	1,247	37	1,877	56	240	7	3,364	100	40	60
Sport utility vehicles	1,142	42	1,367	50	201	7	2,710	100	46	54
Vans	354	56	219	35	59	9	632	100	62	38
Other light trucks	5	25	12	60	3	15	20	100	29	71
Total	**7,400**	**48**	**6,858**	**44**	**1,158**	**8**	**15,416**	**100**	**52**	**48**
Passengers killed										
Passenger car	1,677	52	1,248	39	311	10	3,236	100	57	43
Pickup trucks	274	31	545	62	65	7	884	100	33	67
Sport utility vehicles	419	39	574	53	93	9	1,086	100	42	58
Vans	186	48	153	39	49	13	388	100	55	45
Other light trucks	2	17	7	58	3	25	12	100	22	78
Total	**2,558**	**46**	**2,527**	**45**	**521**	**9**	**5,606**	**100**	**50**	**50**

Source: National Safety Council analysis of NHTSA FARS data.

Air bags

- Air bags, combined with lap/shoulder belts, offer the best available protection for passenger vehicle occupants. Analyses indicate a fatality-reducing effectiveness for frontal air bags of 14% when no safety belt was used and 11% when a safety belt was used in conjunction with air bags.
- Lap/shoulder belts should always be used, even in a vehicle with an air bag. Air bags are a supplemental form of protection, and most are designed to deploy only in moderate-to-severe frontal crashes.
- Children in rear-facing child seats should not be placed in the front seat of vehicles equipped with passenger-side air bags. The impact of the deploying air bag could result in serious injury to the child.

- An estimated 2,388 lives were saved by frontal air bags in 2013, and a total of 39,886 lives were saved from 1987 through 2013 (see table on following page).
- Beginning in September 1997, all new passenger cars were required to have driver and passenger-side air bags. In 1998, the same requirement went into effect for light trucks. Since 1999, driver and passenger-side air bags have been required in all cars, light trucks, and vans.

Occupant Protection (cont.)

Child restraints

- Child restraints saved an estimated 263 lives in 2013 among children younger than 5. An additional 56 lives of such children could have been saved if all had used child safety seats.
- All states and the District of Columbia have had child restraint use laws in effect since 1985.
- Research has shown that child safety seats reduce fatal injury in passenger cars by 71% for infants (younger than 1) and by 54% for toddlers (1-4 years old). For infants and toddlers in light trucks, the corresponding reductions are 58% and 59%, respectively.
- In 2014, there were 183 occupant fatalities among children younger than 4. Of the 167 fatalities among children younger than 4 for which restraint use was known, 36 (22%) were completely unrestrained.
- An estimated 263 lives were saved by child restraints in 2013, and a total of 10,421 lives have been saved by child restraints from 1975 through 2013 (see table below).

Estimated number of lives saved by restraint systems, 1975-2013

Restraint type	1975-2003	2004	2005	2006	2007	2008	2009	2010	2011	2012	2013	Total
Seat belts	179,948	15,548	15,688	15,458	15,223	13,312	12,757	12,670	12,071	12,386	12,584	317,645
Child restraints	7,021	455	424	427	388	286	307	303	262	285	263	10,421
Air bags	14,258[a]	2,660	2,752	2,824	2,800	2,557	2,481	2,403	2,341	2,422	2,388	39,886

Source: National Center for Statistics and Analysis. (2015, April). Traffic Safety Facts Crash Stats: Lives Saved in 2013 by Restraint Use and Miimumb Drinking Age Laws (DOT HS 812 137). Washington, DC: National Highway Traffic Safety Administration.
[a]Total is from 1987 to 2003. Frontal air bags did not exist prior to 1987.

Motorcycle helmets

- Motorcycle helmets are estimated to be 37% effective in preventing fatal injuries to motorcycle operators and 41% effective for motorcycle passengers.
- It is estimated that motorcycle helmets saved the lives of 1,630 motorcyclists in 2013. An additional 715 lives could have been saved in 2013 if all motorcyclists had worn helmets.
- Reported helmet use rates for fatally injured motorcyclists in 2014 were 60% for operators and 52% for passengers, compared with the corresponding rates of 60% and 49%, respectively, in 2013.
- As of December 2015, 19 states and the District of Columbia required helmet use by all motorcycle operators and passengers. Twenty-eight states only required helmet use by a subset of motorcyclists (typically motorcyclists under age 18) and 3 states (Illinois, Iowa, and New Hampshire) do not require helmet use by motorcyclists of any age. In states without universal helmet laws, 59% of motorcyclists killed in 2013 were not wearing helmets, as compared to 8% in states with universal helmet laws.
- According to the National Occupant Protection Use Survey, use of Department of Transportation-compliant helmets by all motorcyclists (riders and passengers) was 64% in 2014, a statistically insignificant increase from 60% in 2013.

Observed helmet use in states with universal helmet laws was significantly higher than in states with weaker or no helmet laws at 89% vs. 48%.

- The economic cost savings due to helmet use was approximately $2,680 million in 2010, and an additional $1,215 million could have been saved if all motorcyclists had worn helmets.

Source: Blinco, L.J., Miller, T.R., Zaloshnja, E., & Lawrence, B.A. (2015, May). The economic and societal impact of motor vehicle crashes, 2010. (Revised). (Report N. DOT HS 812 013). Washington, DC: National Highway Traffic Safety Administration.
National Center for Statistics and Analysis. (2011, March). Traffic Safety Facts Research Note – Determining Estimates of Lives and Costs Saved by Motorcycle Helmets (DOT HS 811 433). Washington, DC: National Highway Traffic Safety Administration.
National Center for Statistics and Analysis. (2015, May). Traffic Safety Facts 2013 Data – Occupant Protection (DOT HS 812 153). Washington, DC: National Highway Traffic Safety Administration.
National Center for Statistics and Analysis. (2015, May). Traffic Safety Facts 2013 Data – Motorcycles (DOT HS 812 148). Washington, DC: National Highway Traffic Safety Administration.
National Center for Statistics and Analysis. (2015, January). Traffic Safety Facts Research Note – Motorcycle Helmet Use in 2014 – Overall Results (DOT HS 812 110). Washington, DC: National Highway Traffic Safety Administration.
Current status of safety belt and motorcycle helmet use laws downloaded December 4, 2015, from the Insurance Institute for Highway Safety at http://www.iihs.org/iihs/topics/laws/helmetuse?topicName=motorcycles.

Alcohol

According to studies conducted by the National Highway Traffic Safety Administration, about 9,967 people were killed in alcohol-impaired crashes in 2014, a decrease of 1.1% from the 10,076 fatalities in 2013. Alcohol-impaired driving crashes involve at least one driver or motorcycle operator with a blood alcohol concentration (BAC) of 0.08 grams per deciliter (g/dL) or higher. The following data summarize the extent of alcohol involvement in motor vehicle crashes with at least one alcohol-impaired driver or motorcycle operator:

- The cost of alcohol-related motor vehicle crashes in 2013 is estimated by the National Highway Traffic Safety Administration at $49.8 billion.
- Traffic fatalities in alcohol-impaired driving crashes as a percentage of total traffic fatalities decreased by less than 1% to 30.5% from 2013 to 2014 but decreased by nearly 9% from 2005 to 2014 (see corresponding chart on bottom of page).
- The 9,967 fatalities in alcohol-impaired driving crashes in 2014 represent an average of one alcohol-impaired driving fatality every 53 minutes.
- Since July 1988, all states and the District of Columbia have had a minimum legal drinking age of 21. The impact these laws had on alcohol-related fatalities was dramatic. Among fatally injured drivers 16-20 years old, the percentage with positive BACs declined from 61% in 1982 to 31% in 1995, a larger decline than for older age groups. These declines occurred among the ages directly affected by increasing the drinking age (ages 18-20) and among young teens not directly affected (ages 16-17).
- In 2014, while people ages 25-34 constituted 20% of all drivers involved in fatal crashes, they were overrepresented among the drivers with a BAC of 0.08 g/dL or higher, comprising 27% of such drivers involved in fatal crashes. Drivers 21-24 years old were similarly overrepresented, accounting for 10% of drivers in fatal crashes and 15% of those with a BAC of 0.08 g/dL or higher. The 35-44 age group also was slightly overrepresented, making up 15% of drivers in fatal crashes and over 17% of those with a BAC of 0.08 g/dL or higher.
- Males continue to comprise the majority – 80% in 2014 – of all drivers involved in fatal crashes with a BAC of 0.08 g/dL or higher. Male drivers showed a 1% decrease while female drivers showed a 2% increase in the proportion of drivers involved in fatal crashes who were alcohol-impaired from 2005 to 2014.
- The corresponding chart on page 115 shows the adjusted crash risk of alcohol-positive drivers compared to alcohol-free drivers. The crash risks are adjusted to factor out the influence of age and gender on crash risk. Drivers with a BrAC (breath alcohol content) of 0.05 are approximately two times as likely to crash than drivers with a zero BrAC. The currently legal limit of 0.08 BrAC results in a crash risk approximately four times greater than 0 BrAC.
- In 2014, the percentage of alcohol-impaired-driving fatalities by state varied from a low of 20% in Vermont to a high of 41% in North Dakota (see corresponding chart on page 115).
- In 2014, all states and the District of Columbia had by law created a threshold making it illegal to drive with a BAC of 0.08 g/dL or higher.

Percent of alcohol-impaired driving fatalities, United States, 1990-2014

Alcohol (cont.)

Adjusted crash risk (adjusted for age and gender)

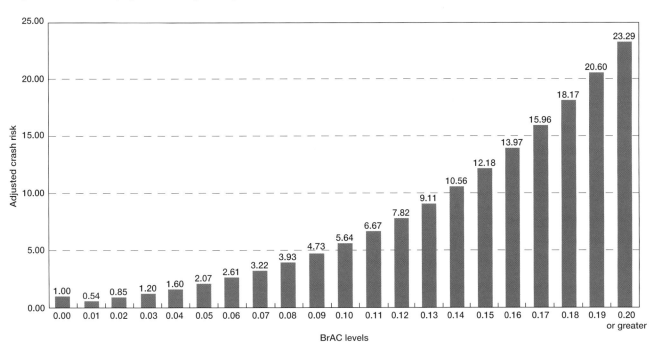

BrAC levels

Percent of fatalities involved in fatal crashes with BAC of 0.08+, by state, 2014

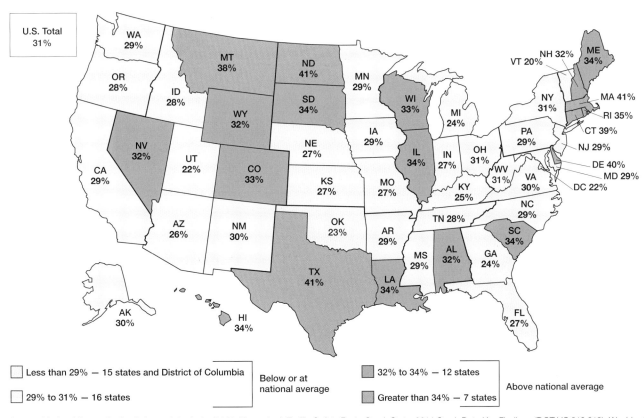

U.S. Total 31%

WA 29%
OR 28%
ID 28%
MT 38%
ND 41%
MN 29%
WI 33%
MI 24%
VT 20%
NH 32%
ME 34%
NY 31%
MA 41%
RI 35%
CT 39%
NJ 29%
DE 40%
MD 29%
DC 22%
SD 34%
WY 32%
NV 32%
UT 22%
CO 33%
NE 27%
IA 29%
IL 34%
IN 27%
OH 31%
PA 29%
WV 31%
VA 30%
CA 29%
KS 27%
MO 27%
KY 25%
NC 29%
AZ 26%
NM 30%
OK 23%
AR 29%
TN 28%
SC 34%
MS 29%
AL 32%
GA 24%
TX 41%
LA 34%
AK 30%
HI 34%
FL 27%

Less than 29% — 15 states and District of Columbia

29% to 31% — 16 states

Below or at national average

32% to 34% — 12 states

Greater than 34% — 7 states

Above national average

Source: National Center for Statistics and Analysis. (2015, November). Traffic Safety Facts Crash Stats: 2014 Crash Data Key Findings (DOT HS 812 219). Washington, DC: National Highway Traffic Safety Administration. National Center for Statistics and Analysis. (2014, December). Traffic Safety Facts Research 2013 Data: Alcohol-Impaired Driving (DOT HS 812 102). Washington, DC: National Highway Traffic Safety Administration. Compton, R.P., & Berning, A. (2015). Traffic Safety Facts Research Note: Drug and Alcohol Risk (DOT HS 812 117). Washington, DC: National Highway Traffic Safety Administration.

Type of Motor-Vehicle Crash

Although motor-vehicle deaths occur more often in collisions between motor vehicles than any other type of incident, this type represents only about 39% of the total. Collisions between a motor vehicle and a fixed object were the next most common type, with about 30% of deaths, followed by pedestrian incidents and noncollisions (rollovers, etc.).

While collisions between motor vehicles accounted for less than half of motor-vehicle fatalities, this crash type represented 77% of injuries, 71% of injury crashes, and 73% of all incidents. Single-vehicle crashes involving collisions with fixed objects,

pedestrians, and noncollisions, on the other hand, accounted for a greater proportion of fatalities and fatal crashes compared to less-serious crashes. These three crash types made up 57% of fatalities and 60% of fatal crashes, but only 25% or less of injuries, injury crashes, or all crashes.

Of collisions between motor vehicles, angle collisions cause the greatest number of deaths, about 6,500 in 2014, and also the greatest number of fatal crashes. The table below shows the estimated number of deaths, injuries, fatal crashes, injury crashes, and all crashes for various types of motor-vehicle crashes.

Motor-vehicle deaths, injuries, and number of crashes by type of crash, 2014

Type of crash	Deaths	Nonfatal injuries[a]	Fatal crashes	Injury crashes	All crashes
Total	35,398	4,100,000	32,500	2,800,000	12,300,000
Collision with...					
Pedestrian	6,300	145,000	5,700	130,000	130,000
Other motor vehicle	13,900	3,150,000	12,000	1,980,000	8,950,000
Angle collision	*6,500*	*1,286,000*	*5,700*	*781,000*	*2,720,000*
Head-on collision	*3,900*	*206,000*	*3,100*	*111,000*	*300,000*
Rear-end collision	*2,400*	*1,406,000*	*2,200*	*916,000*	*4,170,000*
Sideswipe and other two-vehicle collisions	*1,100*	*252,000*	*1,000*	*172,000*	*1,760,000*
Railroad train	144	1,000	100	1,000	2,000
Pedalcycle	1,000	120,000	900	115,000	118,000
Animal, animal-drawn vehicle	100	14,000	100	14,000	560,000
Fixed or other object	10,700	520,000	10,500	440,000	2,280,000
Noncollision	**3,300**	**150,000**	**3,200**	**120,000**	**260,000**

Source: National Safety Council estimates, based on data from the National Highway Traffic Safety Administration Fatality Analysis Reporting System and General Estimates System. Procedures for estimating the number of incidents by type were changed for the 1998 edition and are not comparable to estimates in previous editions (see Technical Appendix).

[a] Nonfatal injury is defined as medically consulted injuries and is not comparable to estimates provided in earlier editions that used the definition of disabling injury. A refinement of the medically consulted injury estimate was also made this year. This refinement makes comparison of medically consulted injuries to previous years inappropriate. Please see the Technical Appendix for more information regarding medically consulted injuries.

Speeding

Speeding is one of the major factors contributing to the occurrence of deaths, injuries, and property damage related to motor-vehicle crashes. The role of speeding in crash causation can be described in terms of its effect on the driver, the vehicle, and the road. Excessive-speed driving reduces the amount of time the driver has to react in a dangerous situation to avoid a crash. Speeding increases vehicle stopping distance and also reduces the ability of road safety structures such as guardrails, impact attenuators, crash cushions, median dividers, and concrete barriers to protect vehicle occupants in a crash.

The National Highway Traffic Safety Administration (NHTSA) estimates that speeding-related crashes[a] cost the nation $51,964 million in 2010, or 21% of the entire cost of motor-vehicle crashes in the United States. This economic loss is equivalent to $142 million per day or $5.9 million per hour.

Speeding was a factor in 28% of all traffic fatalities in 2014, killing an average of 25 people per day for a total of 9,262 speeding-related fatalities. The total number of fatal motor-vehicle crashes attributable to speeding was 8,269. Among young drivers, the impact of speeding is even more severe. Thirty-eight percent of fatalities involving young drivers (ages 15-19) are speeding-related, compared with 27% of fatalities involving drivers older than 19. The figure below shows that the proportion of fatalities by day of the week associated with speeding is greater for young drivers than for older drivers. This speeding related disparity is greatest on weekdays, particularly Monday, and decreases on the weekends.

Percent of fatalities associated with speeding by young driver involvement and day of week, 2014

Young driver related fatalities involving speeding are also elevated during particular times of the day. Speeding related fatalities involving young drivers are particularly pronounced late at night from 8 p.m. until 4 a.m. Another particularly dangerous time for young drivers is from 8 a.m. until noon, when 36% of the fatalities involve speeding.

Percent of fatalities associated with speeding by young driver involvement and time of day, 2014

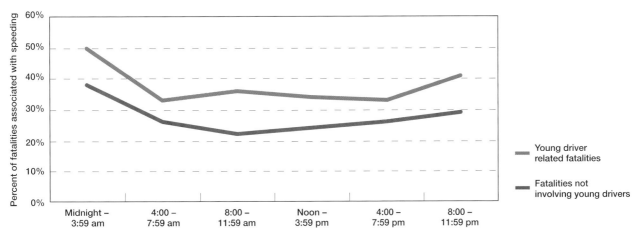

Source: National Safety Council analysis of NHTSA FARS data.
Blincoe, L.J., Miller, T.R., Zaloshnja, E., & Lawrence, B.A. (2015). The economic and societal impact of motor vehicle crashes, 2010. (Revised) (Report No. DOT HS812 013). Washington, DC: National Highway Traffic Safety Administration.

[a] A crash is considered speeding-related if the driver was charged with a speeding-related offense or if racing, driving too fast for conditions, or exceeding the posted speed limit was indicated as a contributing factor in the crash.

Distracted driving as defined by the National Highway Traffic Safety Administration (NHTSA) is a specific type of inattention that occurs when drivers divert their attention away from the driving task to focus on another activity. These distractions can be from electronic sources, such as cell phones or navigation devices, or more conventional distractions such as interacting with passengers and eating. Distracting tasks can affect drivers in different ways, and can be categorized into the following types:

- **Visual distraction:** Tasks that require the driver to look away from the roadway to visually obtain information;
- **Manual distraction:** Tasks that require the driver to take a hand off the steering wheel and manipulate a device;
- **Cognitive distraction:** Tasks that are defined as the mental workload associated with a task that involves thinking about something other than the driving task (NHTSA, 2010).

A recent study measuring brainwaves, eye movement, and other metrics assessed the impact to drivers' mental workload when attempting to complete multiple tasks. Results clearly showed that while simple tasks such as listening to the radio only minimally increased mental workload, more complex tasks such as listening and responding to in-vehicle, voice-activated email features substantially increased mental workload. Talking on cell phones (either hand-held or hands-free) was shown to moderately increase the level of mental workload.

Cognitive Workload Scale

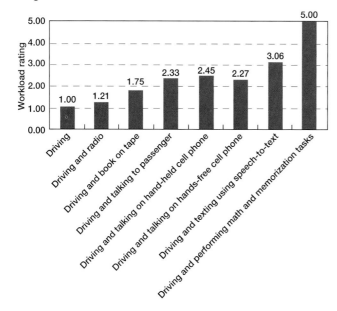

A subsequent phase of this study investigated the mental workload associated with operating original equipment manufacturers' voice-based infotainment systems. Ten vehicles representing the 2015 model year were tested: Chevy Equinox, Buick Lacrosse, Toyota 4Runner, Ford Taurus, Chevy Malibu, VW Passat, Nissan Altima, Chrysler 200c, Hyundai Sonata, Mazda 6. Drivers in the study were asked to perform a number

of simple tasks using voice commands while driving in a residential setting. The tasks included dialing a phone number, calling a contact, changing the radio station, or playing a CD. The subjects then took the vehicles home for five days to practice using the systems. After the practice phase the cognitive workload of interacting with the infotainment systems were then measured using the same scale as the original study (discussed above). As shown in the graph below the cognitive workload required to operate the voice-based systems varies substantially across the different vehicles tested.

Cognitive Workload Scale

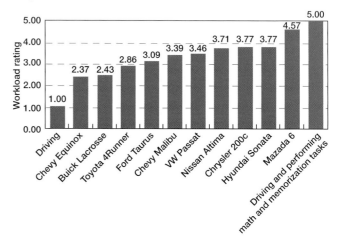

Results also found that practice did not eliminate the cognitive workload of using the systems; the systems too difficult to use prior to practice were still difficult to use following five days of practice. Interestingly, the workload experienced by older drivers was significantly greater than that experienced by younger drivers. The researchers also measured evidence of residual workload that persisted for up to 27 seconds after the subject stopped interacting with the infotainment systems.

Cell phone Driving Prevalence

Over the last two years the prevalence of drivers using hand-held or hands-free cell phones at any given daylight moment has decreased from 9% of drivers in 2012 to 7.82% in 2014. This figure from the National Occupant Protection Use Survey (NOPUS) conducted by the National Highway Traffic Safety Administration is the only national estimate of driver cell phone use based on actual driver observations. As shown in the graph below, the percentage of drivers likely to be on either hand-held or hands-free cell phones decreased from 11% in 2007 and 2008 down to 9% starting in 2009 and continuing through 2012. The corresponding hand-held cell phone use estimate has also dropped from 5.2% of drivers in 2012 to 4.3% drivers in 2014.

The drop in hand-held cell phone use was across all driver age groups, but most pronounced among younger drivers. The percent of young drivers, 16 to 24 years of age, using hand-held cell phones has decreased 44% from 10.4% in 2005 down to 5.85 in 2014.

Distracted Driving (cont.)

Driver use of cell phones 2002-2014

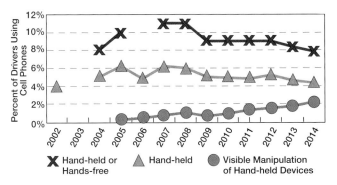

X Hand-held or Hands-free   **▲** Hand-held   **●** Visible Manipulation of Hand-held Devices

A very different trend is apparent regarding the prevalence of drivers observed manipulating hand-held electronic devices. The percent of drivers manipulating hand held electronic devices has increased 1,000% from 0.2% in 2005 to 2.2% in 2014. Among other activities, this observation would include text messaging as well as manipulating devices such as MP3 players. This increase has been driven by younger drivers and middle aged drivers. The percent of younger drivers observed to be manipulating hand-held devices has increased 1,500% while usage among middle age drivers, 25 to 69 years old, has increased 1,900%.

Driver hand-held cell phone use by age, 2005-2014

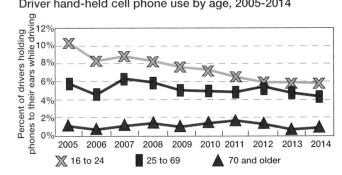

X 16 to 24   **■** 25 to 69   **▲** 70 and older

Driver visibly manipulating hand-held devices by age, 2005-2014

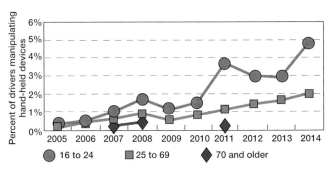

● 16 to 24   **■** 25 to 69   **◆** 70 and older

Cell phone Driving Risk

Two epidemiological studies have found that cell phone use while driving is associated with approximately a quadrupling of crash risk. Researchers in Western Australia analyzed cell phone records of drivers who went to hospital emergency departments due to injuries sustained in a crash. A second group of researchers in Canada analyzed cell phone records of drivers who reported property damage only crashes. Both studies compared cell phone use during a 10-minute period prior to the time of the crash and during non-crash periods, and found cell phone use while driving was associated with a slightly more than four-fold increase in crash risk. Results also showed no significant difference between hand-held and hands-free phone use.

A review of 33 cell phone driving studies published representing a total sample size of approximately 2,000 participants revealed the following:

- Cell phone conversation while driving increases driver reaction time. The total mean increase in reaction time is 0.25 sec.
- Use of hand-held and hands-free phones results in similar increases in reaction time.

State Laws

Although research findings indicate that there is little to no safety advantage of hands-free over hand-held cell phone use, the states that have implemented bans impacting all drivers have focused on hand-held bans. As of September 2015, 14 states and the District of Columbia ban hand held-devices for all drivers while 46 states and the District of Columbia have passed total text ban laws. The only state laws banning any use of cell phones while driving are limited to either young drivers or bus drivers. Thirty-seven states and the District of Columbia ban young or novice drivers from using cell phones. See page 110 for additional information regarding state motor-vehicle laws.

Cooper, J.M., Ingebretsen, H., & Strayer, D. (2014). Mental workload of common voice-based vehicle interactions across six different vehicle systems. Washington, DC: AAA Foundation for Traffic Safety. Downloaded from: https://www.aaafoundation.org/measuring-cognitive-distraction-part-ii-2-new-reports

McEvoy, S.P., Stevenson, M.R., McCartt, A.T., Woodward, M., Haworth, C., Palamar, P., & Cercarelli, R. (2005). Role of mobile phones in motor vehicle crashes resulting in hospital attendance: A case-crossover study. British Medical Journal. Online First BMJ, doi:10.1136/bmj.38537.397512.55 (published online 12 July 2005).

National Highway Traffic Safety Administration [NHTSA]. (2002 - 2015). Traffic Safety Fact Sheets. Available at http://www-nrd.nhtsa.dot.gov/cats/index.aspx.

National Safety Council. (2010). Understanding the distracted brain, why driving while using hands-free cellphones is risky behavior. Downloaded on November 6, 2015 from: http://www.nsc.org/safety_road/Distracted_Driving/Pages/distracted_driving.aspx

Ranney, T.A. (2008, April). Driver distraction: A review of the current state-of-knowledge (Report No. DOT HS 810 787). Washington, DC: National Highway Traffic Safety Administration.

Redelmeier, D.A., & Tibshirani, R.J. (1997). Association between cellular-telephone calls and motor vehicle collisions. New England Journal of Medicine, 336 (7), 453-458.

Schroeder, P., Meyers, M., & Kostyniuk, L. (2013, April). National survey on distracted driving attitudes and behaviors – 2012 (Report No. DOT HS 811 729). Washington, DC: National Highway Traffic Safety Administration. Downloaded from: http://www.nhtsa.gov/staticfiles/nti/pdf/811729.pdf

Strayer, D.L., Cooper, J.M., Turril, J., Coleman, J.R., & Hopman, R.J. (2015). Measuring cognitive distraction in the automobile III: a comparison of ten 2015 in-vehicle information systems. Washington, DC: AAA Foundation for Traffic Safety. Downloaded from: https://www.aaafoundation.org/measuring-cognitive-distraction-automobile-iii-comparison-10-2015-vehicle-information-systems.

Improper Driving

In most motor-vehicle crashes, factors are present relating to the driver, the vehicle, and the road, and it is the interaction of these factors that often sets up the series of events that result in a crash. The table below relates only to the driver, and shows the principal kinds of improper driving in crashes in 2014 as reported by police. The "Other improper driving" category in the table includes driver inattention – however, see page 118 for a discussion of distracted driving issues.

Exceeding the posted speed limit or driving at an unsafe speed was the most common primary error in fatal crashes.

Right-of-way violations predominated in the "Injury crashes" and "All crashes" categories.

While some drivers were under the influence of alcohol or other drugs, this represents the driver's physical condition – not a driving error. See page 114 for a discussion of alcohol involvement in traffic incidents.

Correcting the improper practices listed below could reduce the number of crashes. This does not mean, however, that road and vehicle conditions can be disregarded.

Primary improper driving reported in crashes, 2014

Kind of improper driving	Fatal crashes	Injury crashes	All crashes
Total	100.0%	100.0%	100.0%
Improper driving	**57.9**	**62.7**	**60.4**
Speed too fast or unsafe	15.1	13.5	12.1
Right of way	11.1	19.0	13.8
Failed to yield	*7.6*	*13.8*	*10.5*
Passed stop sign	*1.9*	*2.0*	*1.3*
Disregarded signal	*1.6*	*3.3*	*2.0*
Drove left of center	6.1	1.4	1.0
Improper overtaking	1.1	1.0	1.1
Made improper turn	3.2	3.5	3.5
Followed too closely	1.0	7.6	8.2
Other improper driving	20.3	16.7	20.7
No improper driving stated	**42.1**	**37.3**	**39.6**

Source: Based on reports from 25 state traffic authorities. Percents may not add to totals due to rounding.

Large Trucks

In 2014, 3,903 fatalities resulted from a traffic crash involving a large truck, a 1.5% decrease from 3,964 in 2013. About 73% of these deaths were occupants of vehicles other than the large truck (see figure below). Fatalities among non-occupants in large truck crashes decreased by 11% from 2013 to 2014, while fatalities among truck occupants declined nearly 5% and other vehicle occupants fatalities remained relatively stable, increasing less than 1%. A large truck is one with a gross vehicle weight rating greater than 10,000 pounds.

Large trucks are more likely to be involved in a multiple-vehicle fatal crash than passenger vehicles. In 2014, 79% of large truck fatal crashes were multiple-vehicle crashes, compared with 35% of other fatal crashes.

In two-vehicle fatal crashes involving a large truck, 57% of the vehicles were struck in the front compared with 54% in two-vehicle fatal crashes not involving large trucks. Trucks are more likely to be struck in the rear during a fatal crash than other vehicle types– 22% and 16%, respectively.

Source: National Safety Council analysis of NHTSA FARS data.

Fatalities in crashes involving large trucks, United States, 2014

Non-occupants 10%
Occupants of large trucks 17%
Occupants of other vehicles 73%

Motorcycles

Although motorcycles make up 3% of all registered vehicles and only 0.7% of all vehicle miles traveled in the United States, motorcyclists accounted for 14% of total traffic fatalities, 18% of all occupant fatalities, and 4% of all occupant injuries in 2013.

Fatalities among motorcycle riders and passengers have remained relatively stable between 2005 and 2014, varying from 4,576 to 4,586. However, nonfatal injuries have increased, from 87,000 to 92,000 during the same period. The number of motorcycle fatalities decreased 2% from 2013 to 2014, while injuries increased by 4%.

Exposure also has increased. From 2004 through 2013 (the latest year available), the number of registered motorcycles increased nearly 32% to 8.4 million from 5.7 million. Miles traveled is up 102%, from 10.1 billion to 20.4 billion in 2013 (latest available data). Consequently, the death rate from 2004 to 2013 has decreased 42%, from 39.79 to 22.92 deaths per 100 million miles traveled.

In 2013, 34% of motorcycle operators were speeding at the time of the fatal crash compared to 21% of drivers of passenger vehicles.

In 2013, 27% of motorcycle operators involved in fatal crashes were alcohol-impaired (blood-alcohol content greater than or equal to 0.08 g/dL), compared with 23% for passenger cars, 22% for light trucks, and 2% for large trucks.

In 2014, 1,683 motorcyclists died without a helmet on. Motorcycle helmets are estimated to be 37% effective in preventing fatal injuries to motorcycle operators and 41% effective for motorcycle passengers. The National Highway Traffic Safety Administration estimated helmets saved 1,630 motorcyclists' lives in 2013, and an additional 715 lives could have been saved if all motorcyclists wore helmets. Use of DOT-compliant helmets reached 64% in 2014, statistically unchanged from 60% in 2013. The 2014 helmet use rate is substantially lower than the high of 71% achieved in 2000.

In 2014, 19 states and the District of Columbia had laws requiring helmet use by all motorcyclists. Other states either required only a subset of motorcyclists to use helmets (such as those younger than 18) or had no helmet requirement.

An analysis by the National Safety Council shows a strong relationship between retail gasoline prices and motorcycle fatalities. After correcting for general inflation, as retail gasoline prices go up, so do motorcycle fatalities. The inverse also appears to be true; when gasoline prices trend down, so do motorcycle fatalities. These trends have been consistent for more than 30 years (see chart).

Source: National Center for Statistics and Analysis. (2015). Traffic Safety Facts 2013 Data: Motorcycles. *(DOT HS 812 148.) Washington, DC: National Highway Traffic Safety Administration.*

National Center for Statistics and Analysis. (2015, January). *Traffic Safety Facts Research Note-Motorcycle helmet use in 2014-overall results (DOT HS 812 110).*

Insurance Institute for Highway Safety. (November 2015). Motorcycle and bicycle helmet use laws. Downloaded on November 30, 2015 from http://www.iihs.org/iihs/topics/laws/helmetuse?topicName=motorcycles.
U.S. Department of Energy, Historical Gas Prices. Downloaded on November. 30, 2015 from www.eia.gov/forecasts/steo/realprices.

Motorcycle fatality and gasoline price trends, United States, 1976-2014

School bus-related crashes killed 120 people nationwide in 2014, according to National Safety Council tabulations of data from the National Highway Traffic Safety Administration (NHTSA).

A school bus-related crash is defined by NHTSA to be any crash in which a vehicle, regardless of body design, used as a school bus is directly or indirectly involved, such as a crash involving school children alighting from a vehicle.

From 2007 to 2014, about 70% of the deaths in school bus-related crashes were occupants of vehicles other than the school bus and 18% were pedestrians. About 5% were school bus passengers, 4% were school bus drivers, and another 3% were pedalcyclists.

Out of the people injured in school bus-related crashes from 2007 to 2014, about 37% were school bus passengers, 7% were school bus drivers, and an additional 48% were occupants of other vehicles. The remainder were pedestrians, pedalcyclists, and other or unknown type persons.

Characteristics of school bus transportation

According to the American School Bus Council, an estimated 480,000 yellow school buses provide transportation service daily nationwide and travel approximately 5.8 billion miles each school year. Approximately 26 million elementary and secondary school children ride school buses to and from school each day throughout the United States. This compares to projections from the U.S. Department of Education of enrollments in fall 2013 in grades K-12 of about 55.9 million public school pupils and 5.8 million private school pupils nationwide.

Deaths and injuries in school bus-related crashes, United States, 2007-2014

	2007	2008	2009	2010	2011	2012	2013	2014
Deaths								
Total	142	152	118	130	123	131	130	120
School bus driver	4	4	2	6	7	6	5	4
School bus passenger	1	15	3	10	4	8	6	7
Pedestrian	19	21	21	26	21	27	22	28
Pedalcyclist	6	8	1	3	4	3	3	4
Occupant of other vehicle	112	104	91	84	86	87	92	77
Other non-occupants	0	0	0	1	1	0	2	0
Injuries								
Total	9,000	13,000	13,000	10,000	12,000	9,000	24,000	14,000
School bus driver	1,000	1,000	1,000	1,000	(a)	1,000	2,000	1,000
School bus passenger	2,000	6,000	6,000	3,000	4,000	2,000	11,000	4,000
Pedestrian	(a)	(a)	1,000	(a)	(a)	(a)	1,000	(a)
Pedalcyclist	(a)	(a)	(a)	(a)	(a)	(a)	(a)	(a)
Occupant of other vehicle	5,000	5,000	5,000	5,000	6,000	6,000	9,000	9,000
Other non-occupants	(a)	(a)	(a)	(a)	(a)	(a)	(a)	(a)

Source: Deaths for 2007-2013 – National Center for Statistics and Analysis. (2015). Traffic Safety Facts 2002-2013 Data – School Transportation-Related Crashes (DOT HS 811 746). Washington, DC: National Highway Traffic Safety Administration.
Fatality data for 2014 and pedalcyclist deaths are National Safety Council tabulations of Fatality Analysis Reporting System (FARS) data. Injuries – National Center for Statistics and Analysis. (2007-2013). Traffic Safety Facts, 2007-2013 editions. Washington, DC: National Highway Traffic Safety Administration.
Injury data for 2014 are National Safety Council tabulations of General Estimates System data. School bus transportation data accessed November 25, 2015 from American School Bus Council at http://www.americanschoolbuscouncil.org/issues/environmental-benefits.
Student enrollment data from the Digest of Education Statistics: 2013, accessed November. 25, 2015 from the National Center for Education Statistics at https://nces. ed.gov/programs/digest/d13/tables/dt13_105.10.asp .
[a]Fewer than 500.

In 2014, an estimated 6,300 pedestrian deaths and 145,000 medically consulted nonfatal injuries[a] occurred among pedestrians in motor-vehicle incidents. About 5% of these deaths and injuries occurred when pedestrians failed to obey traffic signs, signals, or officers. Pedestrians improperly crossing roadways or intersections accounted for 3.4% of deaths and injuries, while not being visible to the driver (dark clothing, no lighting, etc.) accounted for about 3%. No improper action or circumstance was reported for over half of the pedestrian deaths and injuries.

Deaths and injuries of pedestrians by age and action/circumstance, United States, 2014

Action or circumstance	Total[a]	Younger than 5	5-9	10-15	16-20	21-24	25-44	45-64	65 or older
				Age of people killed or injured					
Totals[a]	113.6%	113.1%	123.0%	124.0%	116.8%	114.6%	110.8%	111.6%	108.9%
No improper action or circumstance	53.5%	56.4%	23.8%	38.9%	49.1%	50.2%	61.1%	55.7%	58.2%
Other action or circumstance	37.2%	28.4%	57.4%	50.9%	43.1%	42.2%	32.3%	30.6%	36.9%
Failure to obey traffic signs, signals, or officer	5.5%	1.6%	3.1%	15.3%	6.4%	5.6%	4.3%	4.5%	2.6%
Improper crossing of roadway or intersection	3.4%	7.9%	9.3%	3.8%	3.6%	1.7%	2.1%	3.9%	4.6%
Not visible (dark clothing, no lighting, etc.)	2.9%	0.8%	1.4%	2.0%	3.5%	2.6%	3.1%	3.4%	2.7%
Darting or running into roadway	2.4%	13.2%	17.1%	4.0%	1.9%	3.7%	1.0%	1.3%	0.6%
In roadway improperly (standing, lying, working, playing)	2.1%	0.7%	1.7%	0.3%	0.8%	0.9%	2.3%	4.7%	0.2%
Inattentive—talking, eating, etc.	1.9%	1.4%	0.3%	2.6%	2.0%	3.6%	1.4%	2.4%	0.4%
Not reported/unknown	4.6%	2.6%	8.8%	6.3%	6.4%	4.1%	3.3%	5.2%	2.8%

Source: National Safety Council tabulations of National Highway Traffic Safety Administration General Estimates System data.
[a]Totals are greater than 100% as multiple actions/circumstances may be entered for each case. Columns may not sum to totals because of rounding.

A recent study found that drivers are more likely to stop for pedestrians when crossing the road if the pedestrian smiles at the driver. The study conducted in France included both male and female pedestrians who were instructed to either smile or not smile at approaching drivers as they prepared to cross the road at marked crossings. Results clearly showed that drivers, regardless of sex, were more likely to stop for pedestrians who smiled at them than pedestrians who maintained a neutral facial expression (see graph below). Results also found that the positive impact of smiling persisted even when the pedestrian jaywalked.

Percent of drivers stopping at crosswalks for pedestrians smiling or not smiling by sex

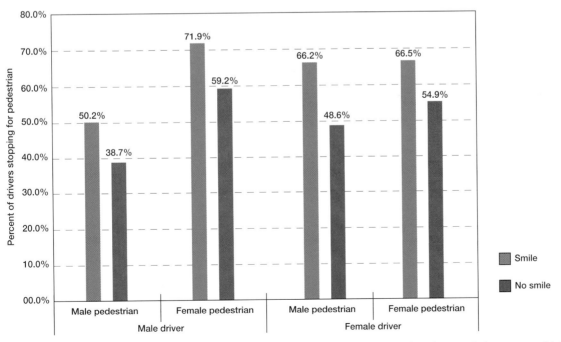

Source: Gueguen, N., Meineri, S., & Eyssartier, C. (2016). A pedestrian's smile and drivers' behavior: when a smile increases careful driving. Journal of Safety Research, 56.
[a]Medically consulted injuries are not comparable to estimates provided in earlier editions that used the definition of disabling injury. Please see the Technical Appendix for more information regarding medically consulted injuries.

According to the latest data available from the National Highway Traffic Safety Administration, 2014 marked the first time in 12 years in which the number of teen motor-vehicle occupant fatalities increased in the United States, now at 2,282 compared to 2,176 in 2013. Motor-vehicle crashes continue to be the number one cause of death for U.S. teens. The total death toll, including pedestrian and bicycle incidents, among teens ages 13 to 19 was 2,623 in 2014, and is equivalent to seven deaths per day.

GDL

A strategy shown to help prevent young driver crashes is the passage and enforcement of state Graduated Driver Licensing (GDL) programs. GDL programs allow for a gradual phasing in of full driving privileges using a three-step process comprising an initial learner's permit phase; an intermediate, or provisional, license phase; and a full licensure phase.

With the advent of state graduated driver licensing programs, fatal crash risk among young drivers have decreased substantially since 1995. Based on mileage estimates from the National Household Travel Survey, the fatal crash rate per 100,000,000 miles driven for 16 year old drivers decreased from 13.4 per 100 million miles driven in 1995-96 down to 9.1 in 2008. Smaller improvements are also evident among other young drivers from ages 17 through 19 years of age (see chart below). However, all of the young driver fatal crash rates remain significantly higher than for the core population of adult drivers, those 30 to 59 years of age.

Mileage-based fatal crash rate per 100,000,000 miles driven by young driver ages compared to the core population of adult drivers by select years

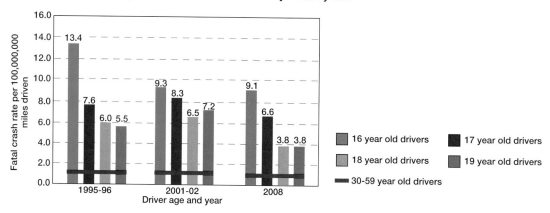

Crashes involving young drivers impact people of all ages. Young driver fatalities account for less than half of the overall fatalities associated with young driver crashes. In 2014, there were 1,717 young driver fatalities, 1,013 fatalities among passengers of young drivers, 1,090 fatalities to occupants of all other vehicles, and 452 non-occupant fatalities.

During the period when GDL programs were being implemented, decreases in the number of young driver involved crashes are evident. Decreases in the number of police-reported crashes are greatest among 16-year-old drivers with a 58% decline in crashes since 1994 and 17 year olds with a 41% decline in crashes. Crashes among 15-year-old drivers have also decreased 52%, but only account for approximately 1% of all young driver crashes.

Number of drivers aged 15 to 19 involved in police-reported crashes each year in relation to driver age, United States, 1994-2013

Driver Education

A recent epidemiological study examined a census of all teen drivers in Nebraska during an eight year period from 2003 to 2010 to assess the impact of participating in a driver education program. Teen driver crash experience were compared between those teens who obtained an intermediate-level provisional operators permit in a graduated driver licensing environment after completing a driver education program versus those teens who obtained a provisional permit by completing a supervised driving certification log without taking driver education. Results showed that teens participating in driver education experienced fewer crashes and violations. This improvement persisted even after controlling for demographic variables such as gender, race/ethnicity, median household income, urban-rural residence, and age. The lower crash and violation prevalence among driver education participants persisted through the first two years of driving with an intermediate license as part of a graduated driver licensing system.

Driver Behavior

A naturalistic driving study using Ltyx DrivCam in-vehicle video camera systems explored the driver behaviors associated with 1,691 young driver crashes from August 2007 through July 2013. Drivers included in the study ranged from 16 to 19 years old and lived in the Midwest region of the United States. Results found that young drivers drove too fast for conditions in 79% of single-vehicle crashes; followed too closely in 36% of rear-end crashes, and failed to yield to another vehicle in 43% of angle crashes. Research findings also show that many of the drivers were involved in distracting behaviors at the time of the crash. About 15% of the young male drivers and 14% of female drivers were interacting with passengers at the time of the crash, while 14% of female drivers and 10% of male drivers were using cell phones (see graph below).

Prevalence of distracting driver behaviors by sex

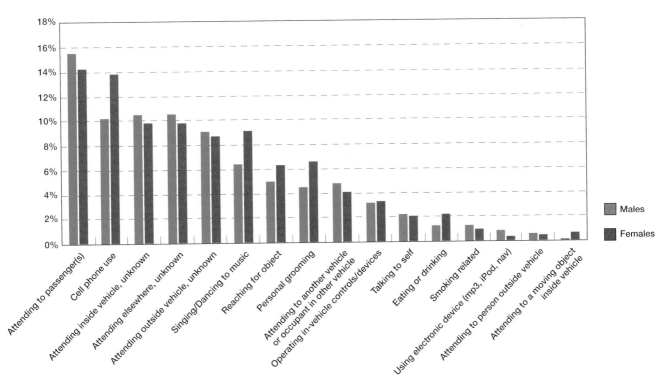

Sources: Carne, C., McGehee, D., Harland, K., Weiss, M., & Raby, M. (2015). *Using naturalistic driving data to assess the prevalence of environmental factors and driver behaviors in teen driver crashes.* Downloaded on November 9, 2015 from: https://www.aaafoundation.org/using-naturalistic-driving-data-assess-vehicle-vehicle-crashes-involving-fleet-drivers.
McCartt, A.T., & Teoh, E.R. (2014). *Tracking progress in teenage crash risk in the United States since the advent of graduated driver licensing programs.* Downloaded on Oct. 13, 2014 from: http://www.iihs.org/frontend/iihs/documents/masterfiledocs.ashx?id=2069.
Shell, D.F., Newman, I.M., Cordova-Cazar, A.L., & Heese, J.M. (2015). *Driver education and teen crashes and traffic violations in the first two years of driving in a graduated licensing system.* Accident Analysis and Prevention, *82 45-52.*
Tefft, B.C. (2015). *Teen driver crashes: 1994-2013.* Downloaded on November 9, 2015 from: https://www.aaafoundation.org/teen-driver-crashes-1994-2013-0.

Age of Driver

The table below shows the total number of licensed drivers and drivers involved in crashes by selected ages and age groups. Also shown is the rate of crash involvement on the basis of the number of drivers in each age group. The fatal crash involvement rates per 100,000 licensed drivers in each age group ranged from a low of 15 for drivers in the 65-74 age group to a high of 39 for drivers age 21. The all-incident involvement rates per 100 drivers in each age group ranged from five for drivers in the 75 and older age group to 28 for drivers age 16.

On the basis of miles driven by each age group, however, involvement rates (not shown in the table) are highest for the youngest drivers. The rates of fatal crashes per mile driven for 16-19 year-olds are about three times the rates for drivers age 20 and older. Passenger vehicle drivers age 16 had the highest fatal crash involvement rate at 9.1 fatal crashes per 100 million vehicle miles traveled in 2008, more than seven times the rate of 1.2 for drivers aged 30-59.

For more details of this mileage-based analysis, please see pages 124 and 125.

Source: National Safety Council estimates based on NHTSA FARS data. Involvement rates per mile driven: McCartt, A.T., & Teoh, E.R., (March 2014). Tracking Progress in Teenage Crash Risk in the United States Since the Advent of Graduated Driver Licensing Programs. Arlington, VA: Insurance Institute for Highway Safety.

Licensed drivers and number in crashes by age of driver, United States, 2014

| Age group | Licensed drivers | | Drivers in... | | | | | |
| | Number | Percent | Fatal crashes | | | All crashes | | |
			Number	Percent	Rate[a]	Number	Percent	Rate[b]
Total	212,800,000	100.0%	48,300	100.0%	23	22,000,000	100.0%	10
Younger than 16	125,000	0.1	200	0.4	(c)	230,000	1.0	(c)
16	1,161,000	0.5	400	0.8	34	320,000	1.5	28
17	1,992,000	0.9	700	1.4	35	500,000	2.3	25
18	2,619,000	1.2	1,000	2.1	38	600,000	2.7	23
19	2,999,000	1.4	1,100	2.3	37	620,000	2.8	21
19 and younger	8,896,000	4.2	3,400	7.0	38	2,270,000	10.3	26
20	3,247,000	1.5	1,100	2.3	34	610,000	2.8	19
21	3,348,000	1.6	1,300	2.7	39	630,000	2.9	19
22	3,513,000	1.7	1,300	2.7	37	630,000	2.9	18
23	3,695,000	1.7	1,200	2.5	32	580,000	2.6	16
24	3,825,000	1.8	1,300	2.7	34	620,000	2.8	16
20-24	17,628,000	8.3	6,200	12.8	35	3,070,000	14.0	17
25-34	36,958,000	17.4	9,900	20.5	27	4,760,000	21.6	13
35-44	35,763,000	16.8	7,600	15.7	21	3,680,000	16.7	10
45-54	39,285,000	18.5	8,100	16.8	21	3,480,000	15.8	9
55-64	36,439,000	17.1	6,600	13.7	18	2,690,000	12.2	7
65-74	23,384,000	11.0	3,600	7.5	15	1,310,000	6.0	6
75 and older	14,447,000	6.8	2,900	6.0	20	740,000	3.4	5

Source: National Safety Council estimates. Drivers in incidents based on data from the National Highway Traffic Safety Administration's Fatality Analysis Reporting System and General Estimates System. Total licensed drivers and age distribution estimated by the National Safety Council based on data from the Federal Highway Administration.
Note: Percents may not add to total due to rounding.
[a]*Drivers in fatal incidents per 100,000 licensed drivers in each age group.*
[b]*Drivers in all incidents per 100 licensed drivers in each age group.*
[c]*Rates for drivers younger than 16 are substantially overstated due to the high proportion of unlicensed drivers involved.*

Twenty-three states and the District of Columbia now allow some form of legal marijuana use, either for medical reasons or recreationally. An additional five states have decriminalized marijuana but do not allow either medical or recreational use. Results from the National Highway Traffic Safety Administration's (NHTSA) 2013-2014 National Roadside Survey of Alcohol and Drug Use by Drivers found that the prevalence of THC[a] among drivers on weekend nights increased 48% since 2007, from 8.6% of drivers to 12.6%. However many states have not yet updated their impaired driving laws to address the growing prevalence of marijuana use and driving. As shown on the U.S. map below, fully 32 states and the District of Columbia have no marijuana-specific impaired driving law.

State marijuana-specific impaired driving laws

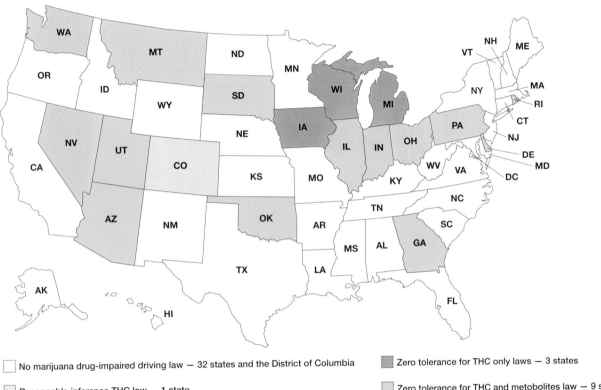

☐ No marijuana drug-impaired driving law — 32 states and the District of Columbia	■ Zero tolerance for THC only laws — 3 states
☐ Reasonable inference THC law — 1 state	■ Zero tolerance for THC and metobolites law — 9 states
☐ THC per se laws — 5 states	

There are several factors that make it difficult to determine the safety impact marijuana use is having on U.S. roads. First, a positive test result for the presence of THC in a driver's system does not necessarily indicate that the driver performance is impaired at the time of the crash. Second, there is no national policy or set of procedures followed by states or municipalities regarding drug testing. Currently there is substantial variation regarding which drivers are tested; how many drivers are tested; type of test used; cut-off levels; equipment used; and which biological specimen (blood, urine, or oral fluid) is used. Because of all of these state-to-state and even municipality-to-municipality differences and because of the large proportion of drivers that are not tested the use of police report crash data is of limited value when assessing the impact of marijuana use on road safety.

Further contributing to the confusion regarding how best to manage the safety implications of marijuana and driving are inconsistent research findings regarding the crash risk posed by marijuana use. Although some previous studies have identified elevated crash risks resulting from marijuana, a recent study conducted by NHTSA over a 20 month period in Virginia Beach, Virginia failed to find a significant crash risk increase.

[a]THC includes delta 9 tetrahydrocannabinol, the psychoactive substance in marijuana, and 11-OH-THC, its active metabolite.

Sources:

State laws: Governors Highway Safety Association downloaded on November 3, 2015 from: www.ghsa.org/html/stateinfo/laws/dre_perse_laws.html.

Berning, A., Compton, R., & Wochinger, K. (2015). Results of the 2013-2014 national roadside survey of alcohol and drug use by drivers. DOT HS 812 118. Washington, DC: U.S. Department of Transportation.

Berning, A., & Smither, D.D. (2014). Understanding the limitations of drug test information, reporting, and testing practices in fatal crashes. DOT HS 812 072. Washington, DC: U.S. Department of Transportation.

Compton, R.P., & Berning, A. (2015). Drug and alcohol crash risk. DOT HS 812 117. Washington, DC: U.S. Department of Transportation.

MOTOR VEHICLE

Motor-Vehicle Crashes by Time of Day and Day of Week

More fatal crashes occurred on Saturday than any other day of the week in 2014, according to data from the National Highway Traffic Safety Administration. More than 18% of fatal crashes occurred on Saturday, compared with 15.8% on Fridays and 15.6% on Sundays. For all crashes, Friday had the highest percentage, with nearly 17%.

Patterns by hour of day for fatal crashes show peaks during afternoon rush hour for weekdays and, especially, late at night during weekends. For all crashes, primary peaks occurred during afternoon rush hours, with secondary peaks during morning rush hours.

Percent of weekly crashes by hour of day and day of week, United States, 2014

Time of day	Fatal crashes								All crashes							
	Total	Sun.	Mon.	Tues.	Wed.	Thurs.	Fri.	Sat.	Total	Sun.	Mon.	Tues.	Wed.	Thurs.	Fri.	Sat.
All hours	100.0%	15.6%	12.5%	12.1%	12.8%	12.9%	15.8%	18.3%	100.0%	10.0%	15.1%	15.0%	15.3%	15.1%	16.8%	12.6%
Midnight to 3:59 a.m.	14.4%	3.9%	1.3%	1.1%	1.3%	1.4%	1.9%	3.6%	5.1%	1.4%	0.5%	0.4%	0.5%	0.5%	0.6%	1.2%
4:00 to 7:59 a.m.	12.7%	1.8%	1.7%	1.8%	1.8%	1.7%	1.8%	2.1%	10.2%	0.7%	1.7%	1.9%	1.7%	1.8%	1.6%	0.9%
8:00 to 11:59 a.m.	12.6%	1.4%	1.8%	1.7%	2.0%	1.8%	1.9%	2.0%	18.9%	1.4%	3.1%	3.2%	3.0%	2.9%	2.9%	2.3%
Noon to 3:59 p.m.	17.7%	2.4%	2.5%	2.4%	2.4%	2.5%	2.7%	2.8%	25.9%	2.6%	4.0%	3.8%	4.0%	3.8%	4.6%	3.2%
4:00 to 7:59 p.m.	21.9%	3.2%	2.9%	2.8%	2.9%	2.8%	3.4%	3.8%	28.1%	2.4%	4.4%	4.3%	4.4%	4.6%	5.0%	3.0%
8:00 to 11:59 p.m.	20.0%	2.6%	2.2%	2.3%	2.4%	2.6%	4.0%	3.9%	11.3%	1.5%	1.4%	1.4%	1.6%	1.5%	2.1%	1.8%

Source: National Safety Council analysis of data from the National Highway Traffic Safety Administration - Fatality Analysis Reporting System (FARS) and General Estimates System (GES).
Note: Column and row totals may not equal sum of parts due to rounding and unreported time of day or day of week data.

Percent of crashes by time of day and day of week, United States, 2014

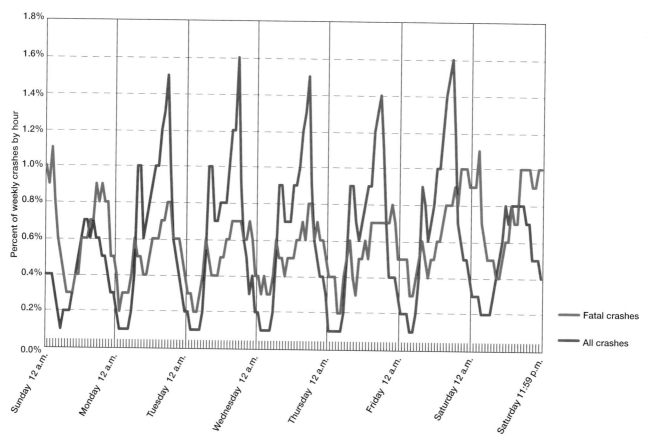

Note: Each daily column represents 24 hours.

Deaths and Mileage Death Rates by Month

Motor-vehicle deaths in 2014 were at their lowest level in February and increased to their highest level in October. In 2014, the highest monthly mileage death rate of 1.31 deaths per 100,000,000 vehicle miles occurred in November. The overall rate for the year was 1.16.

Motor-vehicle deaths and mileage death rates by month, United States, 2014

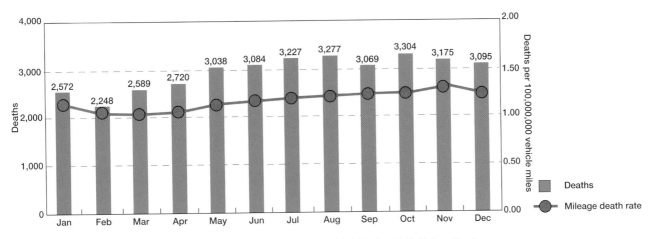

Source: Deaths – National Safety Council estimates. Mileage – Federal Highway Administration, Traffic Volume Trends.

Holidays

Holidays traditionally are a time of travel for families across the United States. Many choose the automobile – with the highest fatality rate of any of the major forms of transportation based on fatalities per passenger mile (see page 156) – as their mode of travel, therefore increasing their risk of dying in a motor-vehicle crash. In addition, holidays are often the cause for celebrations that include drinking alcohol, which is a major contributing factor to motor-vehicle crashes. Nationwide, alcohol-impaired (blood-alcohol content of 0.08 g/dL or higher) fatalities in 2014 represented over 30% of the total traffic fatalities. The table below shows the number of fatalities for each major holiday period and the percent of those fatalities that were alcohol-impaired.

Motor-vehicle deaths and percent alcohol-impaired during holiday periods, United States, 2010-2014

	Holiday period[a]											
	New Year's Day		Memorial Day		Independence Day		Labor Day		Thanksgiving Day		Christmas Day	
Year	Deaths[b]	Alcohol-impaired[c] (%)	Deaths[b]	Alcohol-impaired[c] (%)	Deaths[b]	Alcohol-impaired[c] (%)	Deaths[b]	Alcohol-impaired[c] (%)	Deaths[b]	Alcohol-impaired[c] (%)	Deaths[b]	Alcohol-impaired[c] (%)
2010	286 (3)	48	389 (3)	40	365 (3)	38	390 (3)	35	417 (4)	40	249 (3)	35
2011	304 (3)	43	389 (3)	40	405 (3)	37	373 (3)	37	375 (4)	32	256 (3)	36
2012	348 (3)	39	367 (3)	44	157 (1)	45	378 (3)	38	405 (4)	41	351 (4)	35
2013	343 (4)	44	334 (3)	38	461 (4)	39	371 (3)	38	360 (4)	33	88 (1)	37
2014	126 (1)	—	337 (3)	—	347 (3)	—	362 (3)	—	403 (4)	—	355 (4)	—

Source: Deaths – National Safety Council tabulations of National Highway Traffic Safety Administration (NHTSA), Fatality Analysis Reporting System data. Percent alcohol impaired – NHTSA, Traffic Safety Facts, 2013 edition.
Note: Dashes indicate data not available.
[a]The length of the holiday period depends on the day of the week on which the holiday falls. Memorial Day and Labor Day are always 3.25 days; Thanksgiving is always 4.25 days; and New Year's Day, Independence Day, and Christmas are 3.25 days if the holiday falls on Friday through Monday, 4.25 days if on Tuesday or Thursday, and 1.25 days if on Wednesday.
[b]Number in parentheses refers to the number of whole days in the holiday period.
[c]Highest blood alcohol concentration (BAC) among drivers or motorcycle riders involved in the crash was 0.08 grams per deciliter (g/dL) or higher. The holiday periods used to calculate the percentages conform to the NHTSA holiday period definitions that add another quarter day to the periods noted in footnote (a).

MOTOR VEHICLE
Work Zone Deaths and Injuries

In 2014, 669 people were killed and 30,500 people were injured in work zone crashes (see table below). Of the 669 killed in work zones, 431 were in construction zones, 76 were in maintenance zones, 7 were in utility zones, and 155 were in an unknown type of work zone.

From 2005 through 2014, work zone deaths have ranged from 576 to 1,074 and averaged 733 per year.

According to the Governors Highway Safety Association, nearly all states have laws that increase the penalties for speeding or committing other traffic violations while in a construction work zone.[a] The penalties often involve doubled fines, but also can be a fixed dollar amount. In some cases, the penalty is applicable only when workers are present and/or if signs are posted. Presently, 32 states and the District of Columbia double the fine for speeding or other traffic violations in a work zone. Twenty-four states and the District of Columbia require workers to be present in the construction zone for the increased penalties to take effect.

[a]Retrieved November. 29, 2015 from www.ghsa.org/html/stateinfo/laws/sanctions_laws.html

People killed or injured in work zones, United States, 2014

	Total	Vehicle occupants	Pedestrians	Pedalcyclists	Other nonmotorists
Killed	669	552	109	7	1
Injured	30,500	29,700	410	340	10

Source: National Safety Council analysis of data from National Highway Traffic Safety Administration Fatality Analysis Reporting System and General Estimates Systems.
[a]Vehicle being used as an emergency vehicle at the time of the crash with or without the use of emergency warning equipment.

Work zone deaths, United States, 2000-2014

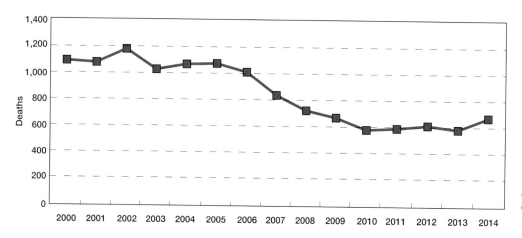

Source: NSC analysis of NHTSA FARS data files.

MOTOR VEHICLE
Emergency Vehicles

Crashes involving emergency vehicles, United States, 2014

	Ambulance		Fire truck/car		Police car	
	Total	Emergency use[a]	Total	Emergency use[a]	Total	Emergency use[a]
Emergency vehicles in fatal crashes	20	10	14	7	75	40
Emergency vehicles in injury crashes	1,600	1,000	200	100	8,200	3,400
Emergency vehicles in all crashes	**6,900**	**2,900**	**2,700**	**1,800**	**24,200**	**7,700**
Emergency vehicle drivers killed	0	0	3	1	18	9
Emergency vehicle passengers killed	7	5	0	0	3	1
Other vehicle occupants killed	12	6	12	3	48	23
Nonmotorists killed	3	1	4	2	20	10
Total killed in crashes	**22**	**12**	**18**	**6**	**89**	**43**
Total injured in crashes	**2,600**	**1,000**	**300**	**200**	**13,200**	**4,600**

Source: National Safety Council analysis of data from National Highway Traffic Safety Administration Fatality Analysis Reporting System and General Estimates Systems.
[a]Vehicle being used as an emergency vehicle at the time of the crash with or without the use of emergency warning equipment.

The National Safety Council (NSC) and the National Highway Traffic Safety Administration (NHTSA) count motor-vehicle crash deaths using somewhat different criteria. NSC counts total motor-vehicle-related fatalities – both traffic and nontraffic – that occur within one year of the crash. This is consistent with the data compiled from death certificates by the National Center for Health Statistics (NCHS). NSC uses NCHS death certificate data less intentional fatalities as the final count of unintentional deaths from all causes.

NHTSA counts only traffic fatalities that occur within 30 days of the crash in its Fatality Analysis Reporting System (FARS). This means that the FARS count omits about 800 to 1,000 motor-vehicle-related deaths each year that occur more than 30 days after the crash. Nontraffic fatalities (those that do not occur on public highways; e.g., parking lots, private roads, and driveways), which account for 900 to 1,900 deaths annually, also are omitted. By using a 30-day cutoff, NHTSA can issue a "final" count about eight months after the reference year.

This edition of *Injury Facts* includes the 2013 and 2014 NCHS final counts by cause of death including motor-vehicle crashes. The graph below shows the NCHS death certificate counts of unintentional motor-vehicle deaths through 2014 compared to the NHTSA FARS counts of traffic deaths.

Motor-vehicle deaths: NSC and NHTSA, 1992-2014

Motor-Vehicle Deaths and Rates

Motor vehicle deaths and rates, United States, 1913-2014

Year	No. of deaths	Estimated no. of vehicles (millions)	Estimated vehicle miles (billions)	Estimated no. of drivers (millions)	Death rates		
					Per 10,000 motor vehicles	Per 100,000,000 vehicle miles	Per 100,000 population
1913	4,200	1.3	(a)	2.0	33.38	(a)	4.4
1914	4,700	1.8	(a)	3.0	26.65	(a)	4.8
1915	6,600	2.5	(a)	3.0	26.49	(a)	6.6
1916	8,200	3.6	(a)	5.0	22.66	(a)	8.1
1917	10,200	5.1	(a)	7.0	19.93	(a)	10.0
1918	10,700	6.2	(a)	9.0	17.37	(a)	10.3
1919	11,200	7.6	(a)	12.0	14.78	(a)	10.7
1920	12,500	9.2	(a)	14.0	13.53	(a)	11.7
1921	13,900	10.5	(a)	16.0	13.25	(a)	12.9
1922	15,300	12.3	(a)	19.0	12.47	(a)	13.9
1923	18,400	15.1	85	22.0	12.18	21.65	16.5
1924	19,400	17.6	104	26.0	11.02	18.65	17.1
1925	21,900	20.1	122	30.0	10.89	17.95	19.1
1926	23,400	22.2	141	33.0	10.54	16.59	20.1
1927	25,800	23.3	158	34.0	11.07	16.33	21.8
1928	28,000	24.7	173	37.0	11.34	16.18	23.4
1929	31,200	26.7	197	40.0	11.69	15.84	25.7
1930	32,900	26.7	206	40.0	12.32	15.97	26.7
1931	33,700	26.1	216	39.0	12.91	15.60	27.2
1932	29,500	24.4	200	36.0	12.09	14.75	23.6
1933	31,363	24.2	201	35.0	12.96	15.60	25.0
1934	36,101	25.3	216	37.0	14.27	16.71	28.6
1935	36,369	26.5	229	39.0	13.72	15.88	28.6
1936	38,089	28.5	252	42.0	13.36	15.11	29.7
1937	39,643	30.1	270	44.0	13.19	14.68	30.8
1938	32,582	29.8	271	44.0	10.93	12.02	25.1
1939	32,386	31.0	285	46.0	10.44	11.35	24.7
1940	34,501	32.5	302	48.0	10.63	11.42	26.1
1941	39,969	34.9	334	52.0	11.45	11.98	30.0
1942	28,309	33.0	268	49.0	8.58	10.55	21.1
1943	23,823	30.9	208	46.0	7.71	11.44	17.8
1944	24,282	30.5	213	45.0	7.97	11.42	18.3
1945	28,076	31.0	250	46.0	9.05	11.22	21.2
1946	33,411	34.4	341	50.0	9.72	9.80	23.9
1947	32,697	37.8	371	53.0	8.64	8.82	22.8
1948	32,259	41.1	398	55.0	7.85	8.11	22.1
1949	31,701	44.7	424	59.3	7.09	7.47	21.3
1950	34,763	49.2	458	62.2	7.07	7.59	23.0
1951	36,996	51.9	491	64.4	7.13	7.53	24.1
1952	37,794	53.3	514	66.8	7.10	7.36	24.3
1953	37,956	56.3	544	69.9	6.74	6.97	24.0
1954	35,586	58.6	562	72.2	6.07	6.33	22.1
1955	38,426	62.8	606	74.7	6.12	6.34	23.4
1956	39,628	65.2	631	77.9	6.07	6.28	23.7
1957	38,702	67.6	647	79.6	5.73	5.98	22.7
1958	36,981	68.8	665	81.5	5.37	5.56	21.3
1959	37,910	72.1	700	84.5	5.26	5.41	21.5
1960	38,137	74.5	719	87.4	5.12	5.31	21.2
1961	38,091	76.4	738	88.9	4.98	5.16	20.8
1962	40,804	79.7	767	92.0	5.12	5.32	22.0
1963	43,564	83.5	805	93.7	5.22	5.41	23.1
1964	47,700	87.3	847	95.6	5.46	5.63	25.0
1965	49,163	91.8	888	99.0	5.36	5.54	25.4
1966	53,041	95.9	930	101.0	5.53	5.70	27.1
1967	52,924	98.9	962	103.2	5.35	5.50	26.8
1968	54,862	103.1	1,016	105.4	5.32	5.40	27.5
1969	55,791	107.4	1,071	108.3	5.19	5.21	27.7
1970	54,633	111.2	1,120	111.5	4.92	4.88	26.8
1971	54,381	116.3	1,186	114.4	4.68	4.57	26.3
1972	56,278	122.3	1,268	118.4	4.60	4.43	26.9
1973	55,511	129.8	1,309	121.6	4.28	4.24	26.3
1974	46,402	134.9	1,290	125.6	3.44	3.59	21.8
1975	45,853	137.9	1,330	129.8	3.33	3.45	21.3
1976	47,038	143.5	1,412	133.9	3.28	3.33	21.6

See source and footnotes on page 133.

Motor vehicle deaths and rates, United States, 1913-2014 (cont.)

Year	No. of deaths	Estimated no. of vehicles (millions)	Estimated vehicle miles (billions)	Estimated no. of drivers (millions)	Death rates		
					Per 10,000 motor vehicles	Per 100,000,000 vehicle miles	Per 100,000 population
1977	49,510	148.8	1,477	138.1	3.33	3.35	22.5
1978	52,411	153.6	1,548	140.8	3.41	3.39	23.6
1979	53,524	159.6	1,529	143.3	3.35	3.50	23.8
1980	53,172	161.6	1,521	145.3	3.29	3.50	23.4
1981	51,385	164.1	1,556	147.1	3.13	3.30	22.4
1982	45,779	165.2	1,592	150.3	2.77	2.88	19.8
1983	44,452	169.4	1,657	154.2	2.62	2.68	19.0
1984	46,263	171.8	1,718	155.4	2.69	2.69	19.6
1985	45,901	177.1	1,774	156.9	2.59	2.59	19.3
1986	47,865	181.4	1,835	159.5	2.63	2.60	19.9
1987	48,290	183.9	1,924	161.8	2.63	2.51	19.9
1988	49,078	189.0	2,026	162.9	2.60	2.42	20.1
1989	47,575	191.7	2,107	165.6	2.48	2.26	19.3
1990	46,814	192.9	2,148	167.0	2.43	2.18	18.8
1991	43,536	192.5	2,172	169.0	2.26	2.00	17.3
1992	40,982	194.4	2,240	173.1	2.11	1.83	16.1
1993	41,893	198.0	2,297	173.1	2.12	1.82	16.3
1994	42,524	201.8	2,360	175.4	2.11	1.80	16.3
1995	43,363	205.3	2,423	176.6	2.11	1.79	16.5
1996	43,649	210.4	2,486	179.5	2.07	1.76	16.5
1997	43,458	211.5	2,562	182.7	2.05	1.70	16.2
1998	43,501	215.0	2,632	185.2	2.02	1.65	16.1
1999	42,401	220.5	2,691	187.2	1.92	1.58	15.5
2000	43,354	225.8	2,747	190.6	1.92	1.58	15.8
2001	43,788	235.3	2,797	191.3	1.86	1.57	15.4
2002	45,380	234.6	2,856	194.3	1.93	1.59	15.8
2003	44,757	236.8	2,890	196.2	1.89	1.55	15.4
2004	44,933	243.0	2,965	199.0	1.85	1.52	15.3
2005	45,343	247.4	2,989	200.5	1.83	1.52	15.3
2006	45,316	250.8	3,014	202.8	1.81	1.50	15.2
2007	43,945	254.4	3,032	205.7	1.73	1.45	14.6
2008	39,790	255.9	2,976	208.3	1.55	1.34	13.1
2009	36,216	254.2	2,957	209.6	1.42	1.22	11.8
2010	35,332	250.3	2,967	210.1	1.41	1.19	11.4
2011	35,303	253.2	2,950	211.9	1.39	1.20	11.3
2012[b]	36,415	253.6	2,969	211.8	1.44	1.23	11.6
2013[b]	35,369	255.9	2,988	212.6	1.38	1.18	11.2
2014[c]	35,398	257.8	3,041	212.8	1.37	1.16	11.1
Changes							
2005 to 2014	-22%	4%	2%	6%	-25%	-24%	-27%
2013 to 2014	(d)	1%	2%	(d)	-1%	-2%	-1%

Source: Deaths from National Center for Health Statistics except 1964 which are National Safety Council estimates based on data from the National Highway Traffic Safety Administration's Fatality Analysis Reporting System. See Technical Appendix for comparability. Motor vehicle registrations, mileage, and drivers estimated by Federal Highway Administration except for 2014 registrations and drivers, which are National Safety Council estimates.

[a] *Mileage data inadequate prior to 1923.*

[b] *Revised.*

[c] *Preliminary.*

[d] *Less than 0.5%.*

Motor-Vehicle Deaths by Type of Incident

Motor vehicle deaths by type of incident, United States, 1913-2014

Year	Total deaths	Pedestrians	Other motor vehicles	Railroad trains	Streetcars	Pedalcycles	Animal-drawn vehicle or animal	Fixed objects	Deaths from noncollision incidents	Nontraffic deaths[a]
			Deaths from collision with...							
1913	4,200	(b)	(b)	(b)	(b)	(b)	(b)	(b)	(b)	(c)
1914	4,700	(b)	(b)	(b)	(b)	(b)	(b)	(b)	(b)	(c)
1915	6,600	(b)	(b)	(b)	(b)	(b)	(b)	(b)	(b)	(c)
1916	8,200	(b)	(b)	(b)	(b)	(b)	(b)	(b)	(b)	(c)
1917	10,200	(b)	(b)	(b)	(b)	(b)	(b)	(b)	(b)	(c)
1918	10,700	(b)	(b)	(b)	(b)	(b)	(b)	(b)	(b)	(c)
1919	11,200	(b)	(b)	(b)	(b)	(b)	(b)	(b)	(b)	(c)
1920	12,500	(b)	(b)	(b)	(b)	(b)	(b)	(b)	(b)	(c)
1921	13,900	(b)	(b)	(b)	(b)	(b)	(b)	(b)	(b)	(c)
1922	15,300	(b)	(b)	(b)	(b)	(b)	(b)	(b)	(b)	(c)
1923	18,400	(b)	(b)	(b)	(b)	(b)	(b)	(b)	(b)	(c)
1924	19,400	(b)	(b)	1,130	410	(b)	(b)	(b)	(b)	(c)
1925	21,900	(b)	(b)	1,410	560	(b)	(b)	(b)	(b)	(c)
1926	23,400	(b)	(b)	1,730	520	(b)	(b)	(b)	(b)	(c)
1927	25,800	10,820	3,430	1,830	520	(b)	(b)	(b)	(b)	(c)
1928	28,000	11,420	4,310	2,140	570	(b)	(b)	540	8,070	(c)
1929	31,200	12,250	5,400	2,050	530	(b)	(b)	620	9,380	(c)
1930	32,900	12,900	5,880	1,830	480	(b)	(b)	720	9,970	(c)
1931	33,700	13,370	6,820	1,710	440	(b)	(b)	870	9,570	(c)
1932	29,500	11,490	6,070	1,520	320	350	400	800	8,500	(c)
1933	31,363	12,840	6,470	1,437	318	400	310	900	8,680	(c)
1934	36,101	14,480	8,110	1,457	332	500	360	1,040	9,820	(c)
1935	36,369	14,350	8,750	1,587	253	450	250	1,010	9,720	(c)
1936	38,089	15,250	9,500	1,697	269	650	250	1,060	9,410	(c)
1937	39,643	15,500	10,320	1,810	264	700	200	1,160	9,690	(c)
1938	32,582	12,850	8,900	1,490	165	720	170	940	7,350	(c)
1939	32,386	12,400	8,700	1,330	150	710	200	1,000	7,900	(c)
1940	34,501	12,700	10,100	1,707	132	750	210	1,100	7,800	(c)
1941	39,969	13,550	12,500	1,840	118	910	250	1,350	9,450	(c)
1942	28,309	10,650	7,300	1,754	124	650	240	850	6,740	(c)
1943	23,823	9,900	5,300	1,448	171	450	160	700	5,690	(c)
1944	24,282	9,900	5,700	1,663	175	400	140	700	5,600	(c)
1945	28,076	11,000	7,150	1,703	163	500	130	800	6,600	(c)
1946	33,411	11,600	9,400	1,703	174	450	130	950	8,900	(c)
1947	32,697	10,450	9,900	1,736	102	550	150	1,000	8,800	(c)
1948	32,259	9,950	10,200	1,474	83	500	100	1,000	8,950	(c)
1949	31,701	8,800	10,500	1,452	56	550	140	1,100	9,100	838
1950	34,763	9,000	11,650	1,541	89	440	120	1,300	10,600	900
1951	36,996	9,150	13,100	1,573	46	390	100	1,400	11,200	966
1952	37,794	8,900	13,500	1,429	32	430	130	1,450	11,900	970
1953	37,956	8,750	13,400	1,506	26	420	120	1,500	12,200	1,026
1954	35,586	8,000	12,800	1,289	28	380	90	1,500	11,500	1,004
1955	38,426	8,200	14,500	1,490	15	410	90	1,600	12,100	989
1956	39,628	7,900	15,200	1,377	11	440	100	1,600	13,000	888
1957	38,702	7,850	15,400	1,376	13	460	80	1,700	11,800	1,016
1958	36,981	7,650	14,200	1,316	9	450	80	1,650	11,600	929
1959	37,910	7,850	14,900	1,202	6	480	70	1,600	11,800	948
1960	38,137	7,850	14,800	1,368	5	460	80	1,700	11,900	995
1961	38,091	7,650	14,700	1,267	5	490	80	1,700	12,200	1,065
1962	40,804	7,900	16,400	1,245	3	500	90	1,750	12,900	1,029
1963	43,564	8,200	17,600	1,385	10	580	80	1,900	13,800	990
1964	47,700	9,000	19,600	1,580	5	710	100	2,100	14,600	1,123
1965	49,163	8,900	20,800	1,556	5	680	120	2,200	14,900	1,113
1966	53,041	9,400	22,200	1,800	2	740	100	2,500	16,300	1,108
1967	52,924	9,400	22,000	1,620	3	750	100	2,350	16,700	1,165
1968	54,862	9,900	22,400	1,570	4	790	100	2,700	17,400	1,061
1969	55,791	10,100	23,700	1,495	2	800	100	3,900[d]	15,700[d]	1,155
1970	54,633	9,900	23,200	1,459	3	780	100	3,800	15,400	1,140
1971	54,381	9,900	23,100	1,378	2	800	100	3,800	15,300	1,015
1972	56,278	10,300	23,900	1,260	2	1,000	100	3,900	15,800	1,064
1973	55,511	10,200	23,600	1,194	2	1,000	100	3,800	15,600	1,164
1974	46,402	8,500	19,700	1,209	1	1,000	100	3,100	12,800	1,088
1975	45,853	8,400	19,550	979	1	1,000	100	3,130	12,700	1,033
1976	47,038	8,600	20,100	1,033	2	1,000	100	3,200	13,000	1,026

See source and footnotes on page 135.

Motor vehicle deaths by type of incident, United States, 1913-2014 (cont.)

Year	Total deaths	Deaths from collision with...							Deaths from noncollision incidents	Nontraffic deaths[a]
		Pedestrians	Other motor vehicles	Railroad trains	Streetcars	Pedalcycles	Animal-drawn vehicle or animal	Fixed objects		
1977	49,510	9,100	21,200	902	3	1,100	100	3,400	13,700	1,053
1978	52,411	9,600	22,400	986	1	1,200	100	3,600	14,500	1,074
1979	53,524	9,800	23,100	826	1	1,200	100	3,700	14,800	1,271
1980	53,172	9,700	23,000	739	1	1,200	100	3,700	14,700	1,242
1981	51,385	9,400	22,200	668	1	1,200	100	3,600	14,200	1,189
1982	45,779	8,400	19,800	554	1	1,100	100	3,200	12,600	1,066
1983	44,452	8,200	19,200	520	1	1,100	100	3,100	12,200	1,024
1984	46,263	8,500	20,000	630	0	1,100	100	3,200	12,700	1,055
1985	45,901	8,500	19,900	538	2	1,100	100	3,200	12,600	1,079
1986	47,865	8,900	20,800	574	2	1,100	100	3,300	13,100	998
1987	48,290	7,500[e]	20,700	554	1	1,000[e]	100	13,200[e]	5,200[e]	993
1988	49,078	7,700	20,900	638	2	1,000	100	13,400	5,300	1,054
1989	47,575	7,800	20,300	720	2	900	100	12,900	4,900	989
1990	46,814	7,300	19,900	623	2	900	100	13,100	4,900	987
1991	43,536	6,600	18,200	541	1	800	100	12,600	4,700	915
1992	40,982	6,300	17,600	521	2	700	100	11,700	4,100	997
1993	41,893	6,400	18,300	553	3	800	100	11,500	4,200	994
1994	42,524	6,300	18,900	549	1	800	100	11,500	4,400	1,017
1995	43,363	6,400	19,000	514	(c)	800	100	12,100	4,400	1,032
1996	43,649	6,100	19,600	373	(c)	800	100	12,100	4,600	1,127
1997	43,458	5,900	19,900	371	(c)	800	100	12,000	4,400	1,118
1998	43,501	5,900	19,700	309	(c)	700	100	12,200	4,600	1,310
1999	42,401	6,100	18,600	314	1	800	100	11,800	4,700	1,436
2000	43,354	5,900	19,100	321	(c)	800	100	12,300	4,800	1,360
2001	43,788	6,100	18,800	324	3	800	100	12,800	4,900	1,345
2002	45,380	6,100	19,200	283	(c)	800	100	13,600	5,300	1,315
2003	44,757	6,000	19,300	245	(c)	800	100	13,100	5,200	1,417
2004	44,933	6,000	19,600	253	(c)	900	100	13,000	5,100	1,501
2005	45,343	6,100	19,000	250	(c)	1,000	100	13,600	5,300	1,676
2006	45,316	6,200	18,500	264	(c)	1,000	100	13,900	5,400	1,652
2007	43,945	6,000	17,700	211	(c)	900	100	13,800	5,200	1,914
2008	39,790	5,600	15,500	199	(c)	900	100	12,900	4,600	1,805
2009	36,216	5,300	14,100	154	(c)	800	100	11,700	4,100	1,731
2010	35,332	5,500	13,600	139	(c)	800	100	11,300	3,900	1,645
2011	35,303	5,700	13,500	139	(c)	900	100	11,200	3,800	1,520
2012[f]	36,415	6,100	13,900	132	(c)	1,000	100	11,500	3,700	1,480
2013[f]	35,369	6,000	13,700	136	(c)	1,000	100	11,000	3,400	1,565
2014	35,398	6,300	13,900	144	(c)	1,000	100	10,700	3,300	1,662
Changes in deaths										
2005 to 2014	-22%	3%	-27%	-42%	—	0%	0%	-21%	-38%	-1%
2013 to 2014	(g)	5%	1%	6%	—	0%	0%	-3%	-3%	6%

Source: Total deaths from National Center for Health Statistics except 1964 and 2013, which are National Safety Council estimates based on data from the National Highway Traffic Safety Administration's Fatality Analysis Reporting System. Most totals by type are estimated and may not add to the total deaths. See Technical Appendix for comparability.

[a]*See definition, page 206. Nontraffic deaths are included in appropriate incident-type totals in the table. In 2013, 39% of the nontraffic deaths were pedestrians, while in 2014 pedestrians accounted for 36% of nontraffic deaths.*

[b]*Insufficient data for approximations.*

[c]*Data not available.*

[d]*1969 through 1986 totals are not comparable to previous years.*

[e]*Procedures and benchmarks for estimating deaths for certain types of incidents were changed for the 1990 edition. Estimates for 1987 and later years are not comparable to earlier years.*

[f]*Revised.*

[g]*Less than 0.5%.*

Motor-Vehicle Deaths by Age

Motor vehicle deaths by age, United States, 1913-2014

Year	All ages	Younger than 5 years	5-14 years	15-24 years	25-44 years	45-64 years	65-74 years	75 and older[a]
1913	4,200	300	1,100	600	1,100	800		300
1914	4,700	300	1,200	700	1,200	900		400
1915	6,600	400	1,500	1,000	1,700	1,400		600
1916	8,200	600	1,800	1,300	2,100	1,700		700
1917	10,200	700	2,400	1,400	2,700	2,100		900
1918	10,700	800	2,700	1,400	2,500	2,300		1,000
1919	11,200	900	3,000	1,400	2,500	2,100		1,300
1920	12,500	1,000	3,300	1,700	2,800	2,300		1,400
1921	13,900	1,100	3,400	1,800	3,300	2,700		1,600
1922	15,300	1,100	3,500	2,100	3,700	3,100		1,800
1923	18,400	1,200	3,700	2,800	4,600	3,900		2,200
1924	19,400	1,400	3,800	2,900	4,700	4,100		2,500
1925	21,900	1,400	3,900	3,600	5,400	4,800		2,800
1926	23,400	1,400	3,900	3,900	5,900	5,200		3,100
1927	25,800	1,600	4,000	4,300	6,600	5,800		3,500
1928	28,000	1,600	3,800	4,900	7,200	6,600		3,900
1929	31,200	1,600	3,900	5,700	8,000	7,500		4,500
1930	32,900	1,500	3,600	6,200	8,700	8,000		4,900
1931	33,700	1,500	3,600	6,300	9,100	8,200		5,000
1932	29,500	1,200	2,900	5,100	8,100	7,400		4,800
1933	31,363	1,274	3,121	5,649	8,730	7,947		4,642
1934	36,101	1,210	3,182	6,561	10,232	9,530		5,386
1935	36,369	1,253	2,951	6,755	10,474	9,562		5,374
1936	38,089	1,324	3,026	7,184	10,807	10,089		5,659
1937	39,643	1,303	2,991	7,800	10,877	10,475		6,197
1938	32,582	1,122	2,511	6,016	8,772	8,711		5,450
1939	32,386	1,192	2,339	6,318	8,917	8,292		5,328
1940	34,501	1,176	2,584	6,846	9,362	8,882		5,651
1941	39,969	1,378	2,838	8,414	11,069	9,829		6,441
1942	28,309	1,069	1,991	5,932	7,747	7,254		4,316
1943	23,823	1,132	1,959	4,522	6,454	5,996		3,760
1944	24,282	1,203	2,093	4,561	6,514	5,982		3,929
1945	28,076	1,290	2,386	5,358	7,578	6,794		4,670
1946	33,411	1,568	2,508	7,445	8,955	7,532		5,403
1947	32,697	1,502	2,275	7,251	8,775	7,468		5,426
1948	32,259	1,635	2,337	7,218	8,702	7,190	3,173	2,004
1949	31,701	1,667	2,158	6,772	8,892	7,073	3,116	2,023
1950	34,763	1,767	2,152	7,600	10,214	7,728	3,264	2,038
1951	36,996	1,875	2,300	7,713	11,253	8,276	3,444	2,135
1952	37,794	1,951	2,295	8,115	11,380	8,463	3,472	2,118
1953	37,956	2,019	2,368	8,169	11,302	8,318	3,508	2,271
1954	35,586	1,864	2,332	7,571	10,521	7,848	3,247	2,203
1955	38,426	1,875	2,406	8,656	11,448	8,372	3,455	2,214
1956	39,628	1,770	2,640	9,169	11,551	8,573	3,657	2,268
1957	38,702	1,785	2,604	8,667	11,230	8,545	3,560	2,311
1958	36,981	1,791	2,710	8,388	10,414	7,922	3,535	2,221
1959	37,910	1,842	2,719	8,969	10,358	8,263	3,487	2,272
1960	38,137	1,953	2,814	9,117	10,189	8,294	3,457	2,313
1961	38,091	1,891	2,802	9,088	10,212	8,267	3,467	2,364
1962	40,804	1,903	3,028	10,157	10,701	8,812	3,696	2,507
1963	43,564	1,991	3,063	11,123	11,356	9,506	3,786	2,739
1964	47,700	2,120	3,430	12,400	12,500	10,200	4,150	2,900
1965	49,163	2,059	3,526	13,395	12,595	10,509	4,077	3,002
1966	53,041	2,182	3,869	15,298	13,282	11,051	4,217	3,142
1967	52,924	2,067	3,845	15,646	12,987	10,902	4,285	3,192
1968	54,862	1,987	4,105	16,543	13,602	11,031	4,261	3,333
1969	55,791	2,077	4,045	17,443	13,868	11,012	4,210	3,136
1970	54,633	1,915	4,159	16,720	13,446	11,099	4,084	3,210
1971	54,381	1,885	4,256	17,103	13,307	10,471	4,108	3,251
1972	56,278	1,896	4,258	17,942	13,758	10,836	4,138	3,450
1973	55,511	1,998	4,124	18,032	14,013	10,216	3,892	3,236
1974	46,402	1,546	3,332	15,905	11,834	8,159	3,071	2,555
1975	45,853	1,576	3,286	15,672	11,969	7,663	3,047	2,640
1976	47,038	1,532	3,175	16,650	12,112	7,770	3,082	2,717

See source and footnotes on page 137.

Motor vehicle deaths by age, United States, 1913-2014 (cont.)

Year	All ages	Younger than 5 years	5-14 years	15-24 years	25-44 years	45-64 years	65-74 years	75 and older[a]
1977	49,510	1,472	3,142	18,092	13,031	8,000	3,060	2,713
1978	52,411	1,551	3,130	19,164	14,574	8,048	3,217	2,727
1979	53,524	1,461	2,952	19,369	15,658	8,162	3,171	2,751
1980	53,172	1,426	2,747	19,040	16,133	8,022	2,991	2,813
1981	51,385	1,256	2,575	17,363	16,447	7,818	3,090	2,836
1982	45,779	1,300	2,301	15,324	14,469	6,879	2,825	2,681
1983	44,452	1,233	2,241	14,289	14,323	6,690	2,827	2,849
1984	46,263	1,138	2,263	14,738	15,036	6,954	3,020	3,114
1985	45,901	1,195	2,319	14,277	15,034	6,885	3,014	3,177
1986	47,865	1,188	2,350	15,227	15,844	6,799	3,096	3,361
1987	48,290	1,190	2,397	14,447	16,405	7,021	3,277	3,553
1988	49,078	1,220	2,423	14,406	16,580	7,245	3,429	3,775
1989	47,575	1,221	2,266	12,941	16,571	7,287	3,465	3,824
1990	46,814	1,123	2,059	12,607	16,488	7,282	3,350	3,905
1991	43,536	1,076	2,011	11,664	15,082	6,616	3,193	3,894
1992	40,982	1,020	1,904	10,305	14,071	6,597	3,247	3,838
1993	41,893	1,081	1,963	10,500	14,283	6,711	3,116	4,239
1994	42,524	1,139	2,026	10,660	13,966	7,097	3,385	4,251
1995	43,363	1,004	2,055	10,600	14,618	7,428	3,300	4,358
1996	43,649	1,035	1,980	10,576	14,482	7,749	3,419	4,408
1997	43,458	933	1,967	10,208	14,167	8,134	3,370	4,679
1998	43,501	921	1,868	10,026	14,095	8,416	3,410	4,765
1999	42,401	834	1,771	10,128	13,516	8,342	3,276	4,534
2000	43,354	819	1,772	10,560	13,811	8,867	3,038	4,487
2001	43,788	770	1,686	10,725	14,020	9,029	2,990	4,568
2002	45,380	733	1,614	11,459	14,169	9,701	3,113	4,591
2003	44,757	766	1,642	10,972	13,794	10,032	2,967	4,584
2004	44,933	778	1,653	10,987	13,699	10,369	2,974	4,473
2005	45,343	763	1,447	10,908	13,987	10,851	3,110	4,277
2006	45,316	728	1,339	11,015	14,025	11,133	2,916	4,160
2007	43,945	675	1,285	10,568	13,457	10,889	2,940	4,131
2008	39,790	566	1,027	8,946	12,242	10,457	2,826	3,726
2009	36,216	574	974	7,688	10,953	9,777	2,693	3,557
2010	35,332	528	890	7,250	10,491	9,727	2,676	3,770
2011	35,303	520	881	7,105	10,352	9,866	2,913	3,666
2012	36,415	531	820	7,062	10,933	10,270	3,112	3,687
2013[b]	35,369	493	852	6,692	10,567	10,030	3,066	3,669
2014	35,398	473	829	6,709	10,518	10,024	3,153	3,692
Changes in deaths								
2005 to 2014	-22%	-38%	-43%	-38%	-25%	-8%	1%	-14%
2013 to 2014	(c)	-4%	-3%	(c)	(c)	(c)	3%	1%

Source: 1913 to 1932 calculated from National Center for Health Statistics data for registration states; 1933 to 1963 and 1965 to 2014 are NCHS totals. All other figures are National Safety Council estimates. See Technical Appendix for comparability.

[a] Includes "age unknown." In 2013, these deaths numbered 4 and in 2014 they numbered 7.

[b] Revised.

[c] Less than 0.5%.

Motor-Vehicle Death Rates by Age

Motor vehicle death rates[a] by age, United States, 1913-2014

Year	All ages	Younger than 5 years	5-14 years	15-24 years	25-44 years	45-64 years	65-74 years	75 and older
1913	4.4	2.3	5.5	3.1	3.8	5.3	8.5	
1914	4.8	2.5	5.7	3.5	4.1	6.2	9.3	
1915	6.6	3.5	7.3	5.0	5.6	8.8	13.5	
1916	8.1	4.7	8.6	6.0	7.0	10.7	15.8	
1917	10.0	5.6	10.6	7.4	8.6	12.6	18.6	
1918	10.3	6.9	12.3	7.7	8.3	13.7	21.2	
1919	10.7	7.5	13.9	7.5	8.1	12.4	24.1	
1920	11.7	8.6	14.6	8.7	8.8	13.5	27.0	
1921	12.9	9.0	14.5	9.2	10.2	15.4	31.0	
1922	13.9	9.2	15.0	10.8	11.1	17.2	34.9	
1923	16.5	9.7	15.6	13.4	13.6	21.0	40.5	
1924	17.1	11.1	16.1	14.3	13.7	21.8	43.7	
1925	19.1	11.0	15.6	17.2	15.8	25.0	48.9	
1926	20.1	11.0	15.9	18.6	17.1	26.3	51.4	
1927	21.8	12.8	16.0	20.0	18.8	28.9	56.9	
1928	23.4	12.7	15.5	21.9	20.2	32.4	62.2	
1929	25.7	13.4	15.6	25.6	22.3	35.6	68.6	
1930	26.7	13.0	14.7	27.4	23.9	37.0	72.5	
1931	27.2	13.3	14.5	27.9	24.8	37.4	70.6	
1932	23.6	11.3	12.0	22.6	22.0	32.9	63.6	
1933	25.0	12.0	12.7	24.8	23.4	34.7	63.1	
1934	28.6	11.7	13.0	28.6	27.2	40.7	71.0	
1935	28.6	12.3	12.2	29.2	27.6	39.9	68.9	
1936	29.7	13.2	12.6	30.8	28.2	41.3	70.5	
1937	30.8	13.0	12.7	33.2	28.2	42.0	75.1	
1938	25.1	11.0	10.8	25.4	22.5	34.3	64.1	
1939	24.7	11.2	10.4	26.5	22.6	32.2	60.2	
1940	26.1	11.1	11.5	28.7	23.5	33.9	62.1	
1941	30.0	12.7	12.6	35.7	27.5	37.0	68.6	
1942	21.1	9.5	8.8	25.8	19.2	26.9	44.5	
1943	17.8	9.4	8.6	20.6	16.1	21.9	37.6	
1944	18.3	9.6	9.1	22.5	16.6	21.6	38.2	
1945	21.2	10.0	10.3	27.8	19.7	24.2	44.1	
1946	23.9	11.9	10.8	34.4	21.1	26.4	49.6	
1947	22.8	10.5	9.7	32.8	20.3	25.7	48.2	
1948	22.1	11.0	9.8	32.5	19.8	24.3	39.6	55.4
1949	21.3	10.7	9.0	30.7	19.9	23.4	37.8	53.9
1950	23.0	10.8	8.8	34.5	22.5	25.1	38.8	52.4
1951	24.1	10.9	9.2	36.0	24.7	26.5	39.5	53.0
1952	24.3	11.3	8.7	38.6	24.7	26.7	38.5	50.8
1953	24.0	11.5	8.5	39.1	24.5	25.8	37.7	52.6
1954	22.1	10.4	8.1	36.2	22.6	24.0	33.9	49.0
1955	23.4	10.2	8.0	40.9	24.5	25.2	35.1	47.1
1956	23.7	9.4	8.4	42.9	24.6	25.3	36.2	46.4
1957	22.7	9.2	8.0	39.7	23.9	24.8	34.4	45.5
1958	21.3	9.1	8.1	37.0	22.3	22.6	33.5	42.3
1959	21.5	9.1	7.9	38.2	22.2	23.2	32.3	41.8
1960	21.2	9.6	7.9	37.7	21.7	22.9	31.3	41.1
1961	20.8	9.2	7.6	36.5	21.8	22.5	30.7	40.5
1962	22.0	9.3	8.1	38.4	22.9	23.7	32.2	41.7
1963	23.1	9.8	8.0	40.0	24.3	25.2	32.6	44.3
1964	25.0	10.5	8.8	42.6	26.8	26.6	35.5	45.2
1965	25.4	10.4	8.9	44.2	27.0	27.0	34.6	45.4
1966	27.1	11.4	9.7	48.7	28.5	27.9	35.4	46.2
1967	26.8	11.2	9.5	48.4	27.8	27.1	35.6	45.4
1968	27.5	11.1	10.1	49.8	28.8	27.0	35.1	46.0
1969	27.7	12.0	9.9	50.7	29.1	26.6	34.3	42.0
1970	26.8	11.2	10.2	46.7	27.9	26.4	32.7	42.2
1971	26.3	10.9	10.5	45.7	27.4	24.7	32.4	41.3
1972	26.9	11.1	10.7	47.1	27.4	25.3	32.0	42.6
1973	26.3	11.9	10.5	46.3	27.2	23.6	29.4	39.1
1974	21.8	9.4	8.6	40.0	22.4	18.8	22.6	30.1
1975	21.3	9.8	8.6	38.7	22.1	17.5	21.9	30.1
1976	21.6	9.8	8.4	40.3	21.8	17.6	21.6	30.1

See source and footnotes on page 139.

Motor vehicle death rates[a] by age, United States, 1913-2014 (cont.)

Year	All ages	Younger than 5 years	5-14 years	15-24 years	25-44 years	45-64 years	65-74 years	75 and older
1977	22.5	9.5	8.5	43.3	22.7	18.1	20.9	29.3
1978	23.6	9.9	8.6	45.4	24.6	18.2	21.5	28.7
1979	23.8	9.1	8.3	45.6	25.6	18.4	20.7	28.1
1980	23.4	8.7	7.9	44.8	25.5	18.0	19.1	28.0
1981	22.4	7.4	7.5	41.1	25.2	17.6	19.4	27.5
1982	19.8	7.5	6.7	36.8	21.5	15.5	17.5	25.2
1983	19.0	7.0	6.6	34.8	20.6	15.0	17.2	26.0
1984	19.6	6.4	6.7	36.4	21.0	15.6	18.2	27.7
1985	19.3	6.7	6.9	35.7	20.5	15.4	17.9	27.5
1986	19.9	6.6	7.0	38.5	21.0	15.2	18.1	28.3
1987	19.9	6.6	7.1	37.1	21.3	15.7	18.8	29.1
1988	20.1	6.7	7.1	37.8	21.2	15.9	19.5	30.2
1989	19.3	6.6	6.5	34.6	20.8	15.9	19.4	29.8
1990	18.8	6.0	5.8	34.2	20.4	15.7	18.5	29.7
1991	17.3	5.6	5.6	32.1	18.3	14.2	17.5	28.9
1992	16.1	5.2	5.2	28.5	17.1	13.6	17.6	27.8
1993	16.3	5.5	5.3	29.1	17.3	13.5	16.7	30.0
1994	16.3	5.8	5.4	29.5	16.8	13.9	18.1	29.4
1995	16.5	5.1	5.4	29.3	17.5	14.2	17.6	29.4
1996	16.5	5.4	5.2	29.2	17.3	14.4	18.3	29.0
1997	16.2	4.9	5.1	27.9	17.0	14.7	18.2	29.9
1998	16.1	4.9	4.8	26.9	16.9	14.7	18.5	29.8
1999	15.5	4.4	4.5	26.8	16.3	14.1	18.0	27.8
2000	15.7	4.3	4.5	27.5	16.8	14.5	16.7	27.0
2001	15.4	4.0	4.1	26.8	16.5	14.0	16.3	26.8
2002	15.8	3.7	3.9	28.2	16.8	14.6	17.0	26.5
2003	15.4	3.9	4.0	26.6	16.4	14.6	16.2	26.0
2004	15.3	3.9	4.1	26.4	16.3	14.7	16.1	25.1
2005	15.3	3.8	3.6	25.9	16.6	14.9	16.7	23.6
2006	15.2	3.6	3.3	26.1	16.8	14.9	15.4	22.7
2007	14.6	3.3	3.2	24.9	16.1	14.2	15.2	22.2
2008	13.1	2.7	2.5	20.8	14.7	13.4	14.0	20.0
2009	11.8	2.7	2.4	17.8	13.2	12.3	13.0	18.9
2010	11.4	2.5	2.2	16.8	12.6	12.0	12.5	19.9
2011	11.3	2.6	2.1	16.2	12.6	11.9	13.0	19.4
2012[b]	11.6	2.7	2.0	16.1	13.2	12.4	13.0	19.2
2013[b]	11.2	2.5	2.1	15.2	12.7	12.1	12.8	18.8
2014	11.1	2.4	2.0	15.3	12.5	12.0	11.9	18.6
Changes in rates								
2005 to 2014	-27%	-37%	-44%	-41%	-25%	-19%	-29%	-21%
2013 to 2014	-1%	-4%	-5%	1%	-2%	-1%	-7%	-1%

Source: 1913 to 1932 calculated from National Center for Health Statistics data for registration states; 1933 to 1963 and 1965 to 2014 are NCHS totals. All other figures are National Safety Council estimates. See Technical Appendix for comparability.
[a]*Death rates are deaths per 100,000 population in each group that were calculated using population data from the U.S. Census Bureau.*
[b]*Revised.*

HOME AND COMMUNITY
Home and Community, 2014 (cont.)

Leading causes of unintentional-injury-related deaths in home and community, United States, 2014

Deaths

- Age 65 and older
- Ages 15-64
- Ages 0-14

...oking*
...cts breathing.

Drowning   Fire, flames or smoke

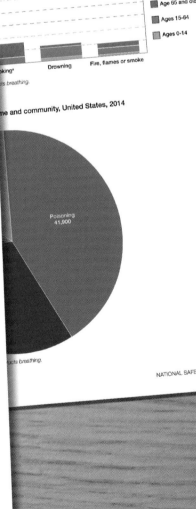

...me and community, United States, 2014

Poisoning
41,900

...cts breathing.

NATIONAL SAFET...

Cost of Sports and Consumer Product Injuries — pg. 153

A recent study finds that three product groups (sports and recreation; home structures and construction materials; and home furnishings and fixtures) account for 77% of the $909 billion annual costs (2009 dollars) of consumer-product-related injuries. The $909 billion includes: medical, work losses, pain and suffering, product liability, insurance administration, and litigation costs. The average cost per incident is estimated to be $63,490 overall, and ranges from $34,606 for non-powered housewares injuries to $71,473 for yard and garden equipment injuries.

143

The home and community venue is the combination of the home class and the public class. Home and community, together with the occupational and transportation venues, make up the totality of unintentional injuries. Home and community includes all unintentional injuries that are not work-related and do not involve motor vehicles on streets and highways.

In 2014, an estimated 98,600 unintentional-injury-related deaths occurred in the home and community venue, or 72% of all unintentional-injury-related deaths that year. The number of deaths was up about 6% from the revised 2013 total of 93,000. An additional 30,500,000 people suffered nonfatal medically consulted injuries. The death rate per 100,000 population was 30.9 – about 5% higher than the revised 2013 rate.

About 1 out of 10 people experienced an unintentional injury in the home and community venue, and about 1 out of 3,200 people died from such an injury in 2014. About 40% of the deaths and injuries involved workers while they were away from work (off the job).

The graph on the next page shows the five leading causes of unintentional-injury-related deaths in the home and community venue and the broad age groups (children, youths and adults, and the elderly) affected by them. This is one way to prioritize issues in this venue. Below is a graph of the trend in deaths and death rates from 1999 to present. Similar graphs for the home and public classes appear on pages 144 and 148.

The National Safety Council adopted the Bureau of Labor Statistics' Census of Fatal Occupational Injuries count for work-related unintentional injuries beginning with 1992 data. Because of the lower work class total resulting from this change, adjustments were made to the home and public classes. Long-term historical comparisons for these three classes should be made with caution. Also, beginning with 1999 data, deaths are now classified according to the 10th revision of the *International Classification of Diseases*. Caution should be used in comparing data classified under the 10th revision with prior revisions. See the Technical Appendix for more information about both changes.

Deaths.. **98,600**
Medically consulted injuries.. **30,500,000ᵃ**
Death rate per 100,000 population **30.9**
Costs .... **$362.5 billion**

ᵃ*Medically consulted injury estimate procedure was revised for the 2016 edition and is not comparable to estimates provided in previous editions.*

Home and community deaths and death rates, United States, 1999-2014

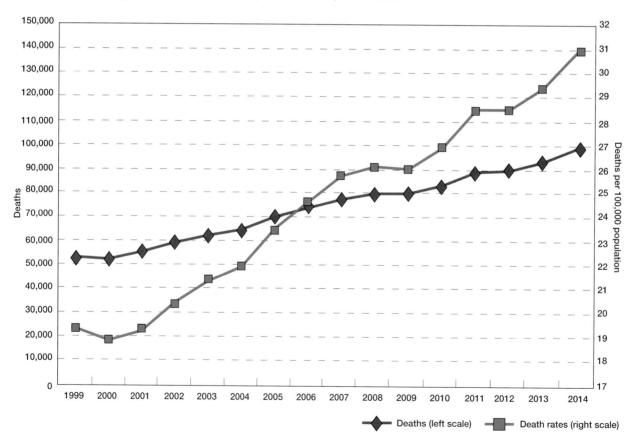

Leading causes of unintentional-injury-related deaths in home and community, United States, 2014

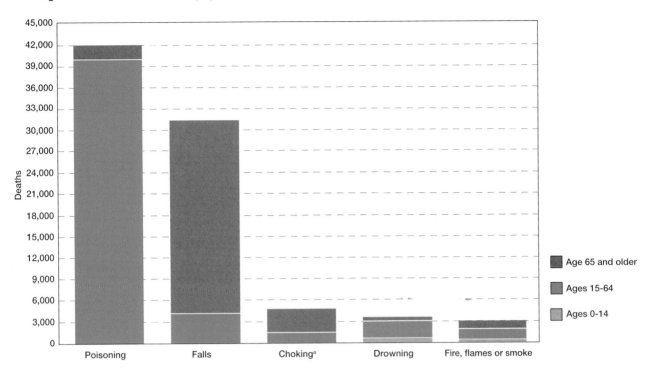

Legend:
- Age 65 and older
- Ages 15-64
- Ages 0-14

Categories: Poisoning, Falls, Choking[a], Drowning, Fire, flames or smoke

[a]Inhalation and ingestion of food or other object that obstructs breathing.

Causes of unintentional-injury-related deaths in home and community, United States, 2014

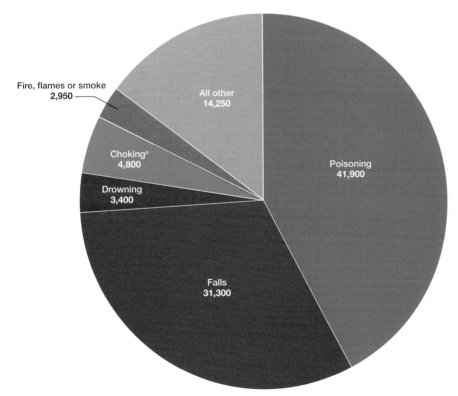

- Fire, flames or smoke 2,950
- All other 14,250
- Choking[a] 4,800
- Poisoning 41,900
- Drowning 3,400
- Falls 31,300

[a]Inhalation and ingestion of food or other object that obstructs breathing.

Between 1912 and 2014, unintentional-home-injury-related deaths per 100,000 population were reduced 22% from 28 to 21.8 (after adjusting for the 1948 classification change). In 1912, when there were 21 million households, an estimated 26,000 to 28,000 people were killed by unintentional-home-related injuries. In 2014, with 123 million households and the population tripled, home-related deaths numbered 69,500. However, the number and rate of unintentional-home-injury-related deaths has been steadily increasing since 2000. This increase in deaths is largely driven by increases in both unintentional poisonings and falls.

The injury total of 20,200,000 means that 1 person in 16 in the United States experienced an unintentional injury in the home in 2014 that was serious enough to consult with a medical professional. The number of medically consulted injuries occurring in the home is greater than the total number of medically consulted injuries that occur in public places, the workplace, and motor-vehicle crashes combined. The National Health Interview Survey estimates that about 52% of all medically attended injuries occurred at home.

The National Safety Council adopted the Bureau of Labor Statistics' Census of Fatal Occupational Injuries count for work-related unintentional injuries beginning with 1992 data. This affected long-term historical comparisons for the work, home, and public classes. Beginning with 1999 data, deaths are classified according to the 10th revision of the *International Classification of Diseases*. Caution should be used in comparing current data with data classified under prior revisions. See the Technical Appendix for more information.

Deaths...69,500
Medically consulted injuries..20,200,000[a]
Death rate per 100,000 population 21.8
Costs ....$241.9 billion

[a]Medically consulted injury estimate procedure was revised for the 2016 edition and is not comparable to estimates provided in previous editions.

Home deaths and death rates, United States, 1999-2014

Principal types of unintentional-home-related injury deaths, United States, 1987-2014

Year	Total home	Poisoning	Falls	Fire, flames, or smoke[a]	Choking[b]	Mechanical suffocation	Drowning	Natural heat or cold	Firearms	Other
1987	21,400	4,100	6,300	3,900	2,500	600	700	(c)	800	2,500
1988	22,700	4,800	6,600	4,100	2,600	600	700	(c)	800	2,500
1989	22,500	5,000	6,600	3,900	2,500	600	700	(c)	800	2,400
1990	21,500	4,500	6,700	3,400	2,300	600	900	(c)	800	2,300
1991	22,100	5,000	6,900	3,400	2,200	700	900	(c)	800	2,200
1992	24,000	5,200	7,700	3,700	1,500	700	900	(c)	1,000	3,300
1993	26,100	6,500	7,900	3,700	1,700	700	900	(c)	1,100	3,600
1994	26,300	6,800	8,100	3,700	1,600	800	900	(c)	900	3,500
1995	27,200	7,000	8,400	3,500	1,500	800	900	(c)	900	4,200
1996	27,500	7,300	9,000	3,500	1,500	800	900	(c)	800	3,700
1997	27,700	7,800	9,100	3,200	1,500	800	900	(c)	700	3,500
1998	29,000	8,400	9,500	2,900	1,800	800	1,000	(c)	600	4,000
1999[d]	30,500	9,300	7,600	3,000	1,900	1,100	900	700	600	5,400
2000	29,200	9,800	7,100	2,700	2,100	1,000	1,000	400	500	4,600
2001	33,200	11,300	8,600	3,000	2,000	1,100	900	400	600	5,300
2002	36,400	13,900	9,700	2,800	1,900	1,100	900	400	500	5,200
2003	38,800	15,900	10,300	2,900	2,100	1,000	800	400	500	4,900
2004	41,700	17,500	11,300	2,900	2,200	1,200	900	400	400	4,900
2005	46,400	20,000	12,000	2,900	2,300	1,300	900	500	500	6,000
2006	49,600	23,300	12,800	2,800	2,300	1,400	1,000	600	400	5,000
2007	53,500	25,800	14,200	3,000	2,100	1,400	1,000	500	400	5,100
2008	55,200	26,800	15,100	2,600	2,300	1,500	900	400	400	5,200
2009	55,800	27,500	15,700	2,600	2,300	1,300	1,000	500	400	4,500
2010	57,900	28,800	16,500	2,500	2,200	1,400	1,000	600	400	4,500
2011	62,400	31,400	17,400	2,400	2,500	1,400	900	700	400	5,300
2012	62,800	31,400	17,900	2,300	2,600	1,400	1,000	500	400	5,300
2013[e]	65,700	33,200	19,300	2,400	2,400	1,500	1,100	500	400	4,900
2014[f]	69,500	35,700	20,400	2,400	2,500	1,500	1,000	600	400	5,000

Source: National Safety Council estimates based on National Center for Health Statistics (NCHS)—Mortality Data compiled from data provided by the 57 vital statistics jurisdictions through the Vital Statistics Cooperative Program. Rates are National Safety Council estimates based on data from NCHS. The Council adopted the Bureau of Labor Statistics' Census of Fatal Occupational Injuries count for work-related unintentional-injuries retroactive to 1992 data. Because of the lower work class total resulting from this change, several thousand unintentional-injury-related deaths that had been classified by the Council as work-related had to be reassigned to the home and public classes. For this reason, long-term historical comparisons for these three classes should be made with caution. See the Technical Appendix for an explanation of the methodological changes.

[a] Includes deaths resulting from conflagration, regardless of nature of injury.
[b] Inhalation and ingestion of food or other object that obstructs breathing.
[c] Included in "Other."
[d] In 1999, a revision was made in the International Classification of Diseases. See the Technical Appendix for comparability with earlier years.
[e] Revised.
[f] Preliminary.

Principal types of home unintentional-injury-related deaths, United States, 2014

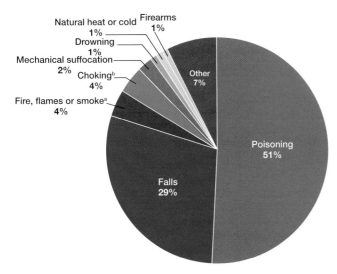

[a]Includes deaths resulting from conflagration, regardless of nature of injury.
[b]Inhalation and ingestion of food or other object that obstructs breathing.

Deaths Due to Unintentional Home Injuries, 2014

Type of event and age of victim

All home

Includes deaths in the home and on home premises to occupants, guests, and trespassers. Also includes hired household workers but excludes other people working on home premises.

	Total	Change from 2013	Death rate[a]
Deaths	69,500	+6%	21.8

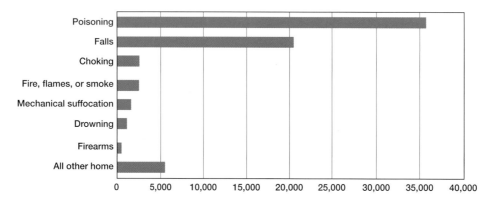

Poisoning

Includes deaths from drugs, medicines, other solid and liquid substances, and gases and vapors. Excludes poisonings from spoiled foods, *Salmonella*, etc., which are classified as disease deaths.

	Total	Change from 2013	Death rate[a]
Deaths	35,700	+8%	11.2

Falls

Includes deaths from falls from one level to another or on the same level in the home or on home premises.

	Total	Change from 2013	Death rate[a]
Deaths	20,400	+6%	6.4

Choking

Includes deaths from unintentional ingestion or inhalation of objects or food resulting in the obstruction of respiratory passages.

	Total	Change from 2013	Death rate[a]
Deaths	2,500	+4%	0.8

See footnotes on page 147.

Type of event and age of victim

Fires, flames, or smoke

Includes deaths from fires, burns, and injuries in conflagrations in the home – such as asphyxiation, falls, and struck by falling objects. Excludes burns from hot objects or liquids.

	Total	Change from 2013	Death rate[a]
Deaths	2,400	0%	0.8

Age	0-4	5-14	15-24	25-44	45-64	65-74	75+
Deaths	120	100	80	300	740	460	600

Mechanical suffocation

Includes deaths from smothering by bed clothes, thin plastic materials, etc.; suffocation by cave-ins or confinement in closed spaces; and mechanical strangulation or hanging.

	Total	Change from 2013	Death rate[a]
Deaths	1,500	0%	0.5

Age	0-4	5-14	15-24	25-44	45-64	65-74	75+
Deaths	960	30	50	160	190	70	40

Drowning

Includes drownings of people in or on home premises – such as in swimming pools and bathtubs. Excludes drowning in floods and other cataclysms.

	Total	Change from 2013	Death rate[a]
Deaths	1,000	-9%	0.3

Age	0-4	5-14	15-24	25-44	45-64	65-74	75+
Deaths	240	50	50	160	240	120	140

Firearms

Includes firearms injuries in or on home premises – such as while cleaning or playing with guns. Excludes deaths from explosive materials.

	Total	Change from 2013	Death rate[a]
Deaths	400	0%	0.1

Age	0-4	5-14	15-24	25-44	45-64	65-74	75+
Deaths	20	20	90	100	100	50	20

All other home

Most important types included are natural heat and cold, struck by or against objects, machinery, and electric current.

	Total	Change from 2013	Death rate[a]
Deaths	5,600	+4%	1.8

Age	0-4	5-14	15-24	25-44	45-64	65-74	75+
Deaths	320	60	80	300	1,150	810	2,880

[a]Deaths per 100,000 population.
[b]Deaths per 100,000 population in each age group.
[c]Death rate less than 0.05.

Between 1912 and 2014, public unintentional-injury-related deaths per 100,000 population were reduced 70% from 30 to 9.1 (after adjusting for the 1948 change in classification). In 1912, an estimated 28,000 to 30,000 people died from public non-motor vehicle injuries. In 2014, with the population tripled, and travel and recreational activity greatly increased, 29,100 people died from public unintentional injuries and 10,300,000 suffered injuries serious enough to consult a medical professional. The public class excludes deaths and injuries involving motor vehicles and people at work or at home.

In 2014, the number of public unintentional-injury-related deaths was up 6.6% from the revised 2013 figure of 27,300. The 2014 death rate per 100,000 population increased 5.8% from 8.6 in 2013 to 9.1.

With an estimated 10,300,000 medically consulted unintentional injuries occurring in public places and a population of over 319 million people, on average about 1 person in 31 experienced such an injury.

The National Safety Council adopted the Bureau of Labor Statistics' Census of Fatal Occupational Injuries count for work-related unintentional-injuries beginning with 1992 data. This affected long-term historical comparisons for the work, home, and public classes. Beginning with 1999 data, deaths are classified according to the 10th revision of the *International Classification of Diseases*. Caution should be used in comparing current data with data classified under prior revisions. See the Technical Appendix for more information.

Deaths.. **29,100**
Medically consulted injuries...**10,300,000**[a]
Death rate per 100,000 population **9.1**
Costs .... **$120.6 billion**

[a]*Medically consulted injury estimate procedure was revised for the 2016 edition and is not comparable to estimates provided in previous editions.*

Public deaths and death rates, United States, 1999-2014

Principal types of public unintentional-injury-related deaths, United States, 1987-2014

Year	Total public[a]	Falls	Poisoning	Drowning	Choking[g]	Fire, flames, or smoke	Firearms	Air transport	Water transport	Rail transport[b]	Mechanical suffocation
1987	18,400	4,000	800	3,200	1,100	500	600	900	800	400	[c]
1988	18,400	4,100	900	3,100	1,100	500	600	700	800	400	[c]
1989	18,200	4,200	900	3,000	1,000	500	600	800	700	400	[c]
1990	17,400	4,300	900	2,800	1,000	400	500	700	800	400	[c]
1991	17,600	4,500	1,000	2,800	900	400	600	700	700	500	[c]
1992	19,000	4,400	1,700	2,500	1,600	200	400	700	700	600	[c]
1993	19,700	4,600	1,900	2,800	1,500	200	400	600	700	600	[c]
1994	19,600	4,700	2,100	2,400	1,500	200	400	600	600	600	[c]
1995	20,100	5,000	2,000	2,800	1,600	200	300	600	700	500	[c]
1996	21,000	5,300	2,100	2,500	1,700	200	300	700	600	500	[c]
1997	21,700	5,600	2,300	2,600	1,700	200	300	500	600	400	[c]
1998	22,600	6,000	2,300	2,900	1,700	200	300	500	600	500	[c]
1999[d]	22,200	4,800	2,800	2,600	2,000	200	300	500	600	400	500
2000	22,700	5,500	2,900	2,400	2,200	200	200	500	500	400	300
2001	21,800	5,600	2,700	2,400	2,100	200	200	700	500	400	300
2002	22,500	5,900	3,600	2,500	2,200	300	200	500	500	400	300
2003	23,200	6,300	3,400	2,400	2,200	300	200	600	500	400	300
2004	22,700	6,700	3,400	2,400	2,200	200	200	400	500	400	200
2005	23,400	6,800	3,500	2,600	2,100	[c]	[c]	400	500	400	200
2006	23,900	7,200	4,100	2,500	2,100	[c]	[c]	400	400	400	200
2007	23,700	7,600	3,900	2,400	2,200	[c]	[c]	400	400	400	200
2008	24,500	8,200	4,200	2,500	2,100	[c]	[c]	400	300	400	200
2009	24,000	8,500	4,200	2,400	2,100	[c]	[c]	400	400	300	200
2010	25,300	8,900	4,100	2,700	2,300	[c]	[c]	300	300	400	200
2011	26,400	9,400	4,700	2,600	2,200	[c]	[c]	300	500	300	200
2012	26,600	10,100	4,800	2,500	2,100	[c]	[c]	300	400	300	200
2013[e]	27,300	10,200	5,600	2,200	2,500	[c]	[c]	300	300	400	200
2014[f]	29,100	10,900	6,200	2,400	2,300	[c]	[c]	300	300	400	200

Source: National Safety Council estimates based on data from the National Center for Health Statistics. The Council adopted the Bureau of Labor Statistics' Census of Fatal Occupational Injuries count for work-related unintentional injuries retroactive to 1992 data. Because of the lower work class total resulting from this change, several thousand unintentional-injury-related deaths that had been classified by the Council as work-related had to be reassigned to the home and public classes. For this reason, long-term historical comparisons for these three classes should be made with caution. See the Technical Appendix for an explanation of the methodological changes.
[a] Includes some deaths not shown separately.
[b] Includes subways and elevateds.
[c] Estimates not available.
[d] In 1999, a revision was made in the International Classification of Diseases. See the Technical Appendix for comparability with earlier years.
[e] Revised.
[f] Preliminary.
[g] Inhalation and ingestion of food or other object that obstructs breathing.

Principal types of public unintentional-injury-related deaths, United States, 2014

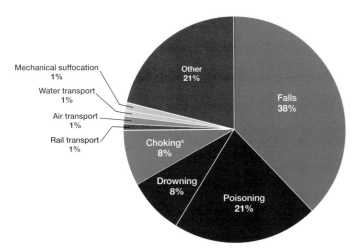

[a] Inhalation and ingestion of food or other object that obstructs breathing.

Deaths Due to Unintentional Public Injuries, 2014

Type of event and age of victim

All public

Includes deaths in public places and not involving motor vehicles. Most sports, recreation, and transportation deaths are included. Excludes work deaths.

	Total	Change from 2013	Death rate[a]
Deaths	29,100	+7%	9.1

Age	0-4	5-14	15-24	25-44	45-64	65-74	75+
Death Rate[b]	1.5	1.0	3.9	6.2	7.9	9.5	62.5
Deaths	300	400	1,700	5,200	6,600	2,500	12,400

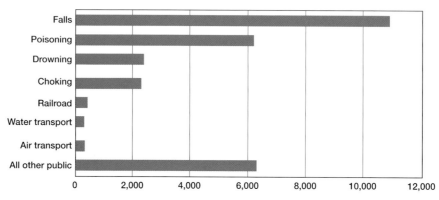

Falls

Includes deaths from falls from one level to another or on the same level in public places. Excludes deaths from falls from moving vehicles.

	Total	Change from 2013	Death rate[a]
Deaths	10,900	+7%	3.4

Age	0-4	5-14	15-24	25-44	45-64	65-74	75+
Death Rate[b]	0.0	(c)	0.3	0.3	1.3	4.3	42.1
Deaths	0	20	110	230	1,060	1,130	8,350

Poisoning

Includes deaths from drugs, medicines, other solid and liquid substances, and gases and vapors. Excludes poisonings from spoiled foods.

	Total	Change from 2013	Death rate[a]
Deaths	6,200	+11%	1.9

Age	0-4	5-14	15-24	25-44	45-64	65-74	75+
Death Rate[b]	0.1	(c)	1.4	3.6	2.8	0.6	0.5
Deaths	10	10	610	2,990	2,340	150	90

Drowning

Includes drownings of people swimming or playing in water, or falling into water, except on home premises or at work. Excludes drownings involving boats, which are included in water transportation.

	Total	Change from 2013	Death rate[a]
Deaths	2,400	+9%	0.8

Age	0-4	5-14	15-24	25-44	45-64	65-74	75+
Death Rate[b]	0.9	0.5	1.0	0.7	0.8	0.7	0.7
Deaths	180	190	450	600	650	190	140

See footnotes on page 151.

Type of event and age of victim

Choking

Includes deaths from unintentional ingestion or inhalation of food or other objects resulting in the obstruction of respiratory passages.

	Total	Change from 2013	Death rate[a]
Deaths	2,300	-8%	0.7

Age	0-4	5-14	15-24	25-44	45-64	65-74	75+
Deaths	20	20	10	80	350	340	1,480

Railroad

Includes deaths arising from railroad vehicles in motion (except involving motor vehicles), subway and elevated trains, and people boarding or alighting from standing trains. Excludes crews and people traveling in the course of employment.

	Total	Change from 2013	Death rate[a]
Deaths	400	0%	0.1

Age	0-4	5-14	15-24	25-44	45-64	65-74	75+
Deaths	0	10	90	140	140	10	10

Water transport

Includes deaths in water transport incidents from falls, burns, etc., as well as drownings. Excludes crews and people traveling in the course of employment.

	Total	Change from 2013	Death rate[a]
Deaths	300	0%	0.1

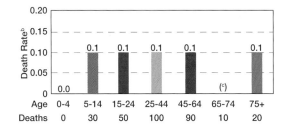

Age	0-4	5-14	15-24	25-44	45-64	65-74	75+
Deaths	0	30	50	100	90	10	20

Air transport

Includes deaths in private flying, passengers in commercial aviation, and deaths of military personnel in the United States. Excludes crews and people traveling in the course of employment.

	Total	Change from 2013	Death rate[a]
Deaths	300	0%	0.1

Age	0-4	5-14	15-24	25-44	45-64	65-74	75+
Deaths	0	20	20	70	130	40	20

All other public

Most important types included are mechanical suffocation; excessive natural heat or cold; firearms; fires, flames, or smoke; and machinery.

	Total	Change from 2013	Death rate[a]
Deaths	6,300	+9%	2.0

Age	0-4	5-14	15-24	25-44	45-64	65-74	75+
Deaths	90	100	360	990	1,840	630	2,290

[a]Deaths per 100,000 population.
[b]Deaths per 100,000 population in each age group.
[c]Rate less than 0.05.

■ *Weather-related deaths down 7% in 2014*

A debris flow/mudslide in rural northwestern Washington State resulting in 43 fatalities was the most deadly weather related event in 2014 (see page 34 for more information on disaster deaths). Overall, deaths in 2014 are down 7% from 2013. A variety of weather events resulted in 546 deaths in the United States in 2014, compared with 586 deaths in 2013. Snow, ice, and winter weather accounted for 24% of the deaths, temperature extremes for 13%, while avalanches and debris flows/mudslides accounted for 12%. Typical levels of weather

related deaths have occurred from 2012 through 2014 compared to 2011, which experienced a total of 1,012 deaths dominated by 587 tornado related deaths.

Data on weather-related deaths were compiled by the National Climatic Data Center (NCDC), which is part of the National Oceanic and Atmospheric Administration. NCDC data may differ from data based on death certificates that appear elsewhere in *Injury Facts*.

Weather-related deaths, United States, 2014

Event	Total	Jan.	Feb.	March	April	May	June	July	Aug.	Sept.	Oct.	Nov.	Dec.
Total	546	91	68	71	60	29	38	50	26	16	17	38	42
Snow, ice, winter weather	130	45	39	7	2	0	1	0	0	0	0	29	7
Temperature extremes	69	32	9	1	0	1	5	11	5	0	1	1	3
Avalanche and Debris flow/mudslide	68	2	11	48	0	4	0	0	0	0	0	1	2
Thunderstorm/high winds	66	2	5	7	3	4	9	10	4	1	7	4	10
Ocean/lake surf/rip current	62	5	0	6	7	7	5	13	5	4	4	2	4
Tornado	49	0	0	0	37	0	2	4	0	0	1	0	5
Flood	41	2	3	0	9	4	9	0	4	8	2	0	0
Lightning	27	0	0	0	0	6	3	9	5	3	1	0	0
Precipitation	25	0	1	1	2	1	4	1	3	0	0	1	11
Wildfire	5	0	0	1	0	2	0	1	0	0	1	0	0
Dust storm	4	3	0	0	0	0	0	1	0	0	0	0	0

Source: National Safety Council analysis of National Climatic Data Center data.

Weather-related fatalities by month, United States, 2014

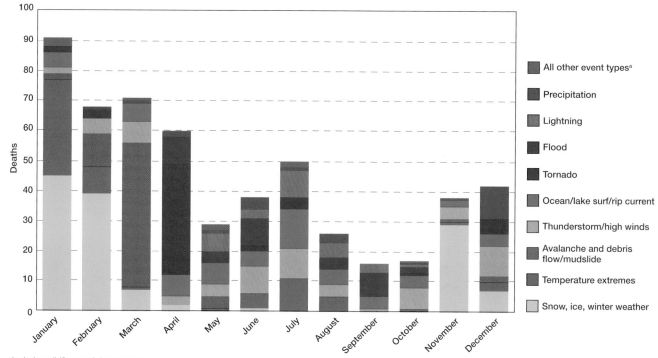

Includes wildfires and dust storms.

Cost of Sports and Consumer Product Injuries

A recent study using emergency department data collected by the Consumer Product Safety Commission provides cost estimates for non-fatal injuries involving consumer products. The study analyzing National Electronic Injury Surveillance System data from 2008 through 2010 found that three product groups (sports and recreation; home structures and construction materials; and home furnishings and fixtures) accounted for 77% of the $909 billion annual costs (2009 dollars). The $909 billion includes: medical, work losses, pain and suffering, product liability, insurance administration, and litigation costs. The average cost per incident is estimated to be $63,490 overall, and ranges by major product group from $34,606 for non-powered housewares injuries to $71,473 for yard and garden equipment injuries. The charts below list the top 10 most expensive product/activity related injuries by both total annual costs and per-incident costs.

Source: Lawrence, B., Spicer, S., & Miller, T. (2015). A fresh look at the costs of non-fatal consumer product injuries. Injury Prevention, 21, 23-29.

Top 10 most expensive product/activity related injuries by average cost per incident, 2009-2010 (2009 dollars)

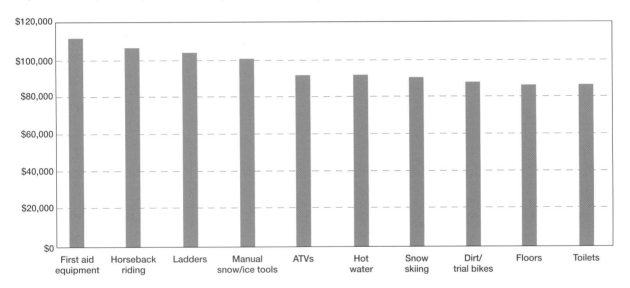

Top 10 most expensive product/activity related injuries by annual total cost, 2009-2010 (2009 dollars)

■ *In the United States in 2014, basketball and bicycle riding injuries each resulted in more than half a million emergency department visits.*

The table below shows estimates of the number of injuries treated in hospital emergency departments associated with various sports and recreational activities. Because this list of sports is not complete and the frequency and duration of participation is not known, no inference should be made concerning the relative hazard of these sports or rank with respect to risk of injury. Since currently available sports participation estimates do not provide a valid estimate of exposure risk, they are inappropriate for use in rate calculations. Because of this limitation, they are not included in the table below.

Sport injuries, United States, 2014

Sport or activity	Injuries	Percent of injuries by age				
		Younger than 5	5-14	15-24	25-64	65 or older
Archery	3,948	2.0	16.9	19.1	50.2	11.9
Baseball	130,376	2.9	49.4	29.4	17.5	0.8
Softball	95,465	0.1	31.4	33.1	33.8	1.6
Basketball	522,817	0.4	34.3	47.0	18.1	0.2
Bicycle riding[a]	502,104	4.5	33.8	17.2	38.3	6.2
Billiards, pool	3,500	15.7	14.1	9.1	57.9	3.2
Bowling	16,613	9.1	13.8	15.5	45.0	16.6
Boxing	16,673	0.1	8.8	43.7	46.8	0.6
Cheerleading	35,894	0.2	49.7	48.5	1.5	0.0
Exercise[b]	368,904	1.6	12.0	19.3	54.9	12.2
Fishing	66,290	3.7	17.8	16.2	51.6	10.7
Football	396,457	0.4	50.6	40.0	8.9	0.1
Golf[c]	30,047	3.5	13.2	6.6	40.0	36.6
Gymnastics[d]	34,550	1.8	75.9	19.8	2.4	0.1
Hockey, field	5,782	1.7	35.8	49.2	13.3	0.0
Horseback riding	50,688	1.0	20.4	23.0	47.7	7.9
Horseshoe pitching[e]	1,449	5.4	6.9	12.4	64.7	10.6
Ice hockey	17,627	0.1	36.9	42.0	20.6	0.4
Ice skating[f]	20,127	1.5	45.7	19.5	30.0	3.3
Martial arts	30,043	0.4	31.7	28.7	38.6	0.6
Mountain biking	8,822	0.0	5.5	18.7	74.1	1.8
Mountain climbing	5,395	0.3	8.2	40.0	49.9	1.6
Racquetball, squash & paddleball	3,375	2.2	6.4	21.7	61.0	8.7
Roller skating[g]	66,601	1.1	56.4	11.3	30.0	1.1
Rugby	11,925	0.0	6.8	74.7	18.5	0.0
Scuba diving	1,220	1.3	10.8	21.2	65.4	1.3
Skateboarding	119,760	0.8	34.0	49.7	15.4	0.1
Snowboarding	31,847	0.4	23.2	51.3	25.1	0.0
Snowmobiling	6,641	1.2	2.5	24.5	70.1	1.6
Soccer	239,943	1.1	43.7	38.8	16.4	0.0
Swimming[h]	179,188	9.6	42.4	16.1	26.5	5.4
Tennis	19,800	0.3	14.3	19.2	36.3	30.0
Track & field	29,484	0.0	39.5	43.5	16.3	0.7
Volleyball	52,548	0.1	36.0	41.9	21.4	0.6
Water skiing	4,807	0.0	9.8	40.1	50.1	0.0
Weight lifting	100,904	2.5	7.7	32.8	53.6	3.5
Wrestling	39,700	0.0	41.8	53.3	5.0	0.0

Source: Consumer Product Safety Commission; figures include only injuries treated in hospital emergency departments.
[a]*Excludes mountain biking.*
[b]*Includes exercise equipment (62,665 injuries) and exercise activity (306,239 injuries).*
[c]*Excludes golf carts (15,225 injuries).*
[d]*Excludes trampolines (104,691 injuries).*
[e]*Data for 2013.*
[f]*Excludes 5,247 injuries in skating, unspecified.*
[g]*Includes roller skating (54,796 injuries) and in-line skating (11,805 injuries).*
[h]*Includes injuries associated with swimming, swimming pools, diving or diving boards, and swimming pool equipment.*

Injuries Associated with Consumer Products

■ *More than 1.5 million injury-related emergency department visits each year are associated with floors or flooring materials.*

The following list of items found in and around the home was selected from the Consumer Product Safety Commission's National Electronic Injury Surveillance System (NEISS) for 2014. NEISS estimates are calculated from a statistically representative sample of hospitals in the United States. Injury totals represent estimates of the number of hospital emergency department-treated cases nationwide associated with various products. However, product involvement may or may not be the cause of the injury.

Consumer product-related injuries treated in hospital emergency departments, 2014
(excluding most sports and sports equipment; also see page 154)

Description	Injuries
Home workshop equipment	
Saws (hand or power)	77,921
Tools, not specified	29,968
Hammers	28,340
Workshop grinders, buffers, or polishers	22,352
Packaging or containers, household	
Household containers and packaging	221,924
Bottles and jars	72,073
Bags	57,862
Paper products	28,941
Housewares	
Knives	378,182
Tableware and flatware (excluding knives)	96,446
Drinking glasses	69,219
Waste containers, trash baskets, etc.	42,046
Manual cleaning equipment (excluding buckets)	35,515
Cookware, bowls and canisters	33,509
Slicers and choppers	25,490
Scissors	25,363
Home furnishing, fixtures, or accessories	
Beds	710,118
Chairs	370,902
Tables, n.e.c.[a]	321,884
Bathtubs and showers	315,098
Household cabinets, racks, & shelves	290,998
Sofas, couches, davenports, divans, etc.	196,613
Rugs and carpets	185,102
Ladders	180,575
Other furniture[b]	114,300
Toilets	112,412
Stools	60,411
Miscellaneous decorating items	40,619
Benches	39,888
Sinks	29,107
Mirrors or mirror glass	24,943
Home structures or construction materials	
Floors or flooring materials	1,591,440
Stairs or steps	1,202,299
Ceilings and walls	355,881
Other doors[c]	290,337
Porches, balconies, open-side floors	149,998
Nails, screws, tacks or bolts	120,629
Fences or fence posts	117,830
Windows	103,143
Door sills or frames	63,043
Counters or countertops	55,236
Handrails, railings or banisters	52,021
Poles	43,453
Glass doors	27,247
General household appliances	
Refrigerators	41,426
Ranges or ovens, not specified	32,086
Heating, cooling, or ventilating equipment	
Pipes (excluding smoking pipes)	29,909

Description	Injuries
Home communication or entertainment equipment	
Televisions	47,732
Computers (equipment & electronic games)	28,422
Telephones or telephone accessories	27,003
Personal use items	
Footwear	198,443
Jewelry	101,992
Daywear	82,382
Razors and shavers	55,042
Other clothing[d]	49,803
Coins	36,965
Desk supplies	29,453
Luggage	28,448
Hair grooming equipment & accessories	24,660
Yard and garden equipment	
Lawn mowers	81,108
Manual snow or ice removal tools	48,817
Pruning, trimming & edging equipment	46,607
Other unpowered garden tools[e]	29,818
Chainsaws	29,687
Sports and recreation	
Bicycles	510,905
Skateboards	119,760
Trampolines	104,691
Swimming pools	87,887
Monkey bars or other playground climbing equipment	79,935
Aquariums and other pet supplies	67,017
Dancing	57,149
Scooters (unpowered)	55,975
Minibikes or trailbikes	54,784
Swings or swing sets	52,257
Slides or sliding boards	50,108
Other playground equipment[f]	48,883
Miscellaneous products	
Carts	53,074
Hot water	39,932
Elevators, escalators, moving walks	24,007
Household chemicals	
Detergents	27,687
Soaps (excl. laundry soaps or detergents)	23,660
Bleaches (noncosmetic)	21,321

Source: U.S. Consumer Product Safety Commission, National Electronic Injury Surveillance System, Product Summary Report, All Products, CY2014.
Note: Products are listed above if the estimate was greater than 21,300 cases. "n.e.c." = not elsewhere classified.
[a]Excludes baby changing tables (3,725 injuries), billiard or pool tables (3,500 injuries), and television tables or stands (11,892 injuries).
[b]Excludes household cabinets, racks, shelves, desks, bureaus, chests, buffets, etc. (290,998 injuries).
[c]Excludes glass doors (27,247 injuries) and garage doors (13,750 injuries).
[d]Excludes costumes or mask (1,217 injuries); day wear (82,382 injuries); footwear (198,443 injuries); nightwear (5,740 injuries); and outerwear (7,117 injuries).
[e]Includes cultivators, hoes, pitchforks, rakes, shovels, spades, and trowels.
[f]Excludes monkey bars (79,935 injuries), see-saws (3,782 injuries), slides (50,108 injuries), and swings (52,257 injuries).

Overall, passenger transportation incidents account for about 2 out of 10 unintentional-injury-related deaths. But the risk of death for the passenger, expressed on a per-mile basis, varies greatly by transportation mode. Highway travel by personal vehicle presents the greatest risk; air, rail, and bus travel have much lower death rates. The tables below show the latest information on passenger transportation deaths and death rates.

In recognition of the current use of vans, sport utility vehicles (SUVs), pickups, and other light trucks as passenger vehicles, the Federal Highway Administration (FHWA) reclassified these vehicles and passenger automobiles as "light duty vehicles" beginning in 2009. Because the data for 2007 and 2008 also meet the requirements of the new FHWA methodology, they are presented with the data for later years in the table below. The statistics for light duty vehicles shown in the tables below represent all use of such vehicles, both intercity and local. The bus data also include intercity and local (transit) bus travel. Railroad includes both intercity (Amtrak) and local commuting travel. Scheduled airlines includes both large airlines and commuter airlines, but excludes on-demand air taxis and charter operations. In comparing the four modes, drivers of light duty vehicles (except taxis) are considered passengers. Bus drivers and airline or railroad crews are not considered passengers.

Other comparisons are possibly based on passenger trips, vehicle miles, or vehicle trips, but passenger miles is the most commonly used basis for comparing the safety of various modes of travel.

Transportation incident death rates, 2011-2013

Mode of transportation	2013			2011-2013 average death rate
	Passenger deaths	Passenger miles (billions)	Deaths per 100,000,000 passenger miles	
Light duty vehicles[a]	21,127	4,471.9	0.47	0.48
Buses[b]	28	62.3	0.04	0.05
Transit buses	0	22.3	0.00	0.01
Intercity buses	13	40.0	0.03	0.05
Railroad passenger trains[c]	6	21.7	0.03	0.03
Scheduled airlines[d]	5	578.7	0.001	< 0.001

Source: Highway passenger deaths – Fatality Analysis Reporting System data. Railroad passenger deaths and miles – Federal Railroad Administration. Airline passenger deaths – National Transportation Safety Board. Airline passenger miles – Bureau of Transportation Statistics. Passenger miles for transit buses – American Public Transit Association. All other figures – National Safety Council estimates.
[a]Includes passenger cars, light trucks, vans, and SUVs regardless of wheelbase. Includes taxi passengers. Drivers of light duty vehicles are considered passengers.
[b]Figures exclude school buses but include "other" and "unknown" bus types.
[c]Includes Amtrak and commuter rail service.
[d]Includes large airlines and scheduled commuter airlines; excludes charter, cargo, on-demand services, and suicide/sabotage.

Passenger deaths and death rates, United States, 2007-2013

Year	Light duty vehicles[a]		Buses		Railroad passenger trains		Scheduled airlines	
	Deaths	Rate[b]	Deaths	Rate[b]	Deaths	Rate[b]	Deaths	Rate[b]
2007	29,075	0.66	18	0.03	5	0.03	0	0.00
2008	25,457	0.59	50	0.08	24	0.13	0	0.00
2009	23,441	0.53	21	0.04	3	0.02	49	0.01
2010	22,271	0.50	28	0.05	3	0.02	0	0.00
2011	21,221	0.48	35	0.06	6	0.03	0	0.00
2012	21,669	0.49	25	0.04	5	0.02	0	0.00
2013	21,127	0.47	28	0.04	6	0.03	5	0.001

Source: See table above.
[a]Includes passenger cars, light trucks, vans, and SUVs regardless of wheelbase. Includes taxi passengers. Drivers of light duty vehicles are considered passengers.
[b]Deaths per 100,000,000 passenger miles.

Passenger death rates, United States, 2011-2013

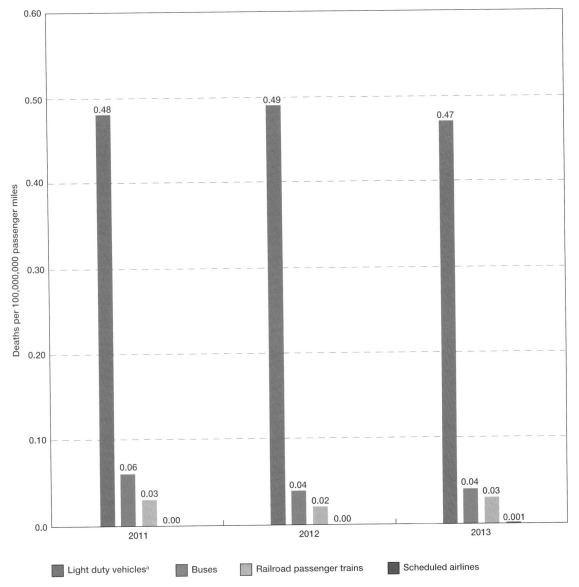

■ Light duty vehicles[a]   ■ Buses   ■ Railroad passenger trains   ■ Scheduled airlines

[a]With the exception of taxi drivers, drivers of these vehicles are considered passengers.

The total number of incidents involving United States registered civil aviation decreased slightly from 1,294 in 2013 to a preliminary estimate of 1,287 in 2014. However, large airlines experienced an increase in the number of incidents from 19 in 2013 to 27 in 2014. Please note that the three fatalities resulting from the crash of Asiana Airlines flight 214 are not included below because the carrier is not registered in the United States.

U.S. civil aviation incidents, deaths, and death rates, 2009-2014

| | Incidents | | | Incident rates | | | |
| | | | | Per 100,000 flight hours | | Per million miles flown | |
Year	Total	Fatal	Total deaths[a]	Total	Fatal	Total	Fatal
Large airlines[b]							
2009	26	1	50	0.151	0.006	0.0036	0.0001
2010	28	0	0	0.162	0	0.0038	0
2011	28	0	0	0.160	0	0.0037	0
2012	27	0	0	0.156	0	0.0036	0
2013	19	0	0	0.11	0	0.0025	0
2014	27	0	0	0.157	0	0.0036	0
Commuter airlines[b]							
2009	2	0	0	0.646	0	0.0441	0
2010	6	0	0	1.907	0	0.1250	0
2011	4	0	0	1.228	0	0.0821	0
2012	4	0	0	1.250	0	0.0808	0
2013	7	2	5	2.183	0.624	0.1418	0.0405
2014	4	0	0	1.145	0	0.0748	0
On-demand air taxis[b]							
2009	47	2	17	1.62	0.07	—	—
2010	30	6	17	0.96	0.19	—	—
2011	50	16	41	—	—	—	—
2012	36	8	12	1.02	0.23	—	—
2013	44	10	25	1.30	0.30	—	—
2014	35	8	20	1.02	0.23	—	—
General aviation[b]							
2009[c]	1,480	275	479	7.08	1.32	—	—
2010[c]	1,440	271	458	6.63	1.24	—	—
2011[c]	1,470	269	452	—	—	—	—
2012[c]	1,470	272	437	7.04	1.30	—	—
2013[c]	1,224	222	391	6.26	1.12	—	—
2014[c]	1,221	253	419	6.74	1.40	—	—

Source: National Transportation Safety Board: 2014 preliminary, 2009-2013 revised; exposure data for rates from the Federal Aviation Administration (FAA). Also note that the 2011 exposure estimates are not currently available. The FAA is engaged in re-calibration efforts. Note: Dash (–) indicates data not available.
[a]*Includes passengers, crew members, and others such as people on the ground.*
[b]*Civil aviation incident statistics collected by the National Transportation Safety Board are classified according to federal air regulations under which the flights were made. The classifications are (1) large airlines operating scheduled service under Title 14, Code of Federal Regulations, part 121 (14 CFR 121); (2) commuter carriers operating scheduled service under 14 CFR 135; (3) unscheduled, "on-demand" air taxis under 14 CFR 135; and (4) "general aviation," which includes incidents involving aircraft flown under rules other than 14 CFR 121 and 14 CFR 135. Not shown in the table is nonscheduled air carrier operations under 14 CFR 121 that experienced (4 incidents/2 fatalities) in 2009, (3/2) in 2010, (3/0) in 2011, (0/0) in 2012, (4/9) in 2013, and (1/0) in 2014. Since 1997, "large airlines" includes aircraft with 10 or more seats, formerly operated as commuter carriers under 14 CFR 135.*
[c]*Suicide/sabotage/terrorism and stolen/unauthorized cases are included in incident and fatality totals but excluded from rates –General Aviation, 2009 (3/0), 2010 (3/2), 2011 (1/0), 2012 (1/1), 2013 (3/3), and 2014 (0/0).*

Civil aviation incidence rates, United States, 1991-2014

Railroad deaths totaled 805 in 2014, an increase of 14% from the 2013 revised total of 707 and also 4% higher than the 2005-2013 average of 772. From 2013 to 2014, there was a 16% increase in fatalities at highway-rail crossings, and a 13% increase in fatalities involving other types of incidents. The latter included 501 deaths, or 94%, to trespassers. Ten employees were killed while on duty, a 23% decrease compared to the 2013 death toll and 41% lower than the 2005-2013 average. Deaths to passengers on trains totaled five, marginally lower than the 2013 total of six deaths and 29% lower than the 2005-2013 average.

The ratio of railroad-related deaths to nonfatal injuries and illnesses is approximately 1:11. In 2014, railroad incidents resulted in 8,471 cases of nonfatal conditions, compared to 8,712 in 2013 and the 2005-2013 average of 8,783. Ten percent of the total, 843, was attributed to highway-rail-crossing incidents, down 13% from the 2013 total of 972 and was 14% lower than the 2005-2013 average of 977. Of the 4,421 nonfatal occupational railroad injuries and illnesses reported in 2014, 1% was attributed to highway-rail-crossing incidents.

Deaths and nonfatal cases in railroad incidents, United States, 2005-2014

Year	Total	Highway rail-crossing incident?		Occurring in other than highway-rail crossing incident		Employees on duty		Passengers on trains[a]	
						At highway-rail crossing?		At highway-rail crossing?	
		Yes	No	Trespassers	Others	Yes	No	Yes	No
Deaths									
2005	884	359	525	458	67	2	23	0	16
2006	903	369	534	511	23	4	12	0	2
2007	851	339	512	470	42	1	16	0	5
2008	804	290	514	457	57	3	23	0	24
2009	695	248	447	416	31	0	16	0	3
2010	734	261	473	440	33	0	20	0	3
2011	691	250	441	405	36	6	15	4	2
2012	677	230	447	413	34	1	15	0	5
2013	707	232	475	432	43	1	13	0	6
2014	805	270	535	501	34	0	10	0	5
Nonfatal conditions									
2005	9,550	1,053	8,497	420	8,077	111	5,711	33	924
2006	8,797	1,070	7,727	481	7,246	96	5,179	95	841
2007	9,669	1,059	8,610	407	8,203	105	5,357	72	1,444
2008	9,062	990	8,072	432	7,640	75	4,925	101	1,231
2009	8,023	743	7,280	344	6,936	72	4,432	61	1,130
2010	8,377	888	7,489	390	7,099	80	4,331	114	1,255
2011	8,425	1,045	7,380	367	7,013	71	4,155	245	1,329
2012	8,429	972	7,457	411	7,046	76	3,903	181	1,397
2013	8,712	972	7,740	431	7,309	84	4,227	108	1,563
2014	8,471	843	7,628	414	7,214	53	4,368	72	1,284

Source: Federal Railroad Administration.
[a]Passenger cases include all circumstances, including getting on/off standing trains, stumbling aboard trains, assaults, train incidents, crossing incidents, etc.

Casualties at public and private highway-rail crossings, United States, 2005-2014

Year	Deaths				Nonfatal conditions			
	Total	Motor vehicle-related	Pedestrians	Others	Total	Motor vehicle-related	Pedestrians	Others
2005	359	284	58	17	1,053	1,006	37	10
2006	369	305	53	11	1,070	1,035	29	6
2007	339	265	59	15	1,059	1,018	32	9
2008	290	221	64	5	990	923	54	13
2009	248	182	59	7	743	697	38	8
2010	261	168	81	12	888	820	49	19
2011	250	169	70	11	1,045	984	43	18
2012	230	163	56	11	972	913	41	18
2013	232	161	55	16	972	899	50	23
2014	270	169	84	17	843	766	57	20

Source: Federal Railroad Administration.

Unintentional Fatal Poisonings

■ *Poisoning deaths were up 7% from 2012 to 2013.*

Deaths from unintentional poisoning numbered 38,851 in 2013, the latest year for which data are available. The death rate per 100,000 population was 12.3. Males are at greatest risk, with a death rate of 16.1 compared with 8.6 for females. Total poisoning deaths increased 7% from 36,332 in 2012 and are more than 1.6 times the 2005 total. See pages 52-55 for long-term trends.

Thirty-nine percent of the poisoning deaths were classified in the "narcotics and psychodysleptics (hallucinogens), not elsewhere classified," category, which includes prescription narcotic analgesics and illegal drugs such as cocaine, heroin, cannabinol, and LSD.

A National Safety Council analysis of National Center for Health Statistics mortality data shows that the greatest number of poisoning deaths in 2013 was due to prescription drug overdoses, accounting for 17,058 deaths or nearly 44% of all unintentional poisoning deaths. Since 1999, total unintentional drug deaths have increased 219% while unintentional prescription drug deaths have increased 287% (see top graph on opposite page). The three drug categories associated with the fastest unintentional fatality increases are prescription opioids,

heroin, and benzodiazepines. Unintentional deaths associated with these drugs have increased 365%, 354%, and 736% since 1999, respectively (see bottom graph on opposite page). In 2014 prescription opioids were involved in 13,486 unintentional deaths or 79% of all unintentional prescription drug deaths while benzodiazepines were involved in 5,663 deaths or 33% of unintentional prescription drug deaths. Please note that prescription opioids and benzodiazepines are often combined and can both be listed in association with a death.

Deaths due to alcohol poisoning increased over 3% from 2012 and totaled 2,244 in 2013. Alcohol poisoning deaths for males outnumbered those for females by more than 3 to 1. The number of alcohol poisoning deaths among males increased by 0.9% from 2012 to 2013, while the number for females increased 10%. It should be noted that alcohol also may be present in combination with other drugs.

Carbon monoxide poisoning is included in the category of "other gases and vapors." Additional information on human poisoning exposure cases may be found on pages 162 and 191.

Unintentional poisoning deaths by type, age, and sex, United States, 2013

Type of poison	All ages	Younger than 5	5-14 years	15-19 years	20-24 years	25-44 years	45-64 years	65 or older
Both sexes								
Total poisoning deaths	**38,851**	**35**	**30**	**587**	**2,706**	**16,625**	**17,039**	**1,829**
Deaths per 100,000 population	*12.3*	*0.2*	*0.1*	*2.8*	*11.9*	*20.0*	*20.5*	*4.1*
Total drug-related poisoning deaths	35,663	24	14	536	2,572	15,540	15,513	1,464
Nonopioid analgesics, antipyretics, and antirheumatics (X40)[a]	*233*	*2*	*0*	*2*	*6*	*86*	*102*	*35*
Antiepileptic, sedative-hypnotic, antiparkinsonism, and psychotropic drugs, n.e.c. (X41)	*2,909*	*6*	*0*	*36*	*136*	*1,072*	*1,537*	*122*
Narcotics and psychodysleptics (hallucinogens), n.e.c. (X42)	*15,241*	*9*	*7*	*253*	*1,381*	*6,903*	*6,260*	*428*
Other drugs acting on the autonomic nervous system (X43)	*24*	*0*	*0*	*1*	*0*	*6*	*15*	*2*
Other and unspecified drugs, medicaments, and biological substances (X44)	*17,256*	*7*	*7*	*244*	*1,049*	*7,473*	*7,599*	*877*
Alcohol (X45)	2,244	0	3	30	72	737	1,236	166
Organic solvents and halogenated hydrocarbons and their vapors (X46)	51	0	0	2	3	19	23	4
Other gases and vapors (X47)	702	8	13	12	42	267	206	154
Pesticides (X48)	5	0	0	0	1	0	1	3
Other and unspecified chemical and noxious substances (X49)	186	3	0	7	16	62	60	38
Males								
Total poisoning deaths	**25,080**	**22**	**15**	**423**	**2,012**	**11,236**	**10,370**	**1,002**
Deaths per 100,000 population	*16.1*	*0.2*	*0.1*	*3.9*	*17.2*	*26.9*	*25.6*	*5.1*
Total drug-related poisoning deaths	22,708	13	8	390	1,912	10,424	9,209	752
Nonopioid analgesics, antipyretics, and antirheumatics (X40)	*104*	*2*	*0*	*0*	*3*	*44*	*47*	*8*
Antiepileptic, sedative-hypnotic, antiparkinsonism, and psychotropic drugs, n.e.c. (X41)	*1,910*	*3*	*0*	*20*	*98*	*735*	*981*	*73*
Narcotics and psychodysleptics (hallucinogens), n.e.c. (X42)	*10,885*	*6*	*4*	*191*	*1,054*	*5,101*	*4,237*	*292*
Other drugs acting on the autonomic nervous system (X43)	*15*	*0*	*0*	*1*	*0*	*5*	*8*	*1*
Other and unspecified drugs, medicaments, and biological substances (X44)	*9,794*	*2*	*4*	*178*	*757*	*4,539*	*3,936*	*378*
Alcohol (X45)	1,688	0	0	18	52	563	932	123
Organic solvents and halogenated hydrocarbons and their vapors (X46)	42	0	0	2	3	14	20	3
Other gases and vapors (X47)	516	6	7	7	32	191	172	101
Pesticides (X48)	4	0	0	0	1	0	1	2
Other and unspecified chemical and noxious substances (X49)	122	3	0	6	12	44	36	21
Females								
Total poisoning deaths	**13,771**	**13**	**15**	**164**	**694**	**5,389**	**6,669**	**827**
Deaths per 100,000 population	*8.6*	*0.1*	*0.1*	*1.6*	*6.2*	*13.0*	*15.7*	*3.3*
Total drug-related poisoning deaths	12,955	11	6	146	660	5,116	6,304	712
Nonopioid analgesics, antipyretics, and antirheumatics (X40)	*129*	*0*	*0*	*2*	*3*	*42*	*55*	*27*
Antiepileptic, sedative-hypnotic, antiparkinsonism, and psychotropic drugs, n.e.c. (X41)	*999*	*3*	*0*	*16*	*38*	*337*	*556*	*49*
Narcotics and psychodysleptics (hallucinogens), n.e.c. (X42)	*4,356*	*3*	*3*	*62*	*327*	*1,802*	*2,023*	*136*
Other drugs acting on the autonomic nervous system (X43)	*9*	*0*	*0*	*0*	*0*	*1*	*7*	*1*
Other and unspecified drugs, medicaments, and biological substances (X44)	*7,462*	*5*	*3*	*66*	*292*	*2,934*	*3,663*	*499*
Alcohol (X45)	556	0	3	12	20	174	304	43
Organic solvents and halogenated hydrocarbons and their vapors (X46)	9	0	0	0	0	5	3	1
Other gases and vapors (X47)	186	2	6	5	10	76	34	53
Pesticides (X48)	1	0	0	0	0	0	0	1
Other and unspecified chemical and noxious substances (X49)	64	0	0	1	4	18	24	17

Source: National Safety Council tabulations of National Center for Health Statistics–Mortality Data for 2013, as compiled from data provided by the 57 vital statistics jurisdictions through the Vital Statistics Cooperative Program.
Note: "n.e.c." means "not elsewhere classified."
[a]Numbers following titles refer to external cause of injury and poisoning classifications in ICD-10.

Unintentional poisoning deaths, United States, 1996-2013

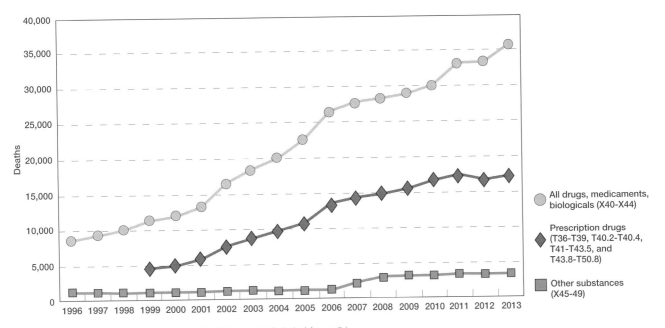

Note: Classification system changed in 1999 (see the Technical Appendix).

Unintentional poisoning deaths by selected drugs, United States, 1999-2013

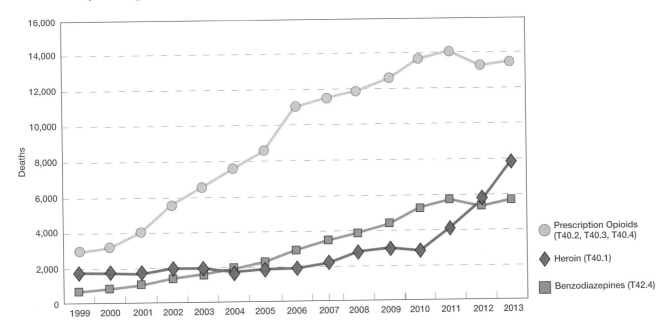

Note: Deaths by drug type are not mutually exclusive, deaths involving multiple drugs are included in the count of each drug.

Fatal Versus Nonfatal Unintentional Poisoning

Most people think of poisoning as a childhood issue. That is true for poisoning exposures, but not for nonfatal and fatal poisonings. The pie charts below show the distribution of poisoning exposures, nonfatal poisonings, and fatal poisonings by age groups. The poisoning exposure data are from the American Association of Poison Control Centers and represent the calls received by poison control centers. The nonfatal data represent emergency department visits, while the fatality data are from death certificates.

Nonfatal exposures occur predominantly among young children, whereas nonfatal and fatal poisonings are overwhelmingly among adults. While 46% of the poisoning exposures involve children four or younger, over 88% of the nonfatal poisonings and 98% of the fatalities occur among adults older than 19.

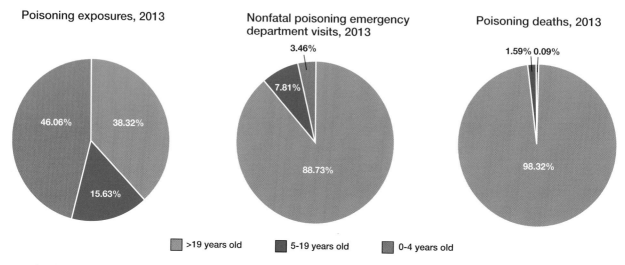

Poisoning exposures, 2013
46.06% · 38.32% · 15.63%

Nonfatal poisoning emergency department visits, 2013
3.46% · 7.81% · 88.73%

Poisoning deaths, 2013
1.59% · 0.09% · 98.32%

Legend: >19 years old · 5-19 years old · 0-4 years old

Nonfatal poisonings increased 8.5% in 2013 and now account for more than one million emergency department visits a year. Fatal poisonings continue to increase, showing a nearly 7% increase from 2012. The charts below illustrate the trends for both categories of poisonings starting in 2002.

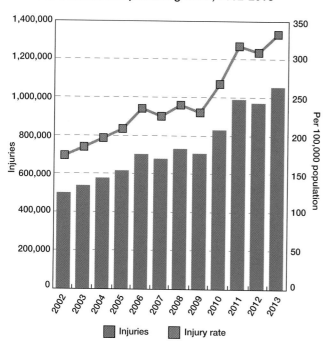

Nonfatal unintentional poisoning trend, 2002-2013

Legend: Injuries · Injury rate

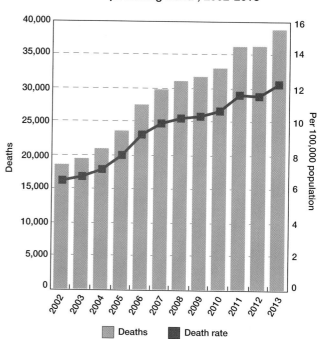

Fatal unintentional poisoning trend[a], 2002-2013

Legend: Deaths · Death rate

Source: Centers for Disease Control and Prevention, NEISS-AIP Source: Centers for Disease Control and Prevention, WISQARS
[a]2013 is the latest official data available. National Safety Council estimates for 2014 are available on pages 53 and 55.

The impact of unintentional falls on the older adult population has been highlighted in numerous editions of *Injury Facts®* (2010-2015, 2008, 2007, etc.).

A recent Center for Disease Control and Prevention (CDC) study assessing the cost-benefit analysis of three older adult fall prevention programs identified a positive return on investment for all three programs. Otago Exercise Program, Tai Chi: Moving for Better Balance, and Stepping On demonstrated that the cost of decreased direct medical costs was greater than the costs associated with implementing the program. Two of these programs, Tai Chi: Moving for Better Balance and Otago Exercise Program, that are delivered to persons aged 80 and older both resulted in return on investments greater than 100%. A similar study found that adults who consistently participate in exercise programs such as EnhanceFitness can reduce their risk of experiencing a medically treated fall by 20 to 30%. EnhancedFitness is an evidence-based community-based group exercise intervention funded by CDC.

Looking at 2013, 25,464 fatalities occurred among adults age 65 or older. From 1999 to 2013, the number of fall-related deaths among individuals 65 or older has increased 152%, while the population death rate has increased 96%. At this same time, the number of fall deaths among individuals younger than 65 increased 55% and the death rate increased 40% (see chart below).

As reported in the 2014 edition of *Injury Facts®*, it is likely that a substantial proportion of the increase in older adult fall deaths is a result of improved death certificate coding and that the more recent estimates more accurately reflect the full extent of the problem.

Source: Greenwood-Hickman, M.A., Rosenberg, D.E., Phelan, E.A., & Fitzpatrick A.L. (2015). *Participation in older adult physical activity programs and risk for falls requiring medical care, Washington State, 2005-2011.* Preventing Chronic Disease, 12: 140574.
Carande-Kulis, V., Stevens, J.A., Florence, C.S., Beattie, B.L., & Aria, I. (2015). *A cost-benefit analysis of three older adult fall prevention interventions.* Journal of Safety Research, 52 (2015) 65-70.

Fall deaths and death rates, United States, 1999-2013

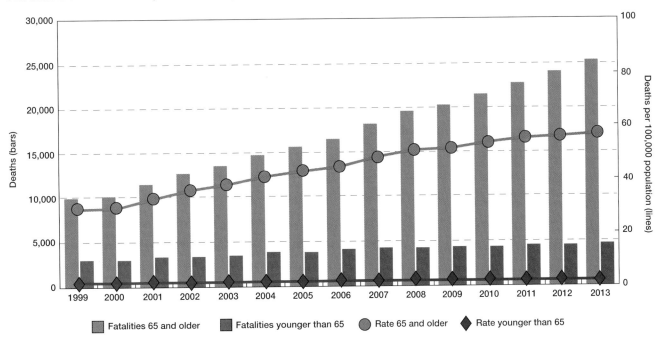

Source: National Safety Council tabulations of National Center for Health Statistics data.

The National Fire Protection Association reports that home structure fire deaths have decreased 47% from 5,200 in 1980 to 2,755 deaths in 2013. However, home fire deaths in 2013 are up 16% from the record low deaths of 2,380 in 2012. As shown in the graph below, nearly all major causes of home fires have decreased since 1980. Fires caused by smoking materials decreased by 73%, heating equipment related fires decreased 60%, electrical distribution or lighting equipment fires decreased 42%, and fires resulting from playing with the heat source have decreased by nearly 91%. The only major cause of home fire deaths that has increased is candle related fires, up 125%.

Civilian deaths resulting from home structure fires, by major cause and year, 1980-2011

Note: Fire data from 1999-2001 are not provided because of data quality limitations.

Young children under five years of age and adults starting at age 50 are over represented by the number of home fire related deaths compared to their representation in the population. For example, while children under five represent 7% of the U.S. population, they account for 8% of the home fire deaths.

Similarly, the 50 to 64 age group represents 18% of the population, but fully 25% of home fire deaths and 20% of the non-fatal injuries. Please see the figure below for additional details.

Percent of home structure fire deaths and injuries by age group, United States, 2007-2011

Smoke inhalation contributes to more home fire deaths than actual burns. From 2007 through 2011, 40% of home fire deaths resulted from smoke inhalation, while only 5% of the deaths resulted from thermal burns only. An additional 46% of home fire deaths resulted from the combination of burns and smoke inhalation.

Source: Ahrens, M. (October 2014). Characteristics of home fire victims. Quincy, MA: National Fire Protection Association.

Pedalcycles

The estimated number of deaths from collisions between pedalcycles and motor vehicles increased from about 750 in 1940 to 1,200 in 1980, and then declined to about 1,000 in 2014.

In 2013, 623 pedalcyclists died in motor vehicle crashes and 302 in other incidents, according to National Center for Health Statistics mortality data. Males accounted for 87% of all pedalcycle deaths, nearly 7 times the female fatalities.

Emergency department-treated injuries associated with bicycles and bicycle accessories were estimated to total 531,340 in 2013 and 510,905 in 2014, according to the Consumer Product Safety Commission (also see page 155).

A meta-analysis of bicycle helmet efficacy by Attewell, Glase, and McFadden (2001) estimated that bicycle helmets reduce the risk of head injury by 60% and brain injury by 58%. As of July 2015, 21 states, the District of Columbia, and more than 201 localities had bicycle helmet-use laws, according to the Bicycle Helmet Safety Institute.

Source: National Safety Council estimates and tabulations of National Center for Health Statistics mortality data obtained via WISQARS at www.cdc.gov/injury/wisqars/index.html. Population data for rates are from the U.S. Census Bureau. Data from Bicycle Helmet Safety Institute was retrieved July 31, 2015, from www.bhsi.org.

Attewell, R.G., Glase, K., & McFadden, M. (2001). Bicycle helmet efficacy: A meta-analysis. Accident Analysis & Prevention, Vol. 33, No. 3, pp. 345-352.

Pedalcycle deaths and death rates by sex and age group, United States, 2013

Source: National Safety Council tabulations based on U.S. Census Bureau and National Center for Health Statistics data.

Pedalcycle fatalities by month, United States, 2013

Source: National Safety Council tabulations of National Center for Health Statistics data.

The leading risks for unintentional injury vary with age and are different for deaths and nonfatal injuries. The tables here and on the next page list, for eight age groups, the five leading causes of unintentional-injury-related deaths and the five leading causes of hospital emergency department visits, which is one measure of nonfatal injuries.

For all ages, the five leading causes account for 86% of all unintentional-injury-related deaths and 72% of unintentional-injury-related emergency department visits. Only motor-vehicle crashes and falls are common to both lists. Motor-vehicle crashes rank second for unintentional-injury-related deaths and fourth for unintentional-injury-related emergency department visits. Falls rank third for unintentional-injury-related deaths and first for emergency department unintentional-injury-related visits.

The five leading causes of unintentional-injury-related deaths account for between 82% and 94% of such deaths depending on the age group. The leading causes of unintentional-injury-related emergency department visits account for between 68% and 89% of such hospital visits.

For deaths, poisoning; motor-vehicle crashes; falls; fire, flames, or smoke; and drowning are most often among the top five, with choking, firearms, and mechanical suffocation sometimes included. For emergency department visits, falls, struck by or against, overexertion, motor-vehicle occupant injuries, and cut or pierce injuries are most often in the top five. In the younger age groups, bites and stings (except dog bites), foreign body injuries, and struck by or against are among the leading risks.

Leading unintentional-injury risks, all ages, United States, 2013

| Rank | Unintentional-injury-related deaths | | | | Emergency department unintentional-injury-related visits | | | |
	Event	Number	Percent	Rate[a]	Event	Number	Percent	Rate[a]
—	Total	130,557	100.0%	41.3	Total	28,649,449	100.0%	9,063
1	Poisoning	38,851	29.8%	12.3	Falls	8,771,656	30.6%	2,775
2	Motor vehicle crashes	35,369	27.1%	11.2	Struck by or against	4,214,125	14.7%	1,333
3	Falls	30,208	23.1%	9.6	Overexertion	3,256,567	11.4%	1,030
4	Choking[b]	4,864	3.7%	1.5	Motor vehicle occupant	2,462,684	8.6%	779
5	Drowning	3,391	2.6%	1.1	Cut or pierce	2,077,775	7.3%	657

Leading unintentional-injury risks, young children (ages 0-4), United States, 2013

| Rank | Unintentional-injury-related deaths | | | | Emergency department unintentional-injury-related visits | | | |
	Event	Number	Percent	Rate[a]	Event	Number	Percent	Rate[a]
—	Total	2,472	100.0%	12.4	Total	2,209,910	100.0%	11,123
1	Mechanical suffocation	1,007	40.7%	5.1	Falls	987,114	44.7%	4,968
2	Motor vehicle crashes	493	19.9%	2.5	Struck by or against	365,703	16.5%	1,841
3	Drowning	416	16.8%	2.1	Bite or sting (except dog)	170,773	7.7%	860
4	Fire, flames, or smoke	145	5.9%	0.7	Foreign body	150,247	6.8%	756
5	Choking[b]	133	5.4%	0.7	Cut or pierce	90,714	4.1%	457

Leading unintentional-injury risks, children and young adolescents (ages 5-14), United States, 2013

| Rank | Unintentional-injury-related deaths | | | | Emergency department unintentional-injury-related visits | | | |
	Event	Number	Percent	Rate[a]	Event	Number	Percent	Rate[a]
—	Total	1,521	100.0%	3.7	Total	3,733,722	100.0%	9,058
1	Motor vehicle crashes	852	56.0%	2.1	Falls	1,183,067	31.7%	2,870
2	Drowning	209	13.7%	0.5	Struck by or against	965,213	25.9%	2,342
3	Fire, flames, or smoke	135	8.9%	0.3	Overexertion	388,282	10.4%	942
4	Mechanical suffocation	54	3.6%	0.1	Cut or pierce	226,918	6.1%	550
5	Firearms	39	2.6%	0.1	Pedalcyclist	172,823	4.6%	419

Leading unintentional-injury risks, teens (ages 15-19), United States, 2013

| Rank | Unintentional-injury-related deaths | | | | Emergency department unintentional-injury-related visits | | | |
	Event	Number	Percent	Rate[a]	Event	Number	Percent	Rate[a]
—	Total	3,652	100.0%	17.3	Total	2,358,715	100.0%	11,148
1	Motor vehicle crashes	2,408	65.9%	11.4	Struck by or against	530,301	22.5%	2,506
2	Poisoning	587	16.1%	2.8	Falls	408,054	17.3%	1,929
3	Drowning	241	6.6%	1.1	Overexertion	360,680	15.3%	1,705
4	Falls	62	1.7%	0.3	Motor vehicle occupant	263,871	11.2%	1,247
5	Firearms	55	1.5%	0.3	Cut or pierce	180,602	7.7%	854

See footnotes on page 167.

Risks by Age Group (cont.)

Leading unintentional-injury risks, young adults (ages 20-24), United States, 2013

Rank	Unintentional-injury-related deaths				Emergency department unintentional-injury-related visits			
	Event	Number	Percent	Rate[a]	Event	Number	Percent	Rate[a]
—	Total	7,967	100.0%	34.9	Total	2,453,120	100.0%	10,761
1	Motor vehicle crashes	4,284	53.8%	18.8	Falls	406,774	16.6%	1,784
2	Poisoning	2,706	34.0%	11.9	Struck by or against	375,358	15.3%	1,647
3	Drowning	260	3.3%	1.1	Motor vehicle occupant	363,694	14.8%	1,595
4	Falls	143	1.8%	0.6	Overexertion	312,266	12.7%	1,370
5	Fire, flames, or smoke	84	1.1%	0.4	Cut or pierce	251,089	10.2%	1,101

Leading unintentional-injury risks, adults (ages 25-44), United States, 2013

Rank	Unintentional-injury-related deaths				Emergency department unintentional-injury-related visits			
	Event	Number	Percent	Rate[a]	Event	Number	Percent	Rate[a]
—	Total	31,563	100.0%	37.9	Total	7,616,892	100.0%	9,144
1	Poisoning	16,625	52.7%	20.0	Falls	1,446,442	19.0%	1,736
2	Motor vehicle crashes	10,567	33.5%	12.7	Overexertion	1,169,167	15.3%	1,404
3	Falls	827	2.6%	1.0	Struck by or against	1,043,429	13.7%	1,253
4	Drowning	791	2.5%	0.9	Motor vehicle occupant	900,534	11.8%	1,081
5	Fire, flames, or smoke	354	1.1%	0.4	Cut or pierce	699,966	9.2%	840

Leading unintentional-injury risks, adults (ages 45-64), United States, 2013

Rank	Unintentional-injury-related deaths				Emergency department unintentional-injury-related visits			
	Event	Number	Percent	Rate[a]	Event	Number	Percent	Rate[a]
—	Total	37,414	100.0%	45.0	Total	6,322,620	100.0%	7,610
1	Poisoning	17,039	45.5%	20.5	Falls	1,844,392	29.2%	2,220
2	Motor vehicle crashes	10,030	26.8%	12.1	Overexertion	727,240	11.5%	875
3	Falls	3,649	9.8%	4.4	Struck by or against	652,772	10.3%	786
4	Choking[b]	940	2.5%	1.1	Motor vehicle occupant	571,090	9.0%	687
5	Fire, flames, or smoke	922	2.5%	1.1	Cut or pierce	471,793	7.5%	568

Leading unintentional-injury risks, older adults (ages 65-74), United States, 2013

Rank	Unintentional-injury-related deaths				Emergency department unintentional-injury-related visits			
	Event	Number	Percent	Rate[a]	Event	Number	Percent	Rate[a]
—	Total	10,967	100.0%	43.5	Total	1,637,905	100.0%	6,495
1	Falls	3,586	32.7%	14.2	Falls	804,304	49.1%	3,190
2	Motor vehicle crashes	3,066	28.0%	12.2	Struck by or against	141,939	8.7%	563
3	Poisoning	1,238	11.3%	4.9	Motor vehicle occupant	119,985	7.3%	476
4	Choking[b]	742	6.8%	2.9	Overexertion	119,727	7.3%	475
5	Fire, flames, or smoke	412	3.8%	1.6	Cut or pierce	102,018	6.2%	405

Leading unintentional-injury risks, elderly (age 75 or older), United States, 2013

Rank	Unintentional-injury-related deaths				Emergency department unintentional-injury-related visits			
	Event	Number	Percent	Rate[a]	Event	Number	Percent	Rate[a]
—	Total	35,001	100.0%	179.6	Total	2,313,622	100.0%	11,872
1	Falls	21,880	62.5%	112.3	Falls	1,691,093	73.1%	8,678
2	Motor vehicle crashes	3,669	10.5%	18.8	Struck by or against	139,340	6.0%	715
3	Choking[b]	2,751	7.9%	14.1	Overexertion	92,565	4.0%	475
4	Fire, flames, or smoke	655	1.9%	3.4	Motor vehicle occupant	77,662	3.4%	399
5	Poisoning	591	1.7%	3.0	Cut or pierce	54,675	2.4%	281

Source: National Safety Council analysis of National Center for Health Statistics—Mortality Data for 2013, as compiled from data provided by the 57 vital statistics jurisdictions through the Vital Statistics Cooperative Program. Rates are National Safety Council estimates based on data from the National Center for Health Statistics and the U.S. Census Bureau. Emergency department data are from NEISS-AIP.
[a]*Deaths or emergency department visits per 100,000 population.*
[b]*Inhalation and ingestion of food or other object obstructing breathing.*

■ *Unintentional firearms-related deaths were down more than 8% in 2013.*

Firearms-related deaths from unintentional, intentional, and undetermined causes totaled 33,677 in 2013, an increase of less than 1% from 33,630 in 2012. Suicides accounted for 62.9% of deaths related to firearms while 33.3% were homicides and 1.5% unintentional deaths. Males dominated all categories of deaths related to firearms and accounted for 86% of the total.

The number of homicide deaths related to firearms decreased by 3.7% from 2012 to 2013 following an increase of 5.4% from 2011 to 2012. Unintentional deaths related to firearms decreased by 7.7% in 2013. Suicide deaths related to firearms increased by 2.5% from 2012 to 2013, marking the seventh consecutive annual increase.

Hospital emergency department surveillance data[a] indicate an estimated 16,864 nonfatal unintentional firearms-related injuries occurred in 2013. Assault was related to an estimated 62,220[b] nonfatal injuries, while the estimated total for intentionally self-inflicted nonfatal injuries was 3,991[b].

[a]*Source: National Center for Injury Prevention and Control injury surveillance data using WISQARS from www.cdc.gov/injury/wisqars/nonfatal.html.*
[b]*Estimate is unstable because of small sample size and should be used with caution.*

Deaths involving firearms by age and sex, United States, 2013

Type and sex	All ages	Younger than 5	5-14 years	15-19 years	20-24 years	25-44 years	45-64 years	65-74 years	75 or older
Total firearms deaths	**33,677**	**82**	**327**	**2,057**	**4,130**	**11,563**	**9,927**	**2,840**	**2,751**
Male	28,831	57	246	1,847	3,651	9,894	8,161	2,461	2,514
Female	4,846	25	81	210	479	1,669	1,766	379	237
Unintentional	**506**	**30**	**39**	**55**	**53**	**130**	**139**	**35**	**25**
Male	441	24	31	51	49	113	118	34	21
Female	65	6	8	4	4	17	21	1	4
Suicide	**21,190**	**—**	**138**	**740**	**1,471**	**5,850**	**7,873**	**2,557**	**2,561**
Male	18,254	—	116	650	1,288	4,955	6,574	2,268	2,403
Female	2,936	—	22	90	183	895	1,299	289	158
Homicide	**11,230**	**51**	**142**	**1,217**	**2,490**	**5,223**	**1,738**	**223**	**146**
Male	9,466	32	93	1,104	2,210	4,500	1,315	140	72
Female	1,764	19	49	113	280	723	423	83	74
Legal intervention	**469**	**0**	**1**	**19**	**78**	**251**	**106**	**10**	**4**
Male	448	0	1	18	77	243	96	9	4
Female	21	0	0	1	1	8	10	1	0
Undetermined[a]	**282**	**1**	**7**	**26**	**38**	**109**	**71**	**15**	**15**
Male	222	1	5	24	27	83	58	10	14
Female	60	0	2	2	11	26	13	5	1

Source: National Safety Council tabulation of National Center for Health Statistics–Mortality Data for 2013, as compiled from data provided by the 57 vital statistics jurisdictions through the Vital Statistics Cooperative Program.
Note: Dashes (–) indicate category not applicable.
[a]*Undetermined means the intentionality of the deaths (unintentional, homicide, suicide) was not determined.*

Firearms deaths by intentionality, United States, 1999-2013

Home and Community, 1987-2014

Principal types of home and community unintentional-injury-related deaths, United States, 1987-2014

Year	Total home and community[a]	Falls	Drowning	Poisoning	Choking[b]	Fire, flames, or smoke	Firearms	Mechanical suffocation	Air transport	Water transport	Rail transport[c]	Other
1987	39,800	10,300	3,900	4,900	3,600	4,400	1,400	(d)	900	800	400	9,200
1988	41,100	10,700	3,800	5,700	3,700	4,600	1,400	(d)	700	800	400	9,300
1989	40,700	10,800	3,700	5,900	3,500	4,400	1,400	(d)	800	700	400	9,100
1990	38,900	11,000	3,700	5,400	3,300	3,800	1,300	(d)	700	800	400	8,500
1991	39,700	11,400	3,700	6,000	3,100	3,800	1,400	(d)	700	700	500	8,400
1992	43,000	12,100	3,400	6,900	3,100	3,900	1,400	(d)	700	700	600	10,200
1993	45,800	12,500	3,700	8,400	3,200	3,900	1,500	(d)	600	700	600	10,700
1994	45,900	12,800	3,300	8,900	3,100	3,900	1,300	(d)	600	600	600	10,800
1995	47,300	13,400	3,700	9,000	3,100	3,700	1,200	(d)	600	700	500	11,400
1996	48,500	14,300	3,400	9,400	3,200	3,700	1,100	(d)	700	600	500	11,600
1997	49,400	14,700	3,500	10,100	3,200	3,400	1,000	(d)	500	600	400	12,000
1998	51,600	15,500	3,900	10,700	3,500	3,100	900	(d)	500	600	500	12,400
1999[e]	52,700	12,400	3,500	12,100	3,900	3,200	900	1,600	500	600	400	13,600
2000	51,900	12,600	3,400	12,700	4,300	2,900	800	1,300	500	500	400	12,500
2001	55,000	14,200	3,300	14,000	4,100	3,200	800	1,400	700	500	400	12,400
2002	58,700	15,600	3,400	17,500	4,100	3,100	700	1,400	500	500	400	11,500
2003	61,800	16,600	3,200	19,300	4,300	3,200	700	1,300	600	500	400	11,700
2004	64,200	18,000	3,300	20,900	4,400	3,100	600	1,400	400	500	400	11,200
2005	69,600	18,800	3,500	23,500	4,400	3,100	(d)	1,500	400	500	400	13,500
2006	73,300	20,000	3,500	27,400	4,400	3,000	(d)	1,600	400	400	400	12,200
2007	77,200	21,800	3,400	29,700	4,300	3,200	(d)	1,600	400	400	400	12,000
2008	79,700	23,300	3,400	31,000	4,400	2,800	(d)	1,700	400	300	400	12,000
2009	79,800	24,200	3,400	31,700	4,400	2,700	(d)	1,500	400	400	300	10,800
2010	83,200	25,400	3,700	32,900	4,500	2,700	(d)	1,600	300	300	400	11,400
2011	88,800	26,800	3,500	36,100	4,700	2,600	(d)	1,600	300	500	300	12,400
2012	89,400	28,000	3,500	36,200	4,700	2,700	(d)	1,600	300	400	300	11,700
2013[f]	93,000	29,500	3,300	38,800	4,900	2,600	(d)	1,700	300	300	400	11,200
2014[g]	98,600	31,300	3,400	41,900	4,800	2,600	(d)	1,700	300	300	400	11,900

Source: National Safety Council estimates based on data from National Center for Health Statistics and state vital statistics departments. The Council adopted the Bureau of Labor Statistics' Census of Fatal Occupational Injuries count for work-related unintentional injuries retroactive to 1992 data. Because of the lower work class total resulting from this change, several thousand unintentional-injury-related deaths that had been classified by the Council as work-related had to be reassigned to the home and public classes. For this reason, long-term historical comparisons for these three classes should be made with caution. See the Technical Appendix for an explanation of the methodological changes.

[a] Includes some deaths not shown separately.
[b] Inhalation and ingestion of food or other object that obstructs breathing.
[c] Includes subways and elevateds.
[d] Estimates for both home and public are not available.
[e] In 1999, a revision was made in the International Classification of Diseases. See the Technical Appendix for comparability with earlier years.
[f] Revised.
[g] Preliminary.

Leading types of home and community unintentional-injury-related deaths, United States, 2001-2014

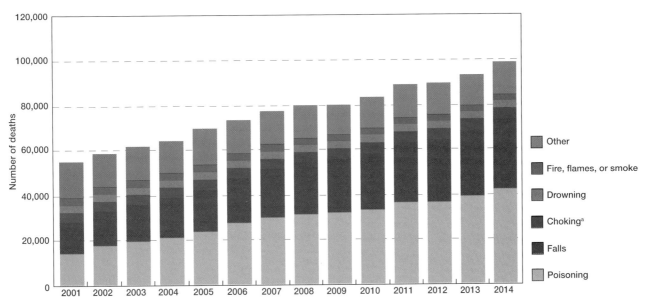

[a] Inhalation and ingestion of food or other object that obstructs breathing.

State Data

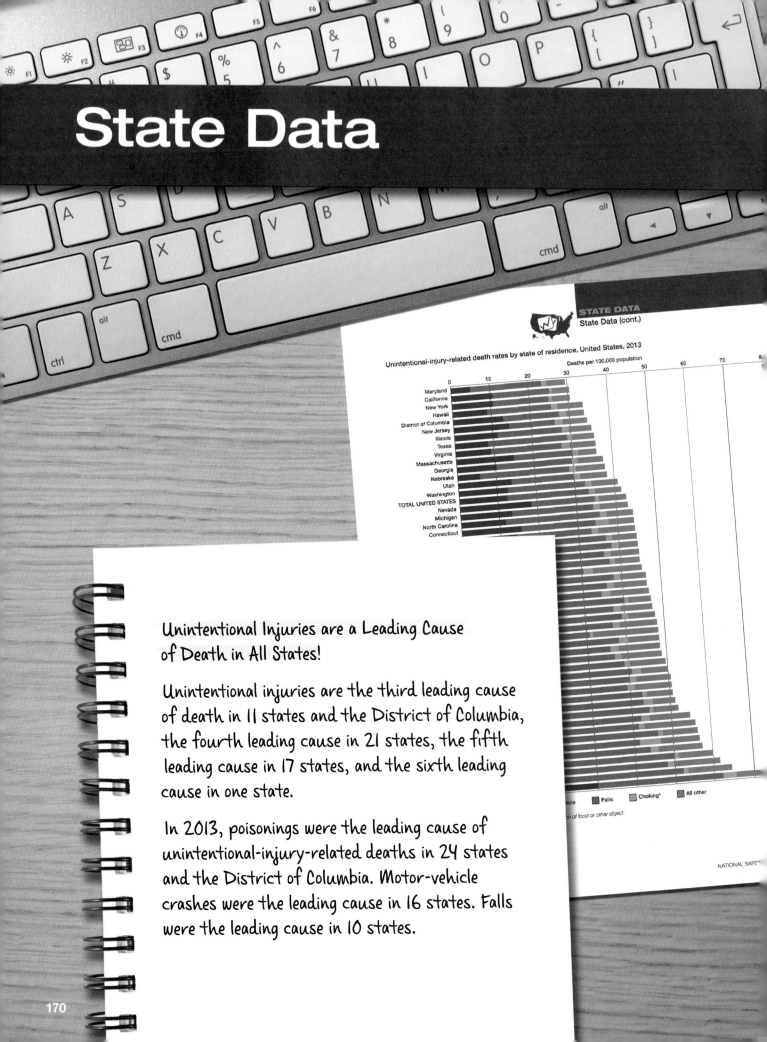

Unintentional-injury-related death rates by state of residence, United States, 2013

Deaths per 100,000 population

Maryland
California
New York
Hawaii
District of Columbia
New Jersey
Illinois
Texas
Virginia
Massachusetts
Georgia
Nebraska
Utah
Washington
TOTAL UNITED STATES
Nevada
Michigan
North Carolina
Connecticut

Falls   Choking*   All other

...n of food or other object.

NATIONAL SAFE...

Unintentional Injuries are a Leading Cause of Death in All States!

Unintentional injuries are the third leading cause of death in 11 states and the District of Columbia, the fourth leading cause in 21 states, the fifth leading cause in 17 states, and the sixth leading cause in one state.

In 2013, poisonings were the leading cause of unintentional-injury-related deaths in 24 states and the District of Columbia. Motor-vehicle crashes were the leading cause in 16 states. Falls were the leading cause in 10 states.

National Safety Council

■ *Poisonings are the leading cause of unintentional-injury-related deaths in 24 states and the District of Columbia.*

This section on state-level data includes data for occupational and motor vehicle injuries, as well as general injury mortality.

Death rates by state of residence for unintentional injuries can vary greatly from one type of injury to the next and from state to state. The graph on the next page shows for each state the death rates (per 100,000 population) for total unintentional-injury-related deaths and the four leading types of unintentional-injury-related deaths nationally – poisonings, motor vehicle crashes, falls, and choking (inhalation or ingestion of food or other object that obstructs breathing).

The map on page 174 shows graphically the overall unintentional-injury-related death rates by state of residence. Rates by region were lowest in Middle Atlantic and highest in East South Central states.

The charts on pages 175-177 show the total unintentional-injury-related deaths by state of residence and where unintentional injuries rank as a cause of death in each state, as well as the five leading causes of unintentional-injury-related deaths in each state.

Unintentional injuries as a whole are the fourth leading cause of death in the United States and in 21 states. Unintentional injuries are the third leading cause of death in 11 states and the District of Columbia, the fifth leading cause in 17 states, and the sixth leading cause in one state.

In 2013, poisonings were the leading cause of unintentional-injury-related deaths in 24 states and the District of Columbia. Motor vehicle crashes were the leading cause in 16 states. Falls were the leading cause in 10 states.

The second leading cause of unintentional-injury-related deaths was motor vehicle crashes in 19 states, while poisoning was the second leading cause in 16 states. Falls were second in 15 states and the District of Columbia.

The most common third leading cause of unintentional-injury-related deaths was falls, in 25 states, while motor vehicle crashes were the third leading cause in 15 states and the District of Columbia. Poisoning ranked third in 10 states.

Choking was the fourth leading cause of unintentional-injury-related deaths in 38 states and the District of Columbia, while the fourth ranking cause was drowning in nine states; natural heat or cold was the fourth ranked in Arizona; mechanical suffocation was fourth in South Dakota; air transportation was fourth in Alaska; and fire, flames or smoke was fourth in Oklahoma.

Fire, flames or smoke was the fifth leading unintentional-injury-related cause of death in 23 states. Drowning was fifth in 18 states and choking ranked fifth in eight states. Natural heat and cold was fifth ranked in the District of Columbia and Nevada, mechanical suffocation was fifth in Wyoming, and struck by or against was fifth in North Dakota.

The table on pages 178-179 shows the number of unintentional-injury-related deaths by state of occurrence for the 15 most common types of injury events. State populations also are shown to facilitate computation of detailed death rates.

The table on page 180 consists of a four-year state-by-state comparison of unintentional-injury-related deaths by state of residence and death rates for 2010 through 2013.

Page 181 shows fatal occupational injuries by state and counts of deaths for some of the principal types of events – transportation incidents, assaults or violent acts, contact with objects or equipment, falls, exposure to harmful substances or environments, and fires or explosions.

Nonfatal occupational injury and illness incidence rates for most states are shown in the table on page 182 and graphically in the map on page 183. States not shown do not have state occupational safety and health plans.

Pages 184 and 185 show motor vehicle-related deaths and death rates by state both in tables and maps. The maps show death rates based on population, vehicle miles traveled, and registered vehicles.

Unintentional-injury-related death rates by state of residence, United States, 2013

Deaths per 100,000 population

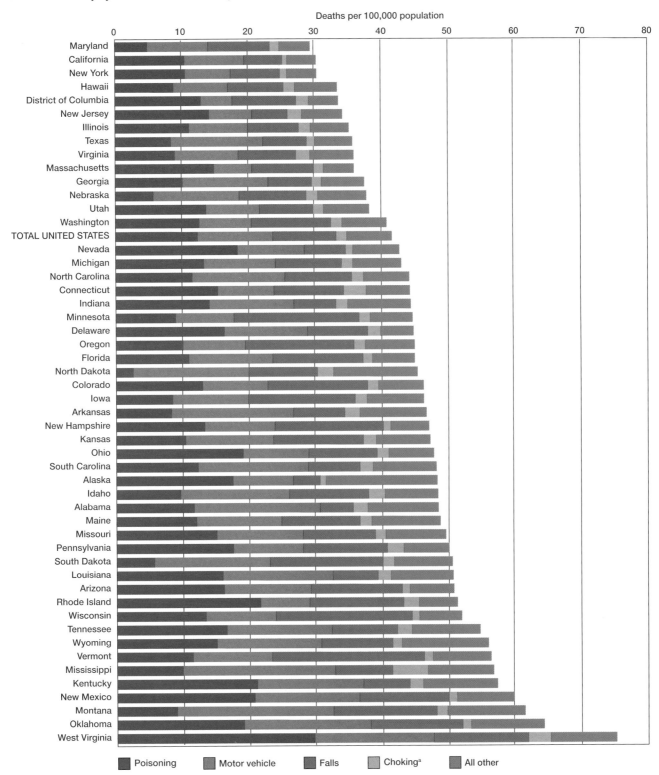

Poisoning Motor vehicle Falls Choking[a] All other

[a]Suffocation by ingestion or inhalation of food or other object.

Unintentional-Injury-Related Death Rates by State

Untentional-injury-related deaths per 100,000 population by state, 2013

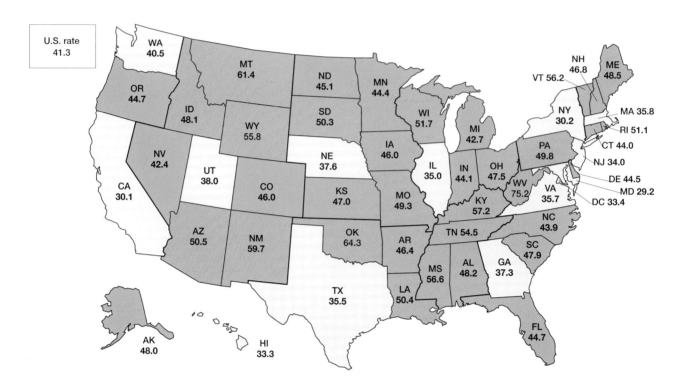

U.S. rate
41.3

WA 40.5

MT 61.4

ND 45.1

MN 44.4

OR 44.7

ID 48.1

WY 55.8

SD 50.3

WI 51.7

NH 46.8

VT 56.2

ME 48.5

NV 42.4

UT 38.0

NE 37.6

IA 46.0

MI 42.7

NY 30.2

MA 35.8

RI 51.1

CA 30.1

CO 46.0

KS 47.0

IL 35.0

IN 44.1

OH 47.5

PA 49.8

CT 44.0

NJ 34.0

WV 75.2

VA 35.7

DE 44.5

MD 29.2

DC 33.4

AZ 50.5

NM 59.7

OK 64.3

MO 49.3

KY 57.2

NC 43.9

AR 46.4

TN 54.5

SC 47.9

MS 56.6

AL 48.2

GA 37.3

TX 35.5

LA 50.4

FL 44.7

AK 48.0

HI 33.3

REGIONAL RATES

NEW ENGLAND (CT, ME, MA, NH, RI, VT)	41.9
MIDDLE ATLANTIC (NJ, NY, PA)	37.1
EAST NORTH CENTRAL (IL, IN, MI, OH, WI)	43.1
WEST NORTH CENTRAL (IA, KS, MN, MO, NE, ND, SD)	46.1
SOUTH ATLANTIC (DE, DC, FL, GA, MD, NC, SC, VA, WV)	41.7
EAST SOUTH CENTRAL (AL, KY, MS, TN)	53.7
WEST SOUTH CENTRAL (AR, LA, OK, TX)	41.1
MOUNTAIN (AZ, CO, ID, MT, NV, NM, UT, WY)	48.2
PACIFIC (AK, CA, HI, OR, WA)	33.0

☐ Below 35.1 — 6 states and District of Columbia

☐ 35.1 to 41.3 — 7 states

Below or at national average

▨ 41.4 to 48.0 — 18 states

▨ Above 48.0 — 19 states

Above national average

Source: National Safety Council analysis of National Center for Health Statistics–Mortality Data for 2013, as compiled from data provided by the 57 vital statistics jurisdictions through the Vital Statistics Cooperative Program. Rates are National Safety Council estimates based on data from the National Center for Health Statistics and the U.S. Census Bureau.

Unintentional-Injury-Related Deaths by State

The following series of tables is a state-by-state ranking of the five leading causes of deaths due to unintentional injuries based on 2013 data. The data are classified by state of residence. The first line of each section gives the rank of unintentional-injury-related deaths among all causes of death, the total number of unintentional-injury-related deaths, and the rate of unintentional-injury-related deaths per 100,000 population in the state. The following lines list the five leading types of unintentional-injury-related deaths in the state, along with the number and rate for each type.

2013

UNITED STATES

Rank	Cause	Deaths	Rate
4	All unintentional injuries	130,557	41.3
1	Poisoning[a]	38,851	12.3
2	Motor vehicle	35,369	11.2
3	Falls	30,208	9.6
4	Choking[b]	4,864	1.5
5	Drowning[c]	3,391	1.1

ALABAMA

Rank	Cause	Deaths	Rate
5	All unintentional injuries	2,329	48.2
1	Motor vehicle	909	18.8
2	Poisoning[a]	561	11.6
3	Falls	242	5.0
4	Choking[b]	102	2.1
5	Fire, flames or smoke	84	1.7

ALASKA

Rank	Cause	Deaths	Rate
3	All unintentional injuries	353	48.0
1	Poisoning[a]	128	17.4
2	Motor vehicle	66	9.0
3	Falls	30	4.1
4	Air transportation	22	3.0
5	Drowning[c]	21	2.9

ARIZONA

Rank	Cause	Deaths	Rate
3	All unintentional injuries	3,349	50.5
1	Poisoning[a]	1,063	16.0
2	Falls	906	13.7
3	Motor vehicle	859	13.0
4	Natural heat or cold	86	1.3
5	Drowning[c]	75	1.1

ARKANSAS

Rank	Cause	Deaths	Rate
5	All unintentional injuries	1,373	46.4
1	Motor vehicle	537	18.1
2	Poisoning[a]	246	8.3
3	Falls	229	7.7
4	Choking[b]	66	2.2
5	Drowning[c]	52	1.8

CALIFORNIA

Rank	Cause	Deaths	Rate
6	All unintentional injuries	11,538	30.1
1	Poisoning[a]	4,015	10.5
2	Motor vehicle	3,375	8.8
3	Falls	2,208	5.8
4	Drowning[c]	405	1.1
5	Choking[b]	259	0.7

COLORADO

Rank	Cause	Deaths	Rate
3	All unintentional injuries	2,422	46.0
1	Falls	792	15.0
2	Poisoning[a]	681	12.9
3	Motor vehicle	510	9.7
4	Choking[b]	81	1.5
5	Drowning[c]	46	0.9

CONNECTICUT

Rank	Cause	Deaths	Rate
3	All unintentional injuries	1,582	44.0
1	Poisoning[a]	549	15.3
2	Falls	378	10.5
3	Motor vehicle	300	8.3
4	Choking[b]	120	3.3
5	Drowning[c]	42	1.2

DELAWARE

Rank	Cause	Deaths	Rate
4	All unintentional injuries	412	44.5
1	Poisoning[a]	150	16.2
2	Motor vehicle	115	12.4
3	Falls	84	9.1
4	Choking[b]	17	1.8
5	Fire, flames or smoke	11	1.2

DISTRICT OF COLUMBIA

Rank	Cause	Deaths	Rate
3	All unintentional injuries	216	33.4
1	Poisoning[a]	83	12.8
2	Falls	62	9.6
3	Motor vehicle	30	4.6
4	Choking[b]	12	1.9
5	Natural heat or cold	—	—

FLORIDA

Rank	Cause	Deaths	Rate
4	All unintentional injuries	8,736	44.7
1	Falls	2,664	13.6
2	Motor vehicle	2,437	12.5
3	Poisoning[a]	2,134	10.9
4	Drowning[c]	356	1.8
5	Choking[b]	261	1.3

GEORGIA

Rank	Cause	Deaths	Rate
4	All unintentional injuries	3,727	37.3
1	Motor vehicle	1,268	12.7
2	Poisoning[a]	1,011	10.1
3	Falls	659	6.6
4	Choking[b]	142	1.4
5	Fire, flames or smoke	134	1.3

HAWAII

Rank	Cause	Deaths	Rate
4	All unintentional injuries	467	33.3
1	Poisoning[a]	124	8.8
2	Falls	118	8.4
3	Motor vehicle	112	8.0
4	Drowning[c]	45	3.2
5	Choking[b]	23	1.6

IDAHO

Rank	Cause	Deaths	Rate
4	All unintentional injuries	776	48.1
1	Motor vehicle	261	16.2
2	Falls	192	11.9
3	Poisoning[a]	155	9.6
4	Choking[b]	38	2.4
5	Drowning[c]	21	1.3

ILLINOIS

Rank	Cause	Deaths	Rate
5	All unintentional injuries	4,511	35.0
1	Poisoning[a]	1,430	11.1
2	Motor vehicle	1,118	8.7
3	Falls	991	7.7
4	Choking[b]	222	1.7
5	Fire, flames or smoke	107	0.8

INDIANA

Rank	Cause	Deaths	Rate
5	All unintentional injuries	2,898	44.1
1	Poisoning[a]	919	14.0
2	Motor vehicle	828	12.6
3	Falls	418	6.4
4	Choking[b]	113	1.7
5	Fire, flames or smoke	88	1.3

IOWA

Rank	Cause	Deaths	Rate
4	All unintentional injuries	1,422	46.0
1	Falls	498	16.1
2	Motor vehicle	346	11.2
3	Poisoning[a]	262	8.5
4	Choking[b]	53	1.7
5	Drowning[c]	36	1.2

KANSAS

Rank	Cause	Deaths	Rate
4	All unintentional injuries	1,359	47.0
1	Falls	392	13.5
2	Motor vehicle	378	13.1
3	Poisoning[a]	300	10.4
4	Choking[b]	53	1.8
5	Drowning[c]	49	1.7

See source and footnotes on page 177.

2013

KENTUCKY

Rank	Cause	Deaths	Rate
4	All unintentional injuries	2,513	57.2
1	Poisoning[a]	921	21.0
2	Motor vehicle	696	15.8
3	Falls	306	7.0
4	Choking[b]	88	2.0
5	Fire, flames or smoke	77	1.8

LOUISIANA

Rank	Cause	Deaths	Rate
3	All unintentional injuries	2,333	50.4
1	Motor vehicle	761	16.5
2	Poisoning[a]	733	15.8
3	Falls	311	6.7
4	Choking[b]	89	1.9
5	Drowning[c]	70	1.5

MAINE

Rank	Cause	Deaths	Rate
4	All unintentional injuries	644	48.5
1	Motor vehicle	168	12.6
2	Poisoning[a]	159	12.0
3	Falls	157	11.8
4	Choking[b]	22	1.7
5	Fire, flames or smoke	15	1.1

MARYLAND

Rank	Cause	Deaths	Rate
5	All unintentional injuries	1,732	29.2
1	Falls	549	9.3
2	Motor vehicle	531	9.0
3	Poisoning[a]	293	4.9
4	Choking[b]	82	1.4
5	Fire, flames or smoke	55	0.9

MASSACHUSETTS

Rank	Cause	Deaths	Rate
4	All unintentional injuries	2,393	35.8
1	Poisoning[a]	990	14.8
2	Falls	625	9.3
3	Motor vehicle	375	5.6
4	Choking[b]	95	1.4
5	Drowning[c]	65	1.0

MICHIGAN

Rank	Cause	Deaths	Rate
5	All unintentional injuries	4,225	42.7
1	Poisoning[a]	1,305	13.2
2	Motor vehicle	1,053	10.6
3	Falls	991	10.0
4	Choking[b]	160	1.6
5	Fire, flames or smoke	119	1.2

MINNESOTA

Rank	Cause	Deaths	Rate
3	All unintentional injuries	2,405	44.4
1	Falls	1,022	18.9
2	Poisoning[a]	487	9.0
3	Motor vehicle	466	8.6
4	Choking[b]	86	1.6
5	Drowning[c]	39	0.7

MISSISSIPPI

Rank	Cause	Deaths	Rate
4	All unintentional injuries	1,692	56.6
1	Motor vehicle	681	22.8
2	Poisoning[a]	294	9.8
3	Falls	256	8.6
4	Choking[b]	159	5.3
5	Fire, flames or smoke	67	2.2

MISSOURI

Rank	Cause	Deaths	Rate
4	All unintentional injuries	2,981	49.3
1	Poisoning[a]	904	15.0
2	Motor vehicle	779	12.9
3	Falls	654	10.8
4	Choking[b]	90	1.5
5	Fire, flames or smoke	89	1.5

MONTANA

Rank	Cause	Deaths	Rate
4	All unintentional injuries	623	61.4
1	Motor vehicle	237	23.3
2	Falls	158	15.6
3	Poisoning[a]	91	9.0
4	Drowning[c]	17	1.7
5	Choking[b]	16	1.6

NEBRASKA

Rank	Cause	Deaths	Rate
5	All unintentional injuries	703	37.6
1	Motor vehicle	237	12.7
2	Falls	189	10.1
3	Poisoning[a]	108	5.8
4	Choking[b]	32	1.7
5	Fire, flames or smoke	18	1.0

NEVADA

Rank	Cause	Deaths	Rate
4	All unintentional injuries	1,184	42.4
1	Poisoning[a]	509	18.2
2	Motor vehicle	278	10.0
3	Falls	174	6.2
4	Drowning[c]	40	1.4
5	Natural heat or cold	38	1.4

NEW HAMPSHIRE

Rank	Cause	Deaths	Rate
4	All unintentional injuries	619	46.8
1	Falls	215	16.2
2	Poisoning[a]	175	13.2
3	Motor vehicle	138	10.4
4	Drowning[c]	16	1.2
5	Choking[b]	14	1.1

NEW JERSEY

Rank	Cause	Deaths	Rate
5	All unintentional injuries	3,028	34.0
1	Poisoning[a]	1,252	14.1
2	Motor vehicle	564	6.3
3	Falls	479	5.4
4	Choking[b]	187	2.1
5	Fire, flames or smoke	58	0.7

NEW MEXICO

Rank	Cause	Deaths	Rate
3	All unintentional injuries	1,245	59.7
1	Poisoning[a]	429	20.6
2	Motor vehicle	326	15.6
3	Falls	282	13.5
4	Choking[b]	25	1.2
4	Drowning[c]	25	1.2

NEW YORK

Rank	Cause	Deaths	Rate
5	All unintentional injuries	5,927	30.2
1	Poisoning[a]	2,069	10.5
2	Falls	1,462	7.4
3	Motor vehicle	1,316	6.7
4	Choking[b]	198	1.0
5	Fire, flames or smoke	146	0.7

NORTH CAROLINA

Rank	Cause	Deaths	Rate
5	All unintentional injuries	4,324	43.9
1	Motor vehicle	1,359	13.8
2	Poisoning[a]	1,129	11.5
3	Falls	994	10.1
4	Choking[b]	169	1.7
5	Drowning[c]	111	1.1

NORTH DAKOTA

Rank	Cause	Deaths	Rate
5	All unintentional injuries	326	45.1
1	Motor vehicle	124	17.1
2	Falls	75	10.4
3	Poisoning[a]	19	2.6
4	Choking[b]	17	2.4
5	Fire, flames or smoke	—	—
5	Struck by or against	—	—

See source and footnotes on page 177.

2013

OHIO

Rank	Cause	Deaths	Rate
5	All unintentional injuries	5,497	47.5
1	Poisoning[a]	2,192	18.9
2	Falls	1,183	10.2
3	Motor vehicle	1,135	9.8
4	Choking[b]	195	1.7
5	Fire, flames or smoke	107	0.9

OKLAHOMA

Rank	Cause	Deaths	Rate
4	All unintentional injuries	2,474	64.3
1	Poisoning[a]	730	19.0
2	Motor vehicle	727	18.9
3	Falls	537	13.9
4	Fire, flames or smoke	64	1.7
5	Drowning[c]	62	1.6

OREGON

Rank	Cause	Deaths	Rate
5	All unintentional injuries	1,755	44.7
1	Falls	644	16.4
2	Poisoning[a]	395	10.1
3	Motor vehicle	361	9.2
4	Choking[b]	65	1.7
5	Drowning[c]	57	1.5

PENNSYLVANIA

Rank	Cause	Deaths	Rate
5	All unintentional injuries	6,359	49.8
1	Poisoning[a]	2,228	17.4
2	Falls	1,604	12.6
3	Motor vehicle	1,334	10.4
4	Choking[b]	312	2.4
5	Fire, flames or smoke	130	1.0

RHODE ISLAND

Rank	Cause	Deaths	Rate
3	All unintentional injuries	537	51.1
1	Poisoning[a]	226	21.5
2	Falls	148	14.1
3	Motor vehicle	77	7.3
4	Choking[b]	24	2.3
5	Fire, flames or smoke	—	—

SOUTH CAROLINA

Rank	Cause	Deaths	Rate
5	All unintentional injuries	2,287	47.9
1	Motor vehicle	786	16.5
2	Poisoning[a]	583	12.2
3	Falls	372	7.8
4	Choking[b]	89	1.9
5	Fire, flames or smoke	73	1.5

SOUTH DAKOTA

Rank	Cause	Deaths	Rate
3	All unintentional injuries	425	50.3
1	Motor vehicle	145	17.2
2	Falls	143	16.9
3	Poisoning[a]	48	5.7
4	Mechanical suffocation	15	1.8
5	Choking[b]	14	1.7

TENNESSEE

Rank	Cause	Deaths	Rate
4	All unintentional injuries	3,540	54.5
1	Poisoning[a]	1,067	16.4
2	Motor vehicle	1,019	15.7
3	Falls	636	9.8
4	Choking[b]	140	2.2
5	Fire, flames or smoke	106	1.6

TEXAS

Rank	Cause	Deaths	Rate
4	All unintentional injuries	9,395	35.5
1	Motor vehicle	3,612	13.7
2	Poisoning[a]	2,223	8.4
3	Falls	1,743	6.6
4	Choking[b]	312	1.2
5	Drowning[c]	298	1.1

UTAH

Rank	Cause	Deaths	Rate
3	All unintentional injuries	1,103	38.0
1	Poisoning[a]	394	13.6
2	Falls	235	8.1
3	Motor vehicle	230	7.9
4	Choking[b]	44	1.5
5	Drowning[c]	29	1.0

VERMONT

Rank	Cause	Deaths	Rate
4	All unintentional injuries	352	56.2
1	Falls	143	22.8
2	Motor vehicle	74	11.8
3	Poisoning[a]	71	11.3
4	Drowning[c]	13	2.1
5	Choking[b]	—	—

VIRGINIA

Rank	Cause	Deaths	Rate
5	All unintentional injuries	2,951	35.7
1	Motor vehicle	775	9.4
2	Poisoning[a]	742	9.0
3	Falls	717	8.7
4	Choking[b]	170	2.1
5	Drowning[c]	84	1.0

WASHINGTON

Rank	Cause	Deaths	Rate
5	All unintentional injuries	2,826	40.5
1	Poisoning[a]	875	12.6
2	Falls	837	12.0
3	Motor vehicle	537	7.7
4	Choking[b]	113	1.6
5	Drowning[c]	102	1.5

WEST VIRGINIA

Rank	Cause	Deaths	Rate
4	All unintentional injuries	1,395	75.2
1	Poisoning[a]	548	29.6
2	Motor vehicle	330	17.8
3	Falls	269	14.5
4	Choking[b]	62	3.3
5	Fire, flames or smoke	33	1.8

WISCONSIN

Rank	Cause	Deaths	Rate
3	All unintentional injuries	2,969	51.7
1	Falls	1,173	20.4
2	Poisoning[a]	764	13.3
3	Motor vehicle	598	10.4
4	Choking[b]	61	1.1
5	Drowning[c]	53	0.9

WYOMING

Rank	Cause	Deaths	Rate
4	All unintentional injuries	325	55.8
1	Motor vehicle	91	15.6
2	Poisoning[a]	87	14.9
3	Falls	62	10.6
4	Drowning[c]	12	2.1
5	Choking[b]	—	—
5	Fire, flames or smoke	—	—
5	Mechanical suffocation	—	—

Source: National Safety Council analysis of National Center for Health Statistics (NCHS)–Mortality Data for 2013, as compiled from data provided by the 57 vital statistics jurisdictions through the Vital Statistics Cooperative Program. Rates are National Safety Council estimates based on data from NCHS and the U.S. Census Bureau. Dashes (—) indicate data values less than 10 as per NCHS publication guidelines.
[a]Solid, liquid, gas, and vapor poisoning.
[b]Inhalation or ingestion of food or other objects.
[c]Excludes transport drownings.

Unintentional-Injury-Related Deaths
by State and Event

Unintentional-injury-related deaths by state of occurrence and type of event, United States, 2013

State	Population (000)	Total[a]	Poisoning	Motor vehicle[b]	Falls	Choking[c]	Drowning[d]	Fire, flames, or smoke	Mechanical suffocation
Total U.S.	316,129	130,557	38,851	35,369	30,208	4,864	3,391	2,760	1,737
Alabama	4,834	2,329	561	909	242	102	67	84	21
Alaska	735	353	128	66	30	–	21	–	11
Arizona	6,627	3,349	1,063	859	906	73	75	66	23
Arkansas	2,959	1,373	246	537	229	66	38	52	23
California	38,333	11,538	4,015	3,375	2,208	259	405	164	84
Colorado	5,268	2,422	681	510	792	81	46	20	33
Connecticut	3,596	1,582	549	300	378	120	42	18	–
Delaware	926	412	150	115	84	17	–	11	–
District of Columbia	646	216	83	30	62	12	–	–	–
Florida	19,553	8,736	2,134	2,437	2,664	261	356	87	153
Georgia	9,992	3,727	1,011	1,268	659	142	95	134	51
Hawaii	1,404	467	124	112	118	23	45	–	–
Idaho	1,612	776	155	261	192	38	21	16	16
Illinois	12,882	4,511	1,430	1,118	991	222	91	107	82
Indiana	6,571	2,898	919	828	418	113	57	88	71
Iowa	3,090	1,422	262	346	498	53	36	26	17
Kansas	2,894	1,359	300	378	392	53	49	27	17
Kentucky	4,395	2,513	921	696	306	88	47	77	33
Louisiana	4,625	2,333	733	761	311	89	70	53	61
Maine	1,328	644	159	168	157	22	14	15	–
Maryland	5,929	1,732	293	531	549	82	44	55	15
Massachusetts	6,693	2,393	990	375	625	95	65	26	10
Michigan	9,896	4,225	1,305	1,053	991	160	82	119	95
Minnesota	5,420	2,405	487	466	1,022	86	39	35	37
Mississippi	2,991	1,692	294	681	256	159	42	67	30
Missouri	6,044	2,981	904	779	654	90	54	89	83
Montana	1,015	623	91	237	158	16	17	11	14
Nebraska	1,869	703	108	237	189	32	–	18	15
Nevada	2,790	1,184	509	278	174	29	40	16	23
New Hampshire	1,323	619	175	138	215	14	16	–	–
New Jersey	8,899	3,028	1,252	564	479	187	54	58	25
New Mexico	2,085	1,245	429	326	282	25	25	19	12
New York	19,651	5,927	2,069	1,316	1,462	198	128	146	72
North Carolina	9,848	4,324	1,129	1,359	994	169	111	101	46
North Dakota	723	326	19	124	75	17	–	–	–
Ohio	11,571	5,497	2,192	1,135	1,183	195	105	107	72
Oklahoma	3,851	2,474	730	727	537	48	62	64	17
Oregon	3,930	1,755	395	361	644	65	57	38	19
Pennsylvania	12,774	6,359	2,228	1,334	1,604	312	98	130	69
Rhode Island	1,052	537	226	77	148	24	–	–	–
South Carolina	4,775	2,287	583	786	372	89	60	73	43
South Dakota	845	425	48	145	143	14	–	12	15
Tennessee	6,496	3,540	1,067	1,019	636	140	78	106	44
Texas	26,448	9,395	2,223	3,612	1,743	312	298	162	123
Utah	2,901	1,103	394	230	235	44	29	–	18
Vermont	627	352	71	74	143	–	13	–	–
Virginia	8,260	2,951	742	775	717	170	84	75	31
Washington	6,971	2,826	875	537	837	113	102	51	28
West Virginia	1,854	1,395	548	330	269	62	14	33	10
Wisconsin	5,743	2,969	764	598	1,173	61	53	46	37
Wyoming	583	325	87	91	62	–	12	–	–

See source and footnotes on page 179.

Unintentional-injury-related deaths by state of occurrence and type of event, United States, 2013

State	Natural heat or cold	Struck by or against	Machinery	Firearms	Rail transportation	Air transportation	Water transportation	Electric current	All other incidents
Total U.S.	1,097	811	588	505	437	412	403	257	8,867
Alabama	17	—	14	25	10	—	11	—	249
Alaska	—	—	—	—	—	22	13	—	31
Arizona	86	—	—	—	—	11	—	—	150
Arkansas	—	13	12	15	—	—	—	—	107
California	80	61	30	35	80	52	22	20	648
Colorado	24	—	—	—	—	16	—	—	190
Connecticut	10	—	—	—	—	—	—	—	144
Delaware	—	—	—	—	—	—	—	—	20
District of Columbia	—	—	—	—	—	—	—	—	12
Florida	19	28	19	22	19	30	37	18	452
Georgia	15	32	13	24	18	—	18	—	236
Hawaii	—	—	—	—	—	—	—	—	26
Idaho	—	10	—	—	—	—	—	—	35
Illinois	51	23	22	18	19	—	10	—	315
Indiana	30	16	14	15	10	—	—	—	305
Iowa	11	11	14	—	—	—	—	—	131
Kansas	11	10	—	—	—	—	—	—	88
Kentucky	19	20	12	21	—	—	—	—	242
Louisiana	16	16	11	19	—	—	13	—	160
Maine	—	—	—	—	—	—	—	—	81
Maryland	23	15	—	—	10	—	—	—	85
Massachusetts	13	10	—	—	—	—	—	—	162
Michigan	44	44	16	10	—	13	11	—	266
Minnesota	29	15	23	—	—	—	—	—	144
Mississippi	—	12	14	17	—	—	12	—	87
Missouri	28	23	25	19	—	—	14	—	206
Montana	—	—	—	—	—	—	—	—	47
Nebraska	—	—	—	—	—	—	—	—	68
Nevada	38	—	—	—	—	12	—	—	50
New Hampshire	—	—	—	—	—	—	—	—	40
New Jersey	25	12	—	—	—	—	—	—	338
New Mexico	23	12	—	—	—	—	—	—	61
New York	67	38	25	—	32	—	14	—	347
North Carolina	15	28	20	18	14	—	16	—	289
North Dakota	—	—	—	—	—	—	—	—	52
Ohio	26	29	29	21	17	—	—	—	369
Oklahoma	16	—	—	15	—	11	—	12	206
Oregon	17	12	—	—	—	—	13	—	110
Pennsylvania	46	41	30	22	23	11	15	19	377
Rhode Island	—	—	—	—	—	—	—	—	33
South Carolina	15	13	—	15	10	18	15	—	179
South Dakota	10	—	—	—	—	—	—	—	19
Tennessee	17	21	17	19	—	—	16	—	347
Texas	53	65	54	38	28	35	24	31	594
Utah	13	—	—	—	—	10	—	—	102
Vermont	—	—	—	—	—	—	—	—	25
Virginia	32	26	13	10	—	—	10	—	246
Washington	30	21	19	11	13	12	13	—	160
West Virginia	—	21	11	—	—	—	—	—	74
Wisconsin	33	18	18	10	—	—	—	—	134
Wyoming	—	—	—	—	—	—	—	—	28

Source: National Safety Council analysis of National Center for Heatlh Statistics (NCHS)–Mortality Data for 2013, as compiled from data provided by the 57 vital statistics jurisdictions through the Vital Statistics Cooperative Program. Dashes (–) indicate data values less than 10 as per NCHS publication guidelines.
[a]*Deaths are by place of occurrence and exclude nonresident aliens.*
[b]*See page 184 for motor vehicle deaths by place of residence.*
[c]*Suffocation by inhalation or ingestion of food or object obstructing breathing.*
[d]*Excludes water transport drownings.*

Unintentional-Injury Trends by State

Nationwide, from 2010 to 2013, unintentional-injury-related deaths increased by 8% and the death rate increased by nearly 6%. By state, the greatest decrease in the number of unintentional-injury-related deaths and death rates occurred in Wyoming (-6% and -9%, respectively). The greatest increase in unintentional-injury-related deaths and death rates occurred in New Jersey (+22% and +20%, respectively).

The table below shows the trend in unintentional-injury-related deaths and death rates by state over the most recent four years for which data are available.

Unintentional-injury-related deaths by state of residence, United States, 2010-2013

State	Deaths[a]				Deaths per 100,000 population			
	2013[b]	2012	2011	2010	2013[b]	2012	2011	2010
Total U.S.	130,557	127,792	126,438	120,859	41.3	40.7	40.6	39.0
Alabama	2,329	2,283	2,662	2,394	48.2	47.4	55.4	50.0
Alaska	353	368	385	366	48.0	50.4	53.2	51.3
Arizona	3,349	3,029	3,096	3,018	50.5	46.2	47.9	47.1
Arkansas	1,373	1,521	1,510	1,461	46.4	51.6	51.4	50.0
California	11,538	10,906	10,824	10,435	30.1	28.7	28.7	28.0
Colorado	2,422	2,403	2,330	2,106	46.0	46.3	45.5	41.7
Connecticut	1,582	1,392	1,339	1,337	44.0	38.8	37.3	37.4
Delaware	412	374	338	357	44.5	40.8	37.2	39.7
District of Columbia	216	194	185	212	33.4	30.6	29.9	35.0
Florida	8,736	8,770	8,901	8,875	44.7	45.4	46.6	47.1
Georgia	3,727	3,731	3,785	3,745	37.3	37.6	38.6	38.5
Hawaii	467	458	517	432	33.3	32.9	37.5	31.7
Idaho	776	699	710	654	48.1	43.8	44.8	41.6
Illinois	4,511	4,488	4,166	3,997	35.0	34.9	32.4	31.1
Indiana	2,898	2,776	2,699	2,534	44.1	42.5	41.4	39.0
Iowa	1,422	1,369	1,369	1,273	46.0	44.5	44.7	41.7
Kansas	1,359	1,319	1,333	1,317	47.0	45.7	46.5	46.1
Kentucky	2,513	2,741	2,608	2,632	57.2	62.6	59.7	60.6
Louisiana	2,333	2,362	2,091	1,999	50.4	51.3	45.7	44.0
Maine	644	602	574	540	48.5	45.3	43.2	40.7
Maryland	1,732	1,696	1,569	1,446	29.2	28.8	26.9	25.0
Massachusetts	2,393	2,195	2,224	2,060	35.8	33.0	33.7	31.4
Michigan	4,225	3,805	3,951	3,770	42.7	38.5	40.0	38.2
Minnesota	2,405	2,301	2,319	2,103	44.4	42.8	43.4	39.6
Mississippi	1,692	1,627	1,724	1,685	56.6	54.5	57.9	56.8
Missouri	2,981	3,002	3,169	2,975	49.3	49.8	52.7	49.6
Montana	623	572	609	548	61.4	56.9	61.0	55.3
Nebraska	703	792	678	700	37.6	42.7	36.8	38.3
Nevada	1,184	1,177	1,155	1,088	42.4	42.7	42.5	40.2
New Hampshire	619	573	553	517	46.8	43.4	42.0	39.3
New Jersey	3,028	2,990	2,685	2,486	34.0	33.7	30.4	28.2
New Mexico	1,245	1,351	1,336	1,233	59.7	64.8	64.3	59.7
New York	5,927	5,786	5,537	5,004	30.2	29.6	28.4	25.8
North Carolina	4,324	4,281	4,297	4,144	43.9	43.9	44.5	43.4
North Dakota	326	318	298	285	45.1	45.3	43.5	42.3
Ohio	5,497	5,420	5,275	5,124	47.5	46.9	45.7	44.4
Oklahoma	2,474	2,388	2,261	2,288	64.3	62.6	59.7	60.9
Oregon	1,755	1,709	1,722	1,566	44.7	43.8	44.5	40.8
Pennsylvania	6,359	6,334	6,216	5,751	49.8	49.6	48.8	45.2
Rhode Island	537	525	541	475	51.1	50.0	51.5	45.1
South Carolina	2,287	2,336	2,285	2,274	47.9	49.5	48.9	49.1
South Dakota	425	426	411	393	50.3	51.1	49.9	48.1
Tennessee	3,540	3,513	3,485	3,539	54.5	54.4	54.5	55.7
Texas	9,395	9,313	9,410	9,212	35.5	35.7	36.7	36.5
Utah	1,103	1,097	1,058	970	38.0	38.4	37.6	35.0
Vermont	352	333	301	298	56.2	53.2	48.1	47.6
Virginia	2,951	2,883	2,809	2,527	35.7	35.2	34.7	31.5
Washington	2,826	2,760	2,709	2,609	40.5	40.0	39.7	38.7
West Virginia	1,395	1,371	1,432	1,234	75.2	73.8	77.2	66.6
Wisconsin	2,969	2,825	2,680	2,525	51.7	49.3	46.9	44.4
Wyoming	325	308	317	346	55.8	53.4	55.9	61.3

Source: Deaths are from the National Center for Health Statistics (NCHS)–Mortality Data for 2010-2013, as compiled from data provided by the 57 vital statistics jurisdictions through the Vital Statistics Cooperative Program. Rates are National Safety Council estimates based on data from NCHS and the U.S. Census Bureau. See Technical Appendix for comparability.
[a]Deaths for each state are by state of residence and exclude nonresident aliens.
[b]Latest official figures.

In general, states with the largest number of people employed have the largest number of work-related fatalities. The four largest states – California, Texas, Florida, and New York – accounted for 27% of the total 2014 work-related fatalities in the United States. Each state's industry mix, geographic features, age of population, and other characteristics of the workforce must be considered when evaluating state fatality profiles. Overall, the six leading events or exposures accounted for all but 11 of the 4,679 total occupational fatalities in all states in 2014.

Fatal occupational injuries by state and event or exposure, United States, 2013-2014

State	Total fatal injuries[a]		Event or exposure[b] 2014					
	2013[c]	2014[d]	Transportation incidents[e]	Falls, slips or trips	Violence and other injuries by persons or animals[f]	Contact with objects and equipment	Exposure to harmful substances or environments	Fire and explostions
Total	4,585	4,679	1,891	793	749	708	390	137
Alabama	78	70	29	8	17	8	5	–
Alaska	32	30	16	–	7	3	–	–
Arizona	95	86	33	12	16	9	14	–
Arkansas	63	67	33	12	7	8	4	3
California	396	337	116	69	72	37	34	3
Colorado	65	83	41	9	12	14	6	–
Connecticut	29	33	11	8	8	2	3	1
Delaware	11	11	8	–	3	–	–	–
District of Columbia	25	11	–	–	5	3	–	–
Florida	239	221	78	50	37	15	39	–
Georgia	117	148	59	30	32	22	3	–
Hawaii	11	31	14	7	4	3	–	–
Idaho	30	34	18	3	3	6	–	–
Illinois	176	163	58	30	31	31	11	–
Indiana	127	127	52	16	25	15	7	12
Iowa	72	90	32	25	6	19	5	3
Kansas	55	69	30	12	8	11	6	–
Kentucky	86	82	35	14	12	14	7	–
Louisiana	114	120	58	15	17	13	9	8
Maine	19	18	11	–	–	6	–	–
Maryland	79	73	21	12	24	11	4	–
Massachusetts	57	51	17	11	11	8	2	2
Michigan	135	138	49	23	31	21	11	3
Minnesota	69	62	25	9	8	14	5	–
Mississippi	68	71	30	11	8	9	9	4
Missouri	118	106	42	23	11	22	6	–
Montana	28	27	9	9	3	5	1	–
Nebraska	39	54	25	9	7	10	1	2
Nevada	42	40	10	6	10	7	6	–
New Hampshire	14	17	6	3	4	–	3	–
New Jersey	102	85	35	24	11	10	–	3
New Mexico	54	50	31	–	6	7	–	–
New York	178	203	69	34	38	38	16	8
North Carolina	109	128	46	24	16	18	18	6
North Dakota	56	38	17	6	–	10	3	–
Ohio	149	184	62	34	31	35	17	5
Oklahoma	92	91	60	7	4	12	3	5
Oregon	49	69	29	10	12	13	4	1
Pennsylvania	183	175	74	25	23	29	16	8
Rhode Island	10	10	–	6	–	–	–	–
South Carolina	75	62	25	11	14	4	4	4
South Dakota	20	28	12	8	–	5	–	–
Tennessee	95	124	56	23	15	16	9	5
Texas	508	524	237	67	66	76	53	24
Utah	37	54	22	3	7	12	9	–
Vermont	7	8	4	–	–	–	–	–
Virginia	128	116	52	18	20	19	7	–
Washington	56	86	23	16	15	21	9	–
West Virginia	61	38	12	10	3	8	4	–
Wisconsin	97	97	38	16	15	22	5	–
Wyoming	26	37	16	9	6	3	–	–

Source: Bureau of Labor Statistics (BLS). National Census of Fatal Occupational Injuries in 2014 (preliminary results), accessed September 18, 2015, from www.bls.gov/news.release/cfoi.nr0.htm.
Note: Dashes (–) indicate no data or data that do not meet publication criteria.
[a]State totals include other events and exposures, such as bodily reaction, in addition to those shown separately.
[b]Based on the BLS Occupational Injury and Illness Classification System 2.01, implemented for 2011 data forward.
[c]Data for 2013 are revised and final.
[d]Data for 2014 are preliminary and include five fatal injuries that occurred within the territorial boundaries of the United States, but a State of incident could not be determined.
[e]Includes highway, nonhighway, air, water, and rail fatal injuries, and fatal injuries resulting from being struck by a vehicle.
[f]Includes violence by persons, self-inflicted injuries, and attacks by animals.

Nonfatal occupational injury and illness rates[a] by state, private industry, 2013

State	Total recordable cases	Cases with days away from work[b]	Cases with job transfer or restriction	Other recordable cases
Private industry[c]	3.3	1.0	0.7	1.6
Alabama	3.3	0.9	0.8	1.6
Alaska	4.3	1.5	0.5	2.2
Arizona	3.3	0.9	1.0	1.4
Arkansas	3.0	0.8	0.6	1.6
California	3.5	1.1	1.0	1.4
Colorado	—	—	—	—
Connecticut	3.8	1.3	0.8	1.7
Delaware	2.7	1.0	0.4	1.3
District of Columbia	1.7	0.7	0.1	0.9
Florida	—	—	—	—
Georgia	2.8	0.8	0.7	1.4
Hawaii	3.7	2.0	0.3	1.4
Idaho	—	—	—	—
Illinois	3.2	1.0	0.7	1.5
Indiana	3.6	0.8	1.0	1.8
Iowa	4.5	1.1	1.2	2.2
Kansas	3.5	0.8	0.8	1.8
Kentucky	4.0	1.1	1.0	2.0
Louisiana	2.2	0.8	0.3	1.1
Maine	5.3	1.4	1.5	2.4
Maryland	3.0	1.1	0.4	1.5
Massachusetts	2.9	1.3	0.3	1.3
Michigan	3.7	1.0	0.9	1.9
Minnesota	3.7	1.0	0.8	2.0
Mississippi	—	—	—	—
Missouri	3.2	0.8	0.7	1.6
Montana	4.7	1.4	0.6	2.6
Nebraska	3.8	1.0	0.8	2.0
Nevada	4.0	1.0	1.1	1.9
New Hampshire	—	—	—	—
New Jersey	2.9	1.1	0.4	1.4
New Mexico	3.2	0.9	0.6	1.7
New York	2.4	1.2	0.1	1.1
North Carolina	2.7	0.8	0.6	1.3
North Dakota	—	—	—	—
Ohio	2.9	0.8	0.6	1.5
Oklahoma	—	—	—	—
Oregon	4.1	1.4	0.8	1.9
Pennsylvania	3.9	1.1	0.9	1.9
Rhode Island	—	—	—	—
South Carolina	2.9	0.8	0.7	1.4
South Dakota	—	—	—	—
Tennessee	3.3	0.9	0.7	1.7
Texas	2.6	0.7	0.7	1.2
Utah	3.4	0.8	0.8	1.8
Vermont	5.2	1.4	0.9	3.0
Virginia	2.6	0.9	0.5	1.3
Washington	4.8	1.6	1.0	2.2
West Virginia	3.7	1.4	0.4	1.8
Wisconsin	4.0	1.0	0.9	2.0
Wyoming	3.4	1.3	0.4	1.7

Source: Bureau of Labor Statistics, U.S. Department of Labor.
Note: Because of rounding, components may not add to totals. Dashes (–) indicate data not available.
[a]Incidence rates represent the number of injuries and illnesses per 100 full-time workers using 200,000 hours as the equivalent.
[b]Days-away-from-work cases include those that result in days away from work with or without job transfer or restriction.
[c]Data cover all 50 states.

Nonfatal Occupational Incidence Rates by State (cont.)

Nonfatal occupational injury and illness incidence rates[a] for total recordable cases by state, private industry, 2013

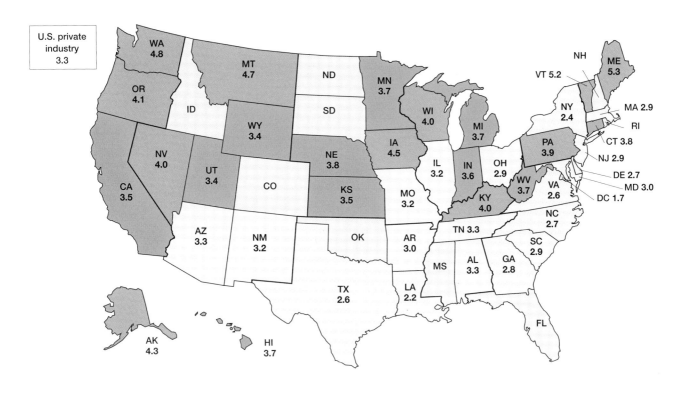

U.S. private industry 3.3

| WA 4.8 |
| OR 4.1 |
| MT 4.7 |
| ND |
| MN 3.7 |
| NH |
| ME 5.3 |
| VT 5.2 |
| ID |
| SD |
| WI 4.0 |
| NY 2.4 |
| MA 2.9 |
| WY 3.4 |
| IA 4.5 |
| MI 3.7 |
| RI |
| NV 4.0 |
| NE 3.8 |
| CT 3.8 |
| UT 3.4 |
| IL 3.2 |
| IN 3.6 |
| OH 2.9 |
| PA 3.9 |
| NJ 2.9 |
| CA 3.5 |
| CO |
| KS 3.5 |
| MO 3.2 |
| WV 3.7 |
| VA 2.6 |
| DE 2.7 |
| MD 3.0 |
| KY 4.0 |
| DC 1.7 |
| AZ 3.3 |
| NM 3.2 |
| OK |
| AR 3.0 |
| TN 3.3 |
| NC 2.7 |
| TX 2.6 |
| MS |
| AL 3.3 |
| GA 2.8 |
| SC 2.9 |
| LA 2.2 |
| FL |
| AK 4.3 |
| HI 3.7 |

Below 2.9 — 7 states and District of Columbia

2.9 to 3.3 — 12 states

States at or less than national average

3.4 to 3.8 — 11 states

Above 3.8 — 11 states

States above national average

Data not available — 9 states

[a]Incidence rates represent the number of injuries and illnesses per 100 full-time workers using 200,000 hours as the equivalent.

Motor-Vehicle Deaths by State

Motor-vehicle deaths by state, United States, 2013-2014

State	Motor-vehicle traffic deaths (Place of incident)				Total motor-vehicle deaths[a] (Place of residence)			
	Number		Mileage rate[b]		Number		Population rate[b]	
	2014[c]	2013	2014	2013	2014[c]	2013	2014	2013
Total U.S.	35,398[a]	33,804	1.2	1.1	35,398	35,369	11.1	11.2
Alabama	821	887	1.2	1.4	896	909	18.5	18.8
Alaska	73	50	1.5	1.0	87	66	11.8	9.0
Arizona	772	827	1.3	1.4	856	859	12.7	13.0
Arkansas	466	482	1.4	1.4	532	537	17.9	18.1
California	3,085	3,169	0.9	1.0	3,438	3,375	8.9	8.8
Colorado	488	519	1.0	1.1	537	510	10.0	9.7
Connecticut	250	289	0.8	0.9	275	300	7.6	8.3
Delaware	125	113	1.3	1.2	126	115	13.5	12.4
District of Columbia	26	45	0.7	1.3	37	30	5.6	4.6
Florida	2,494	2,445	1.3	1.3	2,578	2,437	13.0	12.5
Georgia	1,169	1,217	1.1	1.1	1,282	1,268	12.7	12.7
Hawaii	95	110	0.9	1.1	108	112	7.6	8.0
Idaho	186	225	1.1	1.4	212	261	13.0	16.2
Illinois	924	1,000	0.9	0.9	1,065	1,118	8.3	8.7
Indiana	746	767	0.9	1.0	763	828	11.6	12.6
Iowa	321	325	1.0	1.0	340	346	10.9	11.2
Kansas	385	346	1.2	1.1	381	378	13.1	13.1
Kentucky	672	624	1.4	1.3	716	696	16.2	15.8
Louisiana	740	745	1.5	1.6	804	761	17.3	16.5
Maine	135	145	0.9	1.0	143	168	10.8	12.6
Maryland	443	479	0.8	0.8	475	531	7.9	9.0
Massachusetts	343	337	0.6	0.6	409	375	6.1	5.6
Michigan	901	948	0.9	1.0	1,006	1,053	10.2	10.6
Minnesota	359	412	0.6	0.7	432	466	7.9	8.6
Mississippi	607	624	1.5	1.6	673	681	22.5	22.8
Missouri	766	821	1.1	1.2	798	779	13.2	12.9
Montana	192	226	1.5	1.9	204	237	19.9	23.3
Nebraska	225	219	1.1	1.1	252	237	13.4	12.7
Nevada	291	317	1.2	1.3	316	278	11.1	10.0
New Hampshire	95	132	0.7	1.0	107	138	8.1	10.4
New Jersey	556	551	0.8	0.7	574	564	6.4	6.3
New Mexico	383	329	1.5	1.3	395	326	18.9	15.6
New York	1,026	1,190	0.8	0.9	1,147	1,326	5.8	6.7
North Carolina	1,302	1,326	1.2	1.3	1,393	1,359	14.0	13.8
North Dakota	136	158	1.3	1.6	103	124	13.9	17.1
Ohio	1,008	1,049	0.9	0.9	1,130	1,135	9.7	9.8
Oklahoma	669	681	1.4	1.4	730	727	18.8	18.9
Oregon	356	336	1.0	1.0	378	361	9.5	9.2
Pennsylvania	1,195	1,265	1.2	1.3	1,281	1,334	10.0	10.4
Rhode Island	52	82	0.7	1.1	62	77	5.9	7.3
South Carolina	823	774	1.6	1.6	807	786	16.7	16.5
South Dakota	136	150	1.4	1.6	158	145	18.5	17.2
Tennessee	963	1,094	1.3	1.5	994	1,019	15.2	15.7
Texas	3,541	3,506	1.4	1.4	3,714	3,612	13.8	13.7
Utah	256	208	0.9	0.8	260	230	8.8	7.9
Vermont	44	62	0.6	0.9	46	74	7.3	11.8
Virginia	703	745	0.9	0.9	787	775	9.5	9.4
Washington	464	470	0.8	0.8	578[c]	537	8.2	7.7
West Virginia	272	363	1.4	1.9	324	330	17.5	17.8
Wisconsin	498	541	0.8	0.9	565	598	9.8	10.4
Wyoming	150	79	1.6	0.8	124	91	21.2	15.6

Source: 2014 motor-vehicle traffic deaths are provisional counts from state traffic authorities; 2014 motor-vehicle traffic death figure for Total U.S. and total motor-vehicle deaths are from the National Center for Health Statistics (also see page 178).

[a] Includes both traffic and nontraffic motor-vehicle deaths. See definitions of motor-vehicle traffic and nontraffic incidents on page 206.

[b] The mileage death rate is deaths per 100,000,000 vehicle miles; the population death rate is deaths per 100,000 population. Death rates are National Safety Council estimates.

[c] Latest year available. See Technical Appendix for comparability.

Mileage death rates, 2014
Motor vehicle traffic deaths per 100,000,000 vehicle miles

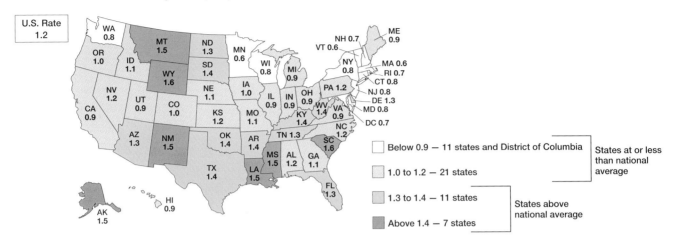

U.S. Rate 1.2

Below 0.9 — 11 states and District of Columbia
1.0 to 1.2 — 21 states
} States at or less than national average

1.3 to 1.4 — 11 states
Above 1.4 — 7 states
} States above national average

Registration death rates, 2014
Motor vehicle traffic deaths per 10,000 motor vehicles

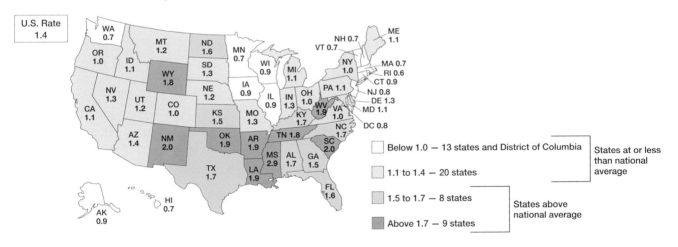

U.S. Rate 1.4

Below 1.0 — 13 states and District of Columbia
1.1 to 1.4 — 20 states
} States at or less than national average

1.5 to 1.7 — 8 states
Above 1.7 — 9 states
} States above national average

Population death rates, 2014
Motor vehicle traffic deaths per 100,000 population

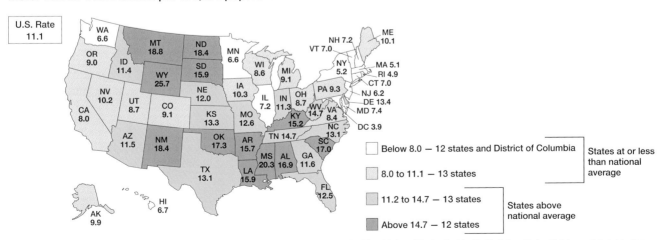

U.S. Rate 11.1

Below 8.0 — 12 states and District of Columbia
8.0 to 11.1 — 13 states
} States at or less than national average

11.2 to 14.7 — 13 states
Above 14.7 — 12 states
} States above national average

Source: Rates estimated by National Safety Council based on data from state traffic authorities, National Center for Health Statistics, Federal Highway Administration, and the U.S. Census Bureau.

INTERNATIONAL

International Unintentional-Injury-Related Deaths and Death Rates

The term "Accidents and Adverse Effects" used in the International Classification of Diseases (ICD) system refers to all causes of unintentional-injury-related deaths, including transportation incidents; unintentional poisonings; falls; fires; burns; natural and environmental factors; drowning; suffocation; medical and surgical complications and misadventures; and other causes, such as those involving machinery, firearms, or electric current. The data presented in the table below are identified by codes

V01-X59 and Y85-Y86 of the 10th revision of ICD (except where noted). World-wide unintentional-injury-related deaths totaled 3,716,000 in 2012, resulting in a death rate of 52.5 per 100,000 population.

The table below and those on pages 190 through 193 show the number of injury-related deaths and the unadjusted death rates for 52 countries for which mortality data and population estimates were obtained.

Unintentional-injury-related deaths and death rates by age group, latest year available

Country	Year	Deaths Total	% male	All ages	0 to 4	5 to 14	15 to 24	25 to 44	45 to 64	65 or older
									17.6	58.4
							30.4	26.0	17.9	116.4
Argentina	2012	11,037	73%	23.8	15.5	5.8	11.1	7.4	24.5	157.7
Austria	2013	2,527	58%	29.8	2.0	1.5	13.0	12.8	42.1	107.6
Belgium	2012	4,369	53%	39.4	5.7	1.1	37.6	38.5	32.3	46.5
Brazil	2012	73,441	78%	36.8	13.5	7.7	18.6	17.8	34.5	105.1
Bulgaria	2012	1,848	76%	25.3	9.9	4.6	15.1	24.0	24.6	70.2
Chile	2012	4,921	74%	28.8	10.6	4.3	21.1	24.5	29.7	138.2
Colombia	2011	10,107	79%	22.6	13.7	6.9	22.9	27.1	31.1	166.4
Costa Rica	2012	1,332	73%	28.7	5.4	5.1	17.3	17.8	24.7	248.3
Croatia	2013	1,976	54%	46.4	4.3	1.7	13.0	16.0	32.9	108.7
	2012	4,890	54%	44.2	11.2	5.0	16.9	16.9	17.3	86.1
					4.0	1.8	7.2	10.0	44.4	66.1
					3.2	2.3	42.3	22.9	26.9	102.2
					25.0	11.5	38.4	41.2	103.8	
					17.5	11.9	28.1	32.5	49.4	135.3
					5.9	6.0	17.5	21.8	35.0	61.5
					2.3	1.4	14.0	34.6	12.4	88.6
					9.0	10.2	25.1	8.0	91.4	214.8
					2.3	1.4	9.2	84.0	8.5	38.8
					16.3	10.8	54.9	5.9	35.4	123.5
					2.3	2.0	2.7	14.1	10.3	77.6
					3.5	2.3	10.9	5.2	13.0	108.3
					5.4	2.7	7.4	11.9	16.0	105.6
					1.8	1.5	11.9	6.2	149.4	130.9
					3.9	1.6	6.3	135.5	73.7	56.1
					32.7	17.3	69.0	50.5	97.3	82.2
					26.8	9.0	21.6	44.6	120.1	106.9
					8.8	6.3	19.5	60.8	37.0	107.1
					6.7	7.6	28.8	31.3	5.2	10.0
					19.9	7.1	28.0	4.4	9.3	121.5
					3.2	2.5	5.1	8.0	35.7	112.4
					2.1	0.8	6.5	29.0	25.5	160.
					14.6	5.1	18.7	17.0	35.3	63
					1.3	1.5	13.3	29.3	34.5	97
					16.5	8.0	24.0	30.8	32.7	81
					12.5	6.4	36.4	26.1	42.9	89
					31.3	7.4	17.9	22.1	16.0	56
					3.8	3.4	21.5	9.8	31.1	11
					2.5	1.7	9.8	12.3	96.8	0
					6.1	3.2	8.8	35.7	50.5	7
					26.2	7.4	21.6	23.3	186.9	16
					14.4	8.8	20.8	167.0	16.1	
					25.6	15.4	90.0	14.6	20.9	
					4.5	3.5	13.7	13.8	71.2	
					3.3	3.4	13.5	88.7	13.5	
					37.0	15.6	54.5	6.7	17.8	
					3.3	1.7	8.7	9.5	35.2	
					1.2	1.1	18.2	11.5	21.4	
					4.5	2.0	14.8	21.9	129.2	
					12.3	6.2	55.8	14.5	15.7	
					21.3	10.9	9.8	98.2	45.0	
					2.8	1.4	26.4	16.9		
					12.4	3.7		37.9		

Deaths per 100,000 population

...on (WHO) data.
...Bureau (International Data Base).
...assault.

NATIONAL SAFETY COU

1.25 Million Road Traffic Deaths in 2013!

The World Health Organization's (WHO) Global Status Report on Road Safety 2015 found that road traffic deaths totaled 1.25 million in 2013. Despite the global increase in population and motorization, the number of deaths has stabilized since 2007. The WHO reports that 68 countries have seen a rise in the number of road traffic deaths since 2010, while 79 countries have seen a decrease. Of those countries with increasing road traffic deaths, 84% have low- or middle-income economies.

National Safety Council

■ *WHO Reports Number of Road Traffic Deaths Plateaued Since 2007.*

This section on international injury and fatalities includes data for occupational and motor-vehicle injuries, as well as general unintentional injury and mortality. The two primary data sources used in this section are the World Health Organization (WHO) and the International Labour Organization.

Looking at specific causes, road traffic incidents are the leading cause of unintentional fatalities for each region in the world. To address the growing road traffic safety issue, *"A Decade of Action for Road Safety 2011-2020 – Saving Millions of Lives"* was officially proclaimed by the United Nations General Assembly in March 2010. This proclamation has been drawn to guide efforts at global, regional, national, and local levels with the goal to stabilize and then reduce the forecasted level of road traffic fatalities around the world.

In addition, WHO's *Global Status Report on Road Safety 2015* found that road traffic deaths totaled 1.25 million in 2013. Despite the global increase in population and motorization the number of deaths have stabilized since 2007. The WHO reports that 68 countries have seen a rise in the number of road traffic deaths since 2010 while 79 countries have seen a decrease. Of those countries with increasing road traffic deaths, 84% have low- or middle-income economies.

The WHO currently ranks road traffic injuries as the ninth leading cause of death in the world while fall deaths ranks 21st. However, by 2030 the WHO projects that road traffic injury deaths will be the 7th leading cause of death and falls will be the 17th leading cause of death in the world.

There are several evidence-based measures recommended to help reduce unintentional injury deaths in the world. Top measures recommended to reduce road traffic crashes include:
• Setting and enforcing laws on speeding
• Setting and enforcing laws on drinking and driving
• Setting and enforcing laws on motorcycle helmets
• Setting and enforcing laws on seat-belts
• Setting and enforcing laws on child restraint

Top measures recommended to reduce fall deaths include:
• Setting and enforcing laws requiring window guards for tall buildings
• Redesigning furniture and other products
• Establishing standards for playground equipment

Another global unintentional injury issue that is often overlooked is drowning. A recent WHO report, *Global report on drowning: preventing a leading killer,* reports that drowning is the third most prevalent unintentional injury death event after motor vehicle and fall deaths. The WHO estimates about 372,000 drowning deaths occur every year. More than 90% of these drowning deaths take place in low- and middle-income countries.

Drowning is in the top 10 leading causes of death among children and young people in every region of the world. Over half of the drowning deaths occur among individuals under the age of 25, with children under the age of 5 at greatest risk.

Data limitations are making it hard to estimate the full extent of the drowning problem. Data collection in many low- and middle- income countries is limited. In addition, current injury coding standards exclude deaths from flood disasters and water transport incidents. Data on non-fatal drowning is often not collected at all in many parts of the developing world.

The WHO identified several risk factors associated with drowning deaths. These risk factors include:
• Lack of physical barriers controlling between people and water
• Lack of or inadequate supervision of young children
• Uncovered or unprotected water supplies and lack of safe water crossings
• Lack of water safety awareness and risky behavior around water
• Travelling on water, especially on overcrowded or poorly maintained vessels
• Flood disasters, whether from extreme rainfall, storm surges, tsunamis or cyclones.

The charts on pages 189-193 provide the unintentional-injury-related deaths and death rates for 52 countries. The most current year of mortality data available is reported for motor vehicle, poisonings, falls, drowning, and overall unintentional-injury-related deaths. Looking at overall age trends across the world, the 65-and-older age group has the highest rate of unintentional-injury-related deaths per 100,000 population, while the 5- to 14-year-old age group has the lowest. Death rates for all causes except poisonings peak for those 65 and older. The poisoning death rate peaks for the 45-to-64 age group. Because of differences in recordkeeping, comparisons among countries are not recommended.

The International Labour Organization has implemented a new occupational injury database. Because of the database change, comparisons prior to 2009 are not recommended. The charts on pages 194 and 195 detail the occupational deaths and death rates by country for the past two years. Because of the wide range of recordkeeping standards used in the world, countries with similar recordkeeping practices are grouped together. Comparison among countries is not recommended even within these recordkeeping groupings.

The charts on pages 196 and 197 detail occupational injuries and injury rates by country. Because of differences in injury definitions among countries, comparisons between countries is not recommended.

Source: World Health Organization. (2011). A Decade of Action for Road Safety 2011-2020 – Saving Millions of Lives. Geneva: Author. Downloaded from www. who.int/violence_injury_prevention/publications/road_traffic/decade_booklet/ en/index.html on Nov. 7, 2012.
World Health Organization. (2015). Global Status Report on Road Safety 2015. Geneva: Author: Downloaded from: http://www.who.int/violence_injury_prevention/road_safety_status/2015/en/ on November. 9, 2015.
World Health Organization. (2014). Global report on drowning: preventing a leading killer. Downloaded from: http://www.who.int/violence_injury_prevention/publications/drowning_global_report/Final_report_full_web.pdf?ua=1 on December 8, 2014.
World Health Organization. (2014). Injuries and violence the facts 2014. Geneva: Author: Downloaded from:
http://www.who.int/violence_injury_prevention/media/news/2015/Injury_violence_facts_2014/en/ on November. 9, 2015.

International Unintentional-Injury-Related Deaths and Death Rates

The term "Accidents and Adverse Effects" used in the International Classification of Diseases (ICD) system refers to all causes of unintentional-injury-related deaths, including transportation incidents; unintentional poisonings; falls; fires; burns; natural and environmental factors; drowning; suffocation; medical and surgical complications and misadventures; and other causes, such as those involving machinery, firearms, or electric current. The data presented in the table below are identified by codes V01-X59 and Y85-Y86 of the 10th revision of ICD (except where noted). World-wide unintentional-injury-related deaths totaled 3,716,000 in 2012, resulting in a death rate of 52.5 per 100,000 population.

The table below and those on pages 190 through 193 show the number of injury-related deaths and the unadjusted death rates for 52 countries for which mortality data and population estimates were obtained.

Unintentional-injury-related deaths and death rates by age group, latest year available

Country	Year	Deaths Total	% male	Deaths per 100,000 population[a] All ages	0 to 4	5 to 14	15 to 24	25 to 44	45 to 64	65 or older
Argentina	2012	11,037	73%	23.8	15.5	5.8	30.4	26.0	17.6	58.4
Austria	2013	2,527	58%	29.8	2.0	1.5	11.1	7.4	17.9	116.4
Belgium	2012	4,369	53%	39.4	5.7	1.1	13.0	12.8	24.5	157.7
Brazil	2012	73,441	78%	36.8	13.5	7.7	37.6	38.5	42.1	107.6
Bulgaria	2012	1,848	76%	25.3	9.9	4.6	18.6	17.8	32.3	46.5
Chile	2012	4,921	74%	28.8	10.6	4.3	15.1	24.0	34.5	105.1
Colombia	2011	10,107	79%	22.6	13.7	6.9	21.1	24.5	24.6	70.2
Costa Rica	2012	1,332	73%	28.7	5.4	5.1	22.9	27.1	29.7	136.2
Croatia	2013	1,976	54%	46.4	4.3	1.7	17.3	17.8	31.1	166.4
Cuba	2012	4,890	54%	44.2	11.2	5.0	13.0	16.0	24.7	248.3
Czech Republic	2013	3,612	64%	34.4	4.0	1.8	16.9	16.9	32.9	106.7
Denmark	2012	1,324	55%	23.7	3.2	2.3	7.2	10.0	17.3	86.1
Ecuador	2012	5,796	78%	38.1	25.0	11.6	38.4	42.3	44.4	102.2
Egypt	2013	18,156	82%	21.5	17.5	11.9	28.1	23.4	22.9	26.9
El Salvador	2012	1,676	80%	27.5	5.9	6.0	17.5	32.5	41.2	103.8
Finland	2013	2,548	65%	46.8	2.3	1.4	14.0	21.8	49.4	135.3
Georgia	2012	1,472	75%	32.8	9.0	10.2	25.1	34.6	35.0	61.5
Germany	2013	20,453	54%	25.4	2.3	1.4	9.2	8.0	12.4	88.6
Guatemala	2012	8,064	81%	57.2	18.3	10.6	54.9	84.0	91.4	214.8
Hong Kong SAR	2013	761	68%	10.6	2.3	2.0	2.7	5.9	8.5	38.8
Hungary	2013	3,642	59%	36.8	3.5	2.3	10.9	14.1	35.4	123.5
Israel	2012	1,072	57%	13.6	5.4	2.7	7.4	5.2	10.3	77.6
Italy	2012	18,460	53%	31.0	1.8	1.5	11.9	11.9	13.0	108.3
Japan	2013	42,018	58%	33.4	3.9	1.6	6.3	6.2	16.0	105.6
Kazakhstan[b]	2012	16,497	78%	98.2	32.7	17.3	69.0	135.5	149.4	130.9
Kyrgyzstan	2013	2,184	76%	38.2	26.8	9.0	21.6	50.5	73.7	56.1
Latvia	2012	1,168	74%	57.4	8.8	6.3	19.5	44.6	97.3	82.2
Lithuania	2012	2,184	75%	73.1	6.7	7.6	28.8	60.8	120.1	106.9
Mexico	2012	36,063	77%	30.7	19.9	7.1	28.0	31.3	37.0	107.1
Morocco	2012	1,477	77%	4.6	3.2	2.5	5.1	4.4	5.2	10.0
Netherlands	2013	4,353	48%	25.9	2.1	0.8	6.5	6.0	9.3	121.5
Nicaragua	2012	1,428	79%	24.9	14.6	5.1	18.7	29.0	35.7	112.0
Norway	2013	1,954	55%	38.5	1.3	1.5	13.3	17.0	25.5	160.6
Panama	2012	940	83%	26.8	16.5	8.0	24.0	29.3	35.3	63.7
Paraguay	2012	1,999	79%	30.6	12.5	6.4	36.4	30.8	34.5	97.6
Peru	2012	7,760	73%	26.3	31.3	7.4	17.9	26.1	32.7	81.7
Poland	2013	13,374	71%	34.7	3.8	3.4	21.5	22.1	42.9	89.9
Portugal	2013	2,037	67%	19.5	2.5	1.7	9.8	9.8	16.0	56.4
Republic of Korea	2012	13,650	69%	27.1	6.1	3.2	8.8	12.3	31.1	111.1
Republic of Moldova	2013	1,847	76%	51.9	25.2	7.4	21.6	35.7	95.8	97.6
Romania	2012	7,528	76%	35.3	14.4	8.8	20.8	23.3	50.5	73.2
Russian Federation[b]	2011	199,358	77%	139.4	25.6	15.4	90.0	167.0	186.9	169.1
Saudi Arabia	2012	3,174	88%	12.0	4.5	3.5	13.7	14.6	16.1	29.8
Serbia	2013	1,438	74%	20.1	3.3	3.4	13.5	13.8	20.9	45.9
South Africa	2013	32,316	75%	60.8	37.0	15.6	54.5	88.7	71.2	115.0
Spain	2013	9,987	59%	21.4	3.3	1.7	6.7	9.5	13.5	78.0
Sweden	2013	3,035	60%	31.6	1.2	1.1	8.7	11.5	17.8	118.6
Switzerland[b]	2012	3,650	59%	45.6	4.5	2.0	18.2	21.9	35.2	157.0
Turkey	2013	15,135	71%	19.9	12.3	6.2	14.8	14.5	21.4	87.0
Ukraine[b]	2012	41,713	78%	91.9	21.3	10.9	55.8	98.2	129.2	115.4
United Kingdom	2013	14,875	58%	23.5	2.8	1.4	9.8	16.9	15.7	76.9
United States of America	2013	130,557	63%	41.3	12.4	3.7	26.4	37.9	45.0	102.8

Source: National Safety Council tabulations of World Health Organization (WHO) data.
[a]*Population estimates based on data from WHO and the U.S. Census Bureau (International Data Base).*
[b]*Data include deaths due to all external causes, including self-harm and assault.*

International Motor Vehicle Injury-Related Deaths and Death Rates

The International Classification of Diseases (ICD) system identifies motor vehicle traffic incidents by codes V02-V04, V09, V12-V14, V19-V79, and V86-V89 of the 10th revision of ICD. A motor vehicle is a mechanically or electrically powered device used in the transportation of people or property on a land highway. A motor vehicle traffic incident involves a motor vehicle in transport (i.e., in motion or on a roadway) on a public highway. World-wide road-injury-related deaths totaled 1,255,000 in 2012, resulting in a death rate of 17.7 per 100,000 population.

Motor vehicle injury-related deaths and death rates by age group, latest year available

Country	Year	Deaths Total	Deaths % male	Deaths per 100,000 population[a] All ages	0 to 4	5 to 14	15 to 24	25 to 44	45 to 64	65 or older
Argentina	2012	4,681	79%	10.1	2.8	2.4	16.7	14.2	8.4	12.0
Austria	2013	257	78%	3.0	0.3	0.4	4.8	2.0	3.1	5.3
Belgium	2012	708	76%	6.4	1.4	0.6	10.4	6.7	6.1	8.9
Brazil	2012	36,804	82%	18.5	2.6	3.0	25.5	24.3	20.8	23.6
Bulgaria	2012	359	79%	4.9	0.3	0.9	7.6	4.8	5.6	5.7
Chile	2012	1,191	78%	7.0	2.1	1.5	7.3	8.8	8.7	8.3
Colombia	2011	5,078	81%	11.4	1.7	2.4	13.1	15.2	11.9	25.7
Costa Rica	2012	583	81%	12.6	1.3	2.5	15.9	16.3	14.0	19.7
Croatia	2013	366	76%	8.6	1.9	1.7	12.7	8.9	8.4	11.4
Cuba	2012	855	81%	7.7	1.3	1.9	6.6	8.3	8.8	13.8
Czech Republic	2013	587	76%	5.6	1.0	0.5	9.8	5.5	5.4	7.6
Denmark	2012	151	73%	2.7	0.9	0.9	4.8	2.0	2.5	4.4
Ecuador	2012	1,256	78%	8.3	2.3	2.1	11.3	10.8	9.1	13.4
Egypt	2013	8,656	83%	10.2	6.2	5.2	12.5	11.1	13.6	15.1
El Salvador	2012	924	80%	15.2	1.9	3.6	9.2	19.3	24.9	48.5
Finland	2013	247	74%	4.5	0.7	0.8	6.1	3.9	4.4	7.9
Georgia	2012	22	95%	0.5	0.0	0.0	0.8	0.5	1.0	0.0
Germany	2013	2,892	74%	3.6	0.4	0.5	6.0	3.4	3.3	5.0
Guatemala	2012	5	80%	0.0	0.0	0.0	0.0	0.1	0.1	0.2
Hong Kong SAR	2013	125	70%	1.7	0.0	0.9	0.8	0.9	1.7	5.4
Hungary	2013	665	72%	6.7	0.4	0.6	5.9	6.9	8.4	9.4
Israel	2012	212	72%	2.7	1.3	0.9	4.0	2.8	2.9	4.3
Italy	2012	3,736	80%	6.3	0.5	0.8	9.3	6.7	5.5	9.0
Japan	2013	5,497	67%	4.4	0.7	0.7	3.7	2.3	3.6	9.4
Kazakhstan[b]	2012	3,181	74%	18.9	5.7	5.7	19.0	26.0	25.2	17.7
Kyrgyzstan	2013	657	74%	11.5	3.0	2.2	8.6	17.6	20.4	14.3
Latvia	2012	178	71%	8.7	1.0	2.6	9.1	9.7	9.6	11.1
Lithuania	2012	321	74%	10.7	0.0	3.8	13.2	12.1	13.2	9.9
Mexico	2012	12,015	79%	10.2	3.1	2.6	13.3	12.8	12.1	18.4
Morocco	2012	627	77%	1.9	0.9	0.7	1.7	2.1	2.6	5.0
Netherlands	2013	483	73%	2.9	0.4	0.4	4.2	2.2	2.2	6.5
Nicaragua	2012	627	85%	10.9	1.8	2.0	10.5	16.6	16.5	22.7
Norway	2013	191	75%	3.8	0.3	0.3	6.0	3.1	4.4	6.1
Panama	2012	439	83%	12.5	3.9	2.3	14.7	16.4	16.9	18.1
Paraguay	2012	1,055	84%	16.1	3.6	2.2	26.0	20.1	17.6	20.9
Peru	2012	588	74%	2.0	0.9	0.3	1.6	2.3	3.1	4.9
Poland	2013	2,929	77%	7.6	0.7	1.6	10.3	6.9	8.7	11.1
Portugal	2013	580	78%	5.5	0.6	0.6	6.0	5.6	5.7	8.7
Republic of Korea	2012	6,278	73%	12.5	1.9	1.6	6.6	7.4	15.6	40.3
Republic of Moldova	2013	353	82%	9.9	1.0	2.4	13.7	10.7	12.5	7.3
Romania	2012	1,767	76%	8.3	1.6	2.7	9.4	7.4	10.1	12.3
Russian Federation[b]	2011	29,342	74%	20.5	3.3	4.4	26.1	27.4	20.3	18.7
Saudi Arabia	2012	2,659	88%	10.0	3.1	2.9	12.3	12.3	13.4	21.1
Serbia	2013	476	76%	6.6	0.0	1.7	8.6	6.7	6.8	9.5
South Africa	2013	5,684	74%	10.7	4.2	3.4	9.3	16.9	14.0	12.1
Spain	2013	1,883	77%	4.0	0.9	0.8	3.7	3.9	4.0	7.3
Sweden	2013	253	77%	2.6	0.2	0.5	3.5	2.5	2.9	3.9
Switzerland[b]	2012	341	75%	4.3	1.7	0.6	5.3	2.9	5.2	7.1
Turkey	2013	1,431	79%	1.9	0.8	0.5	2.0	1.9	2.6	3.8
Ukraine[b]	2012	5,905	75%	13.0	2.3	2.5	16.4	16.5	13.8	11.8
United Kingdom	2013	1,572	75%	2.5	0.3	0.4	4.2	2.6	2.2	3.6
United States of America	2013	35,369	71%	11.2	2.5	2.1	15.2	12.7	12.1	15.1

Source: National Safety Council tabulations of World Health Organization (WHO) data.
[a]Population estimates based on data from WHO and the U.S. Census Bureau (International Data Base).
[b]Data include deaths due to all transportation-related causes, ICD codes V01-V99.

International Poisoning Injury-Related Deaths and Death Rates

The International Classification of Diseases (ICD) system identifies unintentional poisonings by codes X40-X49, which include cases of accidental poisoning by drugs, medicaments, biological substances, alcohol, solvents, gases, vapors, and pesticides. Other accidental poisonings by unspecified chemicals and noxious substances also are included. Worldwide poisoning-related deaths totaled 193,000 in 2012, resulting in a death rate of 2.7 per 100,000 population.

Unintentional poisoning injury-related deaths and death rates by age group, latest year available

Country	Year	Deaths		Deaths per 100,000 population[a]						
		Total	% male	All ages	0 to 4	5 to 14	15 to 24	25 to 44	45 to 64	65 or older
Argentina	2012	325	67%	0.7	0.9	0.2	0.5	0.5	0.7	1.9
Austria	2013	85	13%	1.0	0.5	0.0	0.3	0.1	0.3	0.3
Belgium	2012	373	36%	3.4	0.2	0.0	0.6	2.1	2.4	3.2
Brazil	2012	890	78%	0.4	0.2	0.0	0.6	0.6	0.4	0.6
Bulgaria	2012	141	43%	1.9	0.5	0.0	0.9	1.0	1.3	2.2
Chile	2012	297	71%	1.7	0.3	0.0	0.3	1.9	3.1	2.5
Colombia	2011	186	81%	0.4	0.3	0.0	0.3	0.5	0.6	0.9
Costa Rica	2012	71	61%	1.5	0.5	0.0	0.1	1.2	2.8	1.3
Croatia	2013	109	71%	2.6	0.0	0.0	1.4	3.3	3.3	1.5
Cuba	2012	204	36%	1.8	1.1	0.0	0.3	0.5	1.6	0.8
Czech Republic	2013	463	65%	4.4	0.0	0.1	1.6	3.9	7.0	4.5
Denmark	2012	209	63%	3.7	0.0	0.0	1.6	5.5	4.8	1.4
Ecuador	2012	229	51%	1.5	0.5	0.2	0.6	1.1	1.9	2.6
Egypt	2013	168	49%	0.2	0.2	0.1	0.4	0.2	0.1	0.1
El Salvador	2012	325	49%	5.3	0.2	0.2	0.6	4.7	6.3	5.3
Finland	2013	611	72%	11.2	0.0	0.0	5.5	12.1	20.5	8.6
Georgia	2012	244	24%	5.4	0.3	0.4	1.5	2.1	2.0	1.3
Germany	2013	865	55%	1.1	0.0	0.1	0.3	1.4	0.9	0.7
Guatemala	2012	1,203	80%	8.5	0.8	0.6	6.6	14.3	18.2	24.0
Hong Kong SAR	2013	171	66%	2.4	0.4	0.0	0.3	3.0	2.3	1.3
Hungary	2013	103	67%	1.0	0.2	0.4	1.0	1.0	1.0	1.7
Israel	2012	168	1%	2.1	0.0	0.0	0.0	0.0	0.1	0.0
Italy	2012	774	44%	1.3	0.0	0.0	0.3	1.2	0.7	1.5
Japan	2013	1,176	36%	0.9	0.0	0.0	0.3	0.7	0.7	0.6
Kazakhstan	2012	2,080	74%	12.4	2.5	1.4	3.2	16.8	23.0	18.0
Kyrgyzstan	2013	409	75%	7.2	0.3	0.2	1.0	7.5	21.6	13.1
Latvia	2012	260	54%	12.8	0.0	0.0	2.8	8.9	17.0	6.8
Lithuania	2012	659	55%	22.1	0.7	0.0	4.4	19.8	26.7	10.1
Mexico	2012	1,214	79%	1.0	0.3	0.2	0.7	1.3	1.7	2.5
Morocco	2012	153	46%	0.5	0.1	0.1	0.4	0.4	0.3	0.8
Netherlands	2013	146	60%	0.9	0.0	0.0	0.5	1.4	0.9	0.8
Nicaragua	2012	134	30%	2.3	2.6	0.1	0.2	0.6	2.5	1.9
Norway	2013	321	73%	6.3	0.0	0.0	4.8	9.1	9.6	4.1
Panama	2012	29	55%	0.8	0.0	0.0	0.5	0.5	0.6	3.5
Paraguay	2012	81	15%	1.2	0.7	0.0	0.1	0.4	0.4	0.5
Peru	2012	426	35%	1.4	0.3	0.3	0.5	0.7	1.1	2.0
Poland	2013	1,357	83%	3.5	0.2	0.2	0.9	3.8	6.5	2.6
Portugal	2013	119	25%	1.1	0.2	0.0	0.1	0.5	0.5	0.9
Republic of Korea	2012	366	58%	0.7	0.0	0.0	0.1	0.4	0.8	1.8
Republic of Moldova	2013	561	41%	15.8	3.1	0.8	0.9	6.4	19.3	12.4
Romania	2012	781	68%	3.7	1.3	0.4	0.9	2.5	5.9	7.7
Russian Federation	2011	29,413	77%	20.6	2.3	1.2	6.0	26.6	33.0	17.9
Serbia	2013	373	10%	5.2	0.0	0.0	0.6	1.0	0.5	0.8
South Africa	2013	1,051	44%	2.0	6.7	0.3	0.3	1.0	1.8	2.0
Spain	2013	966	64%	2.1	0.0	0.1	0.4	2.4	2.1	2.9
Sweden	2013	470	73%	4.9	0.0	0.0	3.6	6.8	6.4	3.8
Switzerland	2012	280	34%	3.5	0.2	0.0	1.5	2.9	1.8	0.5
Turkey	2013	1,937	20%	2.5	0.3	0.2	0.5	0.6	1.0	2.4
Ukraine	2012	6,690	79%	14.7	1.5	0.8	3.1	15.6	27.9	12.0
United Kingdom	2013	16,649	12%	26.3	0.0	0.1	2.2	9.4	5.7	1.5
United States of America	2013	38,851	65%	12.3	0.2	0.1	7.5	20.0	20.5	4.1

Source: National Safety Council tabulations of World Health Organization (WHO) data.
[a]*Population estimates based on data from WHO and the U.S. Census Bureau (International Data Base).*

International Fall Injury-Related Deaths and Death Rates

"Accidental falls" are identified by codes W00-W19 in the 10th revision of the International Classification of Diseases (ICD) system. World-wide fall-related deaths totaled 693,000 in 2012, resulting in a death rate of 9.8 per 100,000 population.

Unintentional fall injury-related deaths and death rates by age group, latest year available

Country	Year	Deaths		Deaths per 100,000 population[a]						
		Total	% male	All ages	0 to 4	5 to 14	15 to 24	25 to 44	45 to 64	65 or older
Argentina	2012	287	64%	0.6	0.3	0.1	0.3	0.4	0.4	3.2
Austria	2013	853	55%	10.1	0.0	0.1	0.9	1.0	5.1	45.2
Belgium	2012	1,482	48%	13.4	0.3	0.0	0.1	1.0	7.2	64.1
Brazil	2012	11,649	60%	5.8	0.8	0.3	0.8	2.2	6.5	50.9
Bulgaria	2012	267	72%	3.7	0.8	0.4	0.5	1.5	4.8	9.9
Chile	2012	922	49%	5.4	0.2	0.1	0.4	1.6	3.5	42.7
Colombia	2011	1,134	77%	2.5	0.7	0.3	0.8	1.5	3.5	18.9
Costa Rica	2012	82	83%	1.8	0.0	0.1	0.2	1.5	2.6	11.2
Croatia	2013	1,039	40%	24.4	0.5	0.0	0.2	0.9	7.4	120.5
Cuba	2012	2,067	47%	18.7	1.1	0.4	0.4	1.4	5.6	138.7
Czech Republic	2013	657	62%	6.3	0.3	0.2	1.8	1.5	5.2	24.5
Denmark	2012	511	43%	9.1	0.3	0.2	0.1	0.4	3.4	45.7
Ecuador	2012	468	75%	3.1	1.1	0.5	1.3	2.6	4.7	16.5
Egypt	2013	1,398	74%	1.7	2.9	1.3	1.2	1.3	1.8	3.7
El Salvador	2012	259	66%	4.3	0.4	0.5	1.4	2.4	3.3	40.5
Finland	2013	1,113	54%	20.5	0.0	0.0	0.5	1.4	10.2	90.3
Georgia	2012	12	67%	0.3	0.0	0.0	0.0	0.2	0.2	1.3
Germany	2013	10,842	46%	13.4	0.2	0.1	0.4	0.8	3.4	58.5
Guatemala	2012	6	67%	0.0	0.0	0.0	0.0	0.1	0.1	0.4
Hong Kong SAR	2013	232	65%	3.2	1.2	0.2	0.5	0.6	2.0	16.2
Hungary	2013	1,776	47%	18.0	0.4	0.1	0.1	1.3	9.8	85.8
Israel	2012	119	49%	1.5	0.4	0.0	0.2	0.5	0.8	11.1
Italy	2012	4,178	52%	7.0	0.4	0.1	0.5	0.9	2.4	28.7
Japan	2013	7,766	58%	6.2	0.1	0.1	0.5	0.7	2.4	21.1
Kazakhstan	2012	499	73%	3.0	2.0	0.4	1.5	3.6	4.1	7.6
Kyrgyzstan	2013	77	79%	1.3	0.8	0.2	0.8	1.9	2.4	2.5
Latvia	2012	183	72%	9.0	1.0	0.5	0.8	5.9	14.5	17.4
Lithuania	2012	346	69%	11.6	0.0	0.0	0.7	4.1	16.3	32.8
Mexico	2012	2,274	79%	1.9	0.8	0.2	0.6	1.4	3.5	11.1
Morocco	2012	119	75%	0.4	0.3	0.1	0.3	0.4	0.5	1.5
Netherlands	2013	2,174	43%	12.9	0.1	0.0	0.2	0.9	2.8	69.7
Nicaragua	2012	178	55%	3.1	0.2	0.0	0.3	1.3	2.9	48.8
Norway	2013	498	48%	9.8	0.0	0.3	0.6	0.5	3.2	55.4
Panama	2012	133	79%	3.8	1.2	0.3	1.3	2.1	4.8	25.9
Paraguay	2012	72	81%	1.1	0.2	0.2	0.4	0.5	2.1	7.5
Peru	2012	184	74%	0.6	0.3	0.3	0.2	0.5	0.8	3.5
Poland	2013	4,662	56%	12.1	0.4	0.2	1.6	2.7	10.0	57.3
Portugal	2013	533	60%	5.1	0.4	0.0	0.7	0.7	3.0	20.4
Republic of Korea	2012	2,104	75%	4.2	0.9	0.3	0.5	1.4	5.8	17.2
Republic of Moldova	2013	183	73%	5.1	1.0	0.0	0.7	2.2	9.0	19.1
Romania	2012	1,249	77%	5.9	0.9	0.2	1.2	2.4	9.1	17.3
Russian Federation	2011	8,965	71%	6.3	1.5	0.5	2.7	5.4	8.2	14.5
Saudi Arabia	2012	189	87%	0.7	0.8	0.3	0.3	0.8	1.2	2.5
Serbia	2013	341	69%	4.8	0.6	0.1	0.5	1.1	4.2	17.6
South Africa	2013	181	71%	0.3	0.2	0.1	0.2	0.2	0.6	2.1
Spain	2013	2,672	50%	5.7	0.4	0.1	0.5	0.8	2.4	26.7
Sweden	2013	967	55%	10.1	0.2	0.0	0.1	0.4	2.7	48.0
Switzerland	2012	1,595	44%	19.9	0.7	0.1	0.4	2.0	3.2	106.4
Turkey	2013	3,608	52%	4.7	1.3	0.2	0.5	0.6	2.1	51.2
Ukraine	2012	2,506	74%	5.5	1.0	0.2	1.7	4.1	7.7	12.4
United Kingdom	2013	5,147	50%	8.1	0.1	0.1	0.4	1.0	3.0	40.5
United States of America	2013	30,208	50%	9.6	0.2	0.0	0.5	1.0	4.4	57.0

Source: National Safety Council tabulations of World Health Organization (WHO) data.
[a]*Population estimates based on data from WHO and the U.S. Census Bureau (International Data Base).*

The International Classification of Diseases (ICD) system identifies drowning by codes W65-W74, which include cases of unintentional drowning and submersion while in or following a fall in a bathtub, swimming pool, or natural body of water. Other specified and unspecified cases of drowning and submersion also are included. World-wide drowning-related deaths totaled 372,000 in 2012, resulting in a death rate of 5.3 per 100,000 population.

Unintentional drowning injury-related deaths and death rates by age group, latest year available

Country	Year	Deaths Total	% male	All ages	0 to 4	5 to 14	15 to 24	25 to 44	45 to 64	65 or older
Argentina	2012	499	82%	1.1	2.6	0.8	1.9	0.9	0.5	1.0
Austria	2013	53	72%	0.6	0.3	0.0	0.6	0.2	0.5	1.9
Belgium	2012	53	66%	0.5	0.9	0.0	0.1	0.3	0.7	0.8
Brazil	2012	5,385	86%	2.7	2.9	2.1	3.7	2.6	2.4	2.6
Bulgaria	2012	135	77%	1.8	1.3	1.3	1.6	1.2	2.1	3.2
Chile	2012	342	91%	2.0	2.1	0.6	1.7	1.8	2.5	4.2
Colombia	2011	906	81%	2.0	4.0	1.8	2.7	1.5	1.4	2.3
Costa Rica	2012	116	91%	2.5	1.1	1.6	3.6	2.6	2.7	2.6
Croatia	2013	100	83%	2.3	0.5	0.0	0.8	1.8	3.3	4.4
Cuba	2012	209	91%	1.9	2.7	1.6	2.3	1.9	1.7	1.9
Czech Republic	2013	177	76%	1.7	0.5	0.5	0.6	1.3	2.6	2.6
Denmark	2012	34	82%	0.6	0.3	0.0	0.1	0.8	0.7	1.0
Ecuador	2012	485	82%	3.2	5.0	1.8	4.2	3.0	2.5	4.4
Egypt	2013	1,965	85%	2.3	3.9	2.7	4.1	1.3	1.0	1.1
El Salvador	2012	176	83%	2.9	2.0	1.3	4.6	3.4	2.3	2.8
Finland	2013	131	77%	2.4	1.0	0.2	0.8	1.1	3.0	6.0
Georgia	2012	65	78%	1.4	0.7	2.3	2.3	1.1	1.4	1.0
Germany	2013	465	72%	0.6	0.4	0.3	0.5	0.3	0.5	1.1
Guatemala	2012	346	86%	2.5	1.7	1.3	2.9	2.9	2.3	7.1
Hong Kong SAR	2013	30	83%	0.4	0.0	0.6	0.3	0.4	0.3	1.0
Hungary	2013	123	80%	1.2	0.2	0.4	1.5	1.0	1.7	1.5
Israel	2012	44	80%	0.6	0.6	0.6	0.5	0.2	0.9	0.9
Italy	2012	363	82%	0.6	0.2	0.2	0.6	0.6	0.5	1.0
Japan	2013	7,523	53%	6.0	0.6	0.5	0.8	0.7	2.5	19.8
Kazakhstan	2012	872	84%	5.2	3.9	3.7	5.6	6.5	5.6	2.4
Kyrgyzstan	2013	214	69%	3.7	9.3	2.3	1.8	3.8	3.5	3.7
Latvia	2012	135	79%	6.6	1.9	1.1	3.2	7.2	10.0	7.4
Lithuania	2012	232	81%	7.8	2.7	2.4	3.9	7.5	11.6	9.6
Mexico	2012	2,095	85%	1.8	2.7	1.0	2.4	1.6	1.6	2.6
Morocco	2012	333	83%	1.0	1.0	1.3	1.9	0.7	0.7	0.7
Netherlands	2013	84	70%	0.5	0.7	0.2	0.5	0.3	0.5	0.9
Nicaragua	2012	154	88%	2.7	1.8	0.7	3.4	3.1	3.6	4.5
Norway	2013	52	77%	1.0	0.6	0.0	0.3	0.6	1.7	2.1
Panama	2012	121	88%	3.4	3.6	3.1	2.9	3.3	4.0	4.6
Paraguay	2012	151	89%	2.3	2.9	1.1	3.4	1.8	2.9	2.2
Peru	2012	439	77%	1.5	2.7	1.1	1.5	1.3	1.0	2.9
Poland	2013	884	82%	2.3	0.3	0.5	2.5	1.8	3.5	2.7
Portugal	2013	81	72%	0.8	0.2	0.3	1.0	0.4	0.9	1.3
Republic of Korea	2012	712	80%	1.4	0.3	0.8	0.9	0.9	1.8	3.5
Republic of Moldova	2013	159	75%	4.5	3.6	2.1	2.5	3.9	7.0	5.6
Romania	2012	657	82%	3.1	1.6	2.7	3.2	2.1	4.0	4.2
Russian Federation	2011	8,530	84%	6.0	2.6	3.2	4.7	7.6	7.1	4.5
Saudi Arabia	2012	13	77%	0.0	0.2	0.1	0.0	0.0	0.0	0.0
Serbia	2013	72	76%	1.0	0.3	0.4	1.2	0.7	1.0	1.8
South Africa	2013	1,518	76%	2.9	4.9	3.3	2.4	2.4	2.4	2.4
Spain	2013	422	82%	0.9	0.8	0.5	0.7	0.5	0.9	2.0
Sweden	2013	83	82%	0.9	0.3	0.3	0.7	0.2	1.1	1.9
Switzerland	2012	52	69%	0.7	0.7	0.1	0.6	0.3	0.7	1.4
Turkey	2013	647	81%	0.9	1.3	0.8	1.1	0.6	0.6	1.6
Ukraine	2012	2,713	85%	6.0	2.4	2.9	4.8	6.7	7.8	5.3
United Kingdom	2013	262	76%	0.4	0.2	0.1	0.5	0.4	0.5	0.5
United States of America	2013	3,391	77%	1.1	2.1	0.5	1.1	0.9	1.1	1.2

Source: National Safety Council tabulations of World Health Organization (WHO) data.
[a]*Population estimates based on data from WHO and the U.S. Census Bureau (International Data Base).*

Counts and rates of fatal work-related injuries are shown on this page and the next. Comparisons between countries should be made with caution and take into account the differences in sources, coverage, and kinds of cases included.

Occupational deaths by country, 2010-2014

Country	Deaths					Source of data	Coverage	
	2010	2011	2012	2013	2014		Worker types[a]	Activities excluded
Injuries only – compensated cases								
Australia	216	226	229	197	188	AR	E	none
Bulgaria	92	94	77	81	—	IR	I	none
Chile	—	282	322	283	—	AR	E	none
Finland	33	26	—	—	—	IR	E	none
France	529	—	—	542	—	IR	I	none
Germany	674	664	—	—	—	IR	I	none
Korea, Republic of	1,255	1,271	1,292	1,245	1,123	IR	I	none
Lithuania	50	53	57	60	—	LR	E	none
New Zealand	118	—	48[b]	—	—	IR	—	none
Slovenia	—	18	—	—	—	AR	I	none
South Africa	185	—	—	—	—	AR	—	none
Zimbabwe	—	84	91	—	106	IR	I	none
Injuries only – reported cases								
Armenia	12	—	—	—	—	LR	E	none
Austria	185	73	98	91	—	IR	E	none
Belarus	198	169	147	141	—	S	E	none
Belgium[c]	82	82	67	72	—	IR	E	none
Cuba	88	—	—	—	—	AR	E	none
Cyprus	19	5	9	9	5	LR	E	none
Czech Republic	—	139	105	—	—	LR	—	none
Estonia	17	19	14	20	—	LR	—	none
Hungary	95	80	62	—	—	LR	E	none
Ireland	48	49	—	40	—	LR	—	none
Japan	—	1,024	1,093	1,030	1,057	S	—	Pub. Admn.
Latvia	—	34	34	29	—	LR	E	none
Moldova, Republic of	39	—	—	36	34	S	E	none
Norway	46	53	37	48	—	LR	E	SF, MT, OOE
Poland	446	404	348	—	—	S	E	Priv. Agr
Russian Federation	2,004	1,824	1,820	—	—	S	—	none
Singapore	55	61	56	59	—	AR	E	PDS
Slovakia	48	38	54	53	—	LR	E	none
Spain	342	335	271	232	—	IR	I	none
Sri Lanka	64	—	—	141	77	LR	E	none
Sweden	54	58	45	33	—	AR	—	none
Trinidad and Tobago	9	—	—	—	—	AR	—	—
Turkey	1,454	1,710	745	—	—	IR	I	none
United Kingdom	171	171	—	148	—	LR	E	none
United States[d]	4,547	4,693	4,383	4,405	—	C	E,SE	none
Injuries and commuting accidents – compensated cases								
Croatia	38	38	40	27	—	IR	E, SE	none
Injuries and commuting accidents – reported cases								
El Salvador	96	—	—	—	—	C	E, SE	none
Macau, China[c]	12	13	19	18	—	LR	—	none
Romania	377	297	240	223	—	LR	E,SE	none
Injuries and diseases – compensated cases								
Malta	3	1	6	—	—	AR		none
Injuries and diseases – reported cases								
Argentina	871	558	562	—	—	AR	I	none
Hong Kong, China	183	191	196	188	—	LR	E	none
Nicaragua	42	—	—	—	—	AR	—	none
Injuries, diseases, and commuting accidents – compensated cases								
Thailand	619	—	—	—	—	IR	I	none
Injuries, diseases, and commuting accidents – reported cases								
Mexico	1,433	1,578	1,534	1,314	—	IR	—	none
Panama	12	24	24	22	—	LR	—	—

Source: International Labour Organization (ILO), ILO Department of Statistics, accessed September 28, 2015, from http://laborsta.ilo.org.
Note: Dash (—) means data not available. See footnotes on page 195.

Source of Data
AR = Administrative reports
C = Census
IR = Insurance records
LR = Labor inspectorate records
S = Survey

Worker Types
E = Employees
I = Insured persons
IE = Insured employees
RU = Registered unemployed
SE = Self-employed

Economic Activities
MT = Maritime transport
OOE = Offshore oil extraction
PDS = Private domestic service
Priv. Agr = Private farms in agriculture
SF = Sea fishing

Occupational Death Rates

The International Labour Organization (ILO) estimates that about 2.3 million persons die from work-related incidents and diseases each year. This total equates to about 6,300 worker deaths per day due to an incident or disease from their work, with one worker dying from a work-related incident or disease every 15 seconds. In addition to the human cost of these deaths and injuries, the economic burden of poor safety and health practices is estimated at 4% of global gross domestic product each year.

Source: International Labour Organization. (2015). Accessed October 7, 2015 at http://www.ilo.org/global/topics/safety-and-health-at-work/lang--en/index.htm

Occupational death rates by country, 2010-2014

Country	Coverage[e]	2010	2011	2012	2013	2014
Deaths per 1,000 employees						
Injuries only						
Cuba	RC	0.2	—	—	—	—
Ireland	RC	([f])	—	—	—	—
Slovakia	RC	—	2	3	3	—
Injuries and diseases						
Hong Kong, China	RC	0.1	0.1	0.1	0.1	—
Deaths per 100,000 employed persons						
Injuries only						
Australia	CC	2	2	—	—	—
Austria	RC	—	2.6	3.4	3.1	—
Cyprus	RC	—	1.5	2.8	2.9	1.7
Denmark	RC	—	2	2	—	—
Estonia	RC	3	3.1	2.2	3.2	—
Finland	CC	1.6	1.2	—	—	—
Hungary	RC	—	2.1	1.6	—	—
Kyrgyzstan	RC	—	—	—	6	—
Lithuania	RC	4.6	5.4	5.6	5.8	—
Malaysia	RC	—	9	6	—	—
Netherlands	RC	—	0.7	—	—	—
Norway[g]	RC	1.8	2.1	1.4	1.9	—
Romania	RC	—	—	—	4.7	—
Singapore	RC	2.2	2.3	2.1	2.1	—
Slovakia	RC	—	2	3	3	—
Slovenia	CC	—	2.2	—	—	—
Sweden	RC	1	1	1	1	—
Turkey	RC	—	15.5	6.2	—	—
United Kingdom	RC	0.6	0.6	—	0.5	—
United States[d,h]	RC	3.5	3.5	3.2[b]	—	—
Injuries and commuting accidents						
Brazil	RC	—	7.4	—	—	—
Croatia	CC	—	2.7	2.9	—	—
Israel	CC	—	2.4	2	—	—
Macau, China	RC	3.8[b]	4	5.5	5	—
Romania	RC	8.2	6.4	5.1	—	—
Injuries and and diseases						
Malta	CC	1.8	0.6	3.5	—	—
Injuries, diseases, and commuting accidents						
Israel	CC	2	—	—	—	—
Luxembourg	RC	—	([f])	([f])	([f])	—
Mexico	RC	10	10.5	9.8	8.1	—
Panama	RC	—	1.6	1.5	1.3	—
Deaths per 100,000 persons insured						
Injuries only						
Australia	CC	—	—	2	1.7	1.6
Belize	CC	—	4.5	6.7	—	—
Bulgaria	CC	3.6	3.6	3	3.1	—
Chile	CC	—	5.5	6	5.1	—
Czech Republic	RC	2.8	—	—	—	—
France	CC	([f])	—	—	([f])	—
Germany	CC	1.8	—	—	—	—
Malaysia	RC	—	—	—	5	—
Spain	RC	2.3	2.3	1.9	1.7	—
Thailand	CC	—	—	—	([f])	—
Turkey	RC	20.8	—	—	—	—
Injuries and commuting accidents						
El Salvador	RC	0.1	—	—	—	—
Injuries and diseases						
Argentina	RC	—	67.1	64.9	—	—
Deaths per 1,000,000 Hours Worked						
Injuries only						
Japan[i]	RC	([f])	—	—	—	—
Korea, Republic of	CC	([f])	([f])	([f])	([f])	([f])

See source and limitations of data on page 194.

Note: Dash (—) indicates data not available

[a]*Types of workers included in the data.*
[b]*Provisional.*
[c]*Private sector only.*
[d]*Excludes farms with less than 11 employees.*
[e]*Includes reported cases (RC) and compensated cases (CC) of occupational fatalities*
[f]*Value 0.05 or less.*
[g]*Excludes sea fishing, maritime transport, and offshore oil extraction.*
[h]*Excludes federal jurusdictions.*
[i]*Excludes agriculture.*

Counts and rates of nonfatal work-related injuries are shown on this page and the next. Comparisons between countries should be made with caution and take into account the differences in sources, coverage, and kinds of cases included.

Occupational injuries by country, 2010-2014

Country	Nonfatal injuries					Source of data	Coverage	
	2010	2011	2012	2013	2014		Worker types[a]	Activities excluded
Injuries only – compensated cases								
Australia	92,300	94,714	105,525	107,220	98,980	IR	—	none
Chile	—	225,535	214,986	198,551	—	AR	I	none
Finland	50,557	51,344	—	—	—	IR	E	none
France	658,847	—	—	618,273	—	IR	I	none
Germany	1,045,142	1,007,200	—	—	—	IR	I	none
Lithuania	2,305	2,668	2,840	3,082	—	LR	—	none
Slovenia	—	15,200	—	—	—	AR	—	none
Injuries only – reported cases								
Armenia	21	—	—	—	—	LR	E	none
Austria	117,775	70,374	68,260	59,464	—	IR	E	none
Belgium	86,268	85,329	77,609	71,008	—	IR	E	—
Belize	1,804	1,757	1,756	—	—	AR	—	none
Bulgaria	2,365	2,279	2,314	2,203	—	IR	I	none
Cuba	4,919	—	—	—	—	AR	E	none
Cyprus	2,165	2,005	1,732	1,529	1,613	LR	E	none
Czech Republic	51,557	—	—	42,927	—	AR	I	AF
Denmark	—	42,491	41,710	—	—	AR	—	—
Estonia	3,198	3,725	4,133	4,160	—	LR	—	none
Hungary	19,853	17,215	16,963	—	—	LR	E	AF
Ireland	40,583	—	—	—	—	S	—	AF, Inst.
Latvia	—	1,363	1,476	1,566	—	LR	E	none
Netherlands	—	834,200	908,000	831,800	—	S	E	—
New Zealand	20,229	—	15,369	—	—	IR	E, SE	none
Norway	15,370	—	—	—	—	LR	—	SF, MT, OOE
Panama	40	22	30	42	—	LR	—	—
Singapore	10,264	10,060	11,057	11,842	—	AR	—	PDS
Slovakia	9,124	8,789	8,469	8,482	—	LR	E	none
Spain	568,080	511,051	407,073	402,718	—	IR	—	none
Sri Lanka	1,456	—	—	—	1,440	LR	E	none
Sweden	28,311	28,702	29,906	30,480	—	AR	E, SE	none
Trinidad and Tobago	833	—	—	—	—	AR	—	—
Turkey	2,085	2,216	2,209	—	—	IR	I	AF, Inst.
United Kingdom	117,469	113,535	—	79,917	—	LR	E	—
United States[b]	1,191,100	—	—	—	—	S	E, SE	Fed., Inst., OT
Injuries and commuting accidents - compensated cases								
Croatia	15,791	18,116	15,718	15,432	—	IR	—	none
Injuries and commuting accidents - reported cases								
Macau, China	3,759[c]	4,247	3,352	5,632	—	LR	E	AF, Inst.
Romania	3,767	3,264	3,251	3,352	—	LR	E, SE	AF
Injuries and diseases - compensated cases								
Malta	3,314	3,024	3,057	—	—	AR	—	none
Injuries and diseases - reported cases								
Argentina	568,162	466,086	441,113	—	—	AR	—	none
Hong Kong, China	41,724	40,387	39,711	37,839	—	LR	E	none
Nicaragua	25,838	—	—	—	—	AR	—	none
Switzerland	—	93,770	—	—	—	IR	I	none
Injuries, diseases, and commuting accidents - compensated cases								
Israel	62,519	63,294	66,264	—	—	IR	I	none
Thailand	145,892	—	—	—	—	IR	I	none
Injuries, diseases, and commuting accidents - reported cases								
Ecuador	—	9,338	13,657	—	—	AR	—	none
Mexico	506,528	536,322	557,782	542,373	—	IR	—	none

Source: International Labour Organization, Department of Statistics, accessed September 30, 2015, from http://www.ilo.org/ilostat/faces/home/statisticaldata
Note: Dash (—) means data not available. See footnotes on page 197.

Source of Data
AR = Administrative reports
IR = Insurance records
LR = Labor inspectorate records
S = Survey

Worker Types
E = Employees
I = Insured persons
SE = Self-employed

Economic Activities
AF = Armed forces
Agr = Agriculture
Fed. = Federal jurisdictions
Inst. = Institutional population
M = Manufacturing
MT = Maritime transport
OOE = Offshore oil extraction
OT = Overseas territories
PDS = Private domestic service
Priv. Agr = Private farms in agriculture
SF = Sea fishing

The International Labour Organization (ILO) estimates that about 317 million nonfatal occupational injuries occur annually, many of which result in extended absences from work. This means that every 15 seconds, 153 workers suffer a work-related injury. Provided below are nonfatal injury and illness rates for 42 countries included in the ILO dataset.

Source: International Labour Organization. (2015). Safety and health at work. Accessed October 7, 2015 from www.ilo.org/global/topics/safety-and-health-at-work/lang--en/index.htm

Occupational injury rates by country, 2010-2014

Country	Coverage[d]	2010	2011	2012	2013	2014
Injuries per 1,000 employees						
Injuries only						
Cuba	RC	10.2	—	—	—	—
Ireland	RC	21.8	22.5	—	—	—
Injuries and diseases						
Hong Kong, China	RC	15.4	14.5	14	—	—
Injuries per 1,000 insured employees						
Injuries and diseases						
Argentina	RC	—	56.1	50.9	—	—
Injuries per 100,000 employed persons						
Injuries only						
Australia	CC	912.5	907.5	—	1,011.5	912.8
Austria	RC	—	2,478	2,368	2,051	—
Bulgaria	CC	—	—	—	84.7	—
Cyprus	RC	—	613.6	534.4	494.4	541.5
Denmark	RC	—	1,588	1,560	—	—
Estonia	RC	560.2	611.6	661.9	669.6	—
Finland	CC	2,385	2,397	—	—	—
France	CC	—	—	—	22.7	—
Hungary	RC	—	451.6	437.4	—	—
Kyrgyzstan	RC	—	—	—	38	—
Lithuania	RC	—	269.3	281.1	299.7	—
Malaysia	RC	—	747	703	—	—
Netherlands	RC	—	11,800	12,800	11,900	—
New Zealand	CC	—	—	800	—	—
Norway[e]	RC	613.1	—	—	—	—
Panama[f]	RC	—	—	—	2.5	—
Qatar[g]	CC	—	8.9	5.4	3.6[f]	—
Romania	RC	—	—	—	70.5	—
Slovakia	RC	—	452	430	431.2	—
Slovenia	CC	—	1,858.6	—	—	—
Sweden	RC	643	636	662	666	—
Turkey	RC	—	20.1	18.5	—	—
United Kingdom	RC	402.7	387.8	—	270.1	—
United States[b, e]	RC	1,179	—	—	—	—
Injuries and commuting accidents						
Brazil	RC	—	1,609.3	—	—	—
Croatia	CC	—	1,284.6	1,127.3	1,093.9	—
Israel	CC	—	2,419.5	2,259.6	—	—
Macau, China[f]	RC	1,181[c]	1,296.4	976.7	1,560.1	—
Romania	RC	82.4	70	69.3	—	—
Injuries and diseases						
Malta	CC	2,013.2	1,792.4	1,770.1	—	—
Switzerland	RC	—	2,437.7	—	—	—
Injuries, diseases, and commuting accidents						
Israel	CC	2,438.8	—	—	—	—
Mexico	RC	3,532	3,582.4	3,559.2	3,343	—
Panama[f]	RC	—	1.4	1.9	—	—
Injuries per 100,000 persons insured						
Injuries only						
Australia	CC	—	—	1,016.4	—	—
Belize	CC	—	1,996.9	1,954.4	—	—
Bulgaria	CC	—	88.1	90.2	—	86.5
Chile	CC	—	5,488.3	4,876.2	—	—
Czech Republic[e]	RC	1,196	—	—	—	—
France	CC	23.3	—	—	—	—
Germany	CC	2,738	—	—	—	—
Malaysia[f]	RC	—	—	—	681	—
Spain	RC	3,861.1	3,504.7	2,838.7	2,997.6	—
Injuries per 1,000,000 Hours Worked						
Injuries only						
Belgium[f]	RC	22.2	21.4	19.4	17.6	—
Injuries, diseases, and commuting accidents						
Luxembourg	RC	—	12.5	12.3	12	—

See source and limitations of data on page 196.
Note: Dash (–) indicates data not available
[a] *Types of workers included in the data.*
[b] *Excludes federal jurisdictions, occupational diseases, and farms with less than 11 employees.*
[c] *Provisional.*
[d] *Includes reported cases (RC) and compensated cases (CC) of occupational fatalities*
[e] *See activities excluded in table on page 196.*
[f] *Private sector only.*
[g] *Excluding injuries not resulting in some degree of disability.*

Technical Appendix (cont.)

Berkowitz, M., & Burton, J.F., Jr. (1987). *Permanent Disability Benefits in Workers' Compensation.* Kalamazoo, MI: W.E. Upjohn Institute for Employment Research.

Blincoe, L. J., Miller, T. R., Zaloshnja, E., & Lawrence, B. A. (2015, May). The economic and societal impact of motor vehicle crashes, 2010. (Revised) (Report No. DOT HS 812 013). Washington, DC: National Highway Traffic Safety Administration.

Bureau of Labor Statistics [BLS]. (2012). *Occupational Injury & Illness Classification Manual Version 2.01.* Downloaded from http://www.bls.gov/iif/oshoiics.htm on August 29, 2013.

Bureau of Labor Statistics [BLS]. (2014, December). Workplace Injuries and Illnesses in 2013. Press release USDL-14-2183.

Hensler, D.R., Marquis, M.S., Abrahamse, A.F., Berry, S.H., Ebener, P.A., Lewis, E.D., Lind, E.A., MacCoun, R.J., ... M.E. (1991). ... *States.* Santa

...phy, S.L., & ... 1999. *National*

...mpensation Paid ...A: The RAND

...F., & Miller, ...a, IL: Statistics

...N., Gellert, W., ...G. (1991). *The* ...tional Technical

Miller, T.R., Brigham, P.A., Cohen, M.A., Douglass, J ... Galbraith, M.S., Lestina, D.C., Nelkin, V.S., Pindus, N.... & Smith-Regojo, P. (1993a). Estimating the costs to society cigarette fire injuries. *Report to Congress in Response to the Fire Cigarette Act of 1990.* Washington, DC: U.S. Consumer Pro... Safety Commission.

Miller, T.R., Pindus, N.M., Douglass, J.B., & Rossman, (1993b). *Nonfatal Injury Incidence, Costs, and Consequences: A Book.* Washington, DC: The Urban Institute Press.

Occupational Safety and Health Administration. (... *OSHA recordkeeping handbook.* OSHA 3245-01R.

Rice, D.P., & MacKenzie, E.J. (1989). *Cost of Injury in the States: A Report to Congress.* Atlanta, GA: Centers for ... Control and Prevention.

Adams, P.F., Heyman, K.M., Vickerie, J.L. (2009). Su... health statistics for the U.S. population: National... interview survey, 2008. *Vital and Health Statistics, S No. 243.* Hyattsville, MD: National Center of Health S...

Toscano, G., & Windau, J. (1994). The changing cha... fatal work injuries. *Monthly Labor Review, 117*(10), 17-2...

World Health Organization. (1977). *Manual of the In... Statistical Classification of Diseases, Injuries, and Causes...* Geneva, Switzerland: Author.

World Health Organization. (1992). *Internationa... Classification of Diseases and Related Health Problems – Te...* Geneva, Switzerland: Author.

This appendix gives a brief explanation of some of the sources and methods used by the National Safety Council Statistics Department in preparing the estimates of deaths, injuries, and costs presented in this book.

The Council uses four classes to categorize unintentional injuries. The four classes are Motor Vehicle, Work, Home, and Public. Each class represents an environment and an intervention route for injury prevention through a responsible authority such as a police department, an employer, a home owner, or a public health department.

National Safety Council

This appendix gives a brief explanation of some of the sources and methods used by the National Safety Council Statistics Department in preparing the estimates of deaths, injuries, and costs presented in this book. Because many of the estimates depend on death certificate data provided by the National Center for Health Statistics (NCHS), it begins with a brief introduction to the certification and classification of deaths.

Certification and classification. The medical certification of death involves entering information on the death certificate about the disease or condition directly leading to death, antecedent causes, and other significant conditions. The death certificate is then registered with the appropriate authority and a code is assigned for the underlying cause of death. The underlying cause is defined as "(a) the disease or injury which initiated the train of morbid events leading directly to death, or (b) the circumstances of the accident or violence which produced the fatal injury" (World Health Organization [WHO], 1992). Deaths are classified and coded on the basis of a WHO standard, the *International Statistical Classification of Diseases and Related Health Problems*, commonly known as the International Classification of Diseases or ICD (WHO, 1992). For deaths due to injury and poisoning, the ICD provides a system of "external cause" codes to which the underlying cause of death is assigned. (See pages 22–23 of *Injury Facts* for a condensed list of external cause codes.)

Comparability across ICD revisions. The ICD is revised periodically and these revisions can affect comparability from year to year. The sixth revision (1948) substantially expanded the list of external causes and provided for classifying the place of occurrence. Changes in the classification procedures for the sixth revision as well as the seventh (1958) and eighth (1968) revisions classified as diseases some deaths previously classified as injuries. The eighth revision also expanded and reorganized some external cause sections. The ninth revision (1979), provided more detail on the agency involved, the victims' activity, and the place of occurrence. The tenth revision, which was adopted in the United States effective with 1999 data, completely revised the transportation-related categories. Specific external cause categories affected by the revisions are noted in the historical tables.

The table at the end of this appendix (page 203) shows the ICD-9 codes, the ICD-10 codes, and a comparability ratio for each of the principal causes of unintentional injury death. The comparability ratio represents the net effect of the new revision on statistics for the cause of death. The comparability ratio was obtained by classifying a sample of death certificates under both ICD-9 and ICD-10 and then dividing the number of deaths for a selected cause classified under ICD-10 by the number classified to the most nearly comparable ICD-9 cause. A comparability ratio of 1.00 indicates no net change due to the new classification scheme. A ratio less than 1.00 indicates fewer deaths assigned to a cause under ICD-10 than under ICD-9. A ratio greater than 1.00 indicates an increase in assignment of

deaths to a cause under ICD-10 compared to ICD-9.

The broad category of "accidents" or "unintentional injuries" under ICD-9 included complications and misadventures of surgical and medical care (E870-E879) and adverse effects of drugs in therapeutic use (E930-E949). These categories are not included in "accidents" or "unintentional injuries" under ICD-10. In 1998, deaths in these two categories numbered 3,228 and 276, respectively.

Under ICD-9, the code range for falls (E880-E888) included a code for "fracture, cause unspecified" (E887). A similar code does not appear in ICD-10 (W00-W19), which probably accounts for the low comparability ratio (0.8409). In 1998, deaths in code E887 numbered 3,679.

Beginning with 1970 data, tabulations published by NCHS no longer include deaths of nonresident aliens. In 2013, there were 812 such unintentional deaths, of which 281 were motor vehicle related

Fatality estimates. The Council uses four classes and three venues to categorize unintentional injuries. The four classes are Motor Vehicle, Work, Home, and Public. Each class represents an environment and an intervention route for injury prevention through a responsible authority such as a police department, an employer, a home owner, or public health department. The three venues are Transportation, Work, and Home and Community.

Motor vehicle. The Motor Vehicle class can be identified by the underlying cause of death (see the table on page 203).

Work. The National Safety Council adopted the Bureau of Labor Statistics' Census of Fatal Occupational Injuries (CFOI) figure, beginning with the 1992 data year, as the authoritative count of unintentional work-related deaths. The CFOI system is described in detail in Toscano and Windau (1994).

The 2-Way Split. After subtracting the Motor Vehicle and Work figures from the unintentional injury total (ICD-10 codes V01-X59, Y85-Y86), the remainder belong to the Home and Public classes. The Home class can be identified by the "place of occurrence" subclassification (code .0) used with most nontransport deaths; the Public class is the remainder. Missing "place of occurrence" information, however, prevents the direct determination of the Home and Public class totals. Because of this, the Council allocates non-motor vehicle, nonwork deaths into the Home and Public classes based on the external cause, age group, and cases with specified "place of occurrence." This procedure, known as the 2-Way Split, uses the most recent death certificate data available from the NCHS and the CFOI data for the same calendar year. For each cause-code group and age group combination, the Motor Vehicle and Work deaths are subtracted and the remainder, including those with "place of occurrence" unspecified, are allocated to Home and Public in the same proportion as those with "place of occurrence" specified.

The table on page 204 shows the ICD-10 cause-codes and CFOI event codes for the most common causes of unintentional-injury death. The CFOI event codes (BLS, 1992) do not match exactly with ICD cause codes, so there is some error in the allocation of deaths among the classes.

Linking up to current year. The benchmark data published by NCHS are usually two years old and the final CFOI data are usually one year old. Starting with the 2011 edition of *Injury Facts*, an exponential smoothing technique is used to make current year estimates. Exponential smoothing is a statistical technique used to make short term forecasts. In exponential smoothing (as opposed to in moving averages smoothing) older data are given progressively less relative weight (importance) whereas newer data are given progressively greater weight. The results of the exponential smoothing is then compared against the latest reported state data for validation.

Revisions of prior years. When the figures for a given year are published by NCHS, the 2-Way Split based on those figures and the CFOI become the final estimate of unintentional injury deaths by class, age group, and type of event or industry. Subsequent years are revised by repeating the exponential smoothing and state data process described above. For example, in the current edition of *Injury Facts*, the 2013 NCHS and CFOI data were used to produce final estimates using the 2-Way Split, and the new 2014 estimates were made with 2014 preliminary CFOI data.

Nonfatal injury estimates. Starting with the 2011 edition of *Injury Facts*, the Council adopted the concept of "medically consulted injury" to define the kinds of injuries included in its estimates. Prior editions of *Injury Facts* used the definition of disabling injury. There is no national injury surveillance system that provides injury estimates on a current basis. The National Health Interview System, a household survey conducted by NCHS (see page 25), produces national estimates using its own definition of medically consulted injury (Adams, Heyman, & Vickerie, 2009). A medically consulted injury as defined by NCHS is an injury serious enough that a medical professional was consulted. The Council uses the medically consulted injury estimates from the National Health Interview survey for its motor vehicle, home, and public injury estimates. Starting with the 2016 edition of *Injury Facts* a further refinement of the nonfatal injury estimate was implemented to better account for and remove intentional injuries. Because of this refinement, nonfatal estimates published in the 2016 edition are not comparable with previous years. In addition, the Occupational Safety and Health Administration defines injury or illness using criteria including "Medical treatment beyond first aid." The Council uses the total recordable case estimate defined by OSHA and published by the Bureau of Labor Statistics to estimate the number of workplace injuries. Because BLS's estimate excludes the self-employed, unpaid family workers, and federal government employees, the Council uses total employment estimates, as well as BLS nonfatal estimates, to calculate the total number of nonfatal medically consulted injuries.

Injury-to-death ratios. Because estimates for medically consulted injuries are not available for the current year, the Council uses injury-to-death ratios to estimate nonfatal medically consulted injuries for the current year. Complete documentation of the procedure, effective with the 1993 edition, may be found in Landes, Ginsburg, Hoskin, and Miller (1990). The resulting estimates are not direct measures of nonfatal injuries and should not be compared with prior years.

Population sources. All population figures used in computing rates are estimates taken from various reports published by the Bureau of the Census, U.S. Department of Commerce, on their website (www.census.gov). *Resident* population is used for computing rates.

Costs (pages 6-9). The procedures for estimating the economic losses due to fatal and nonfatal unintentional injuries were extensively revised for the 2016 edition of *Accident Facts*. New components were added, new benchmarks adopted, and a new discount rate assumed. All of these changes resulted in significantly higher cost estimates. For this reason, it must be re-emphasized that the cost estimates should not be compared to those in earlier editions of the book.

The Council's general philosophy underlying its cost estimates is that the figures represent income not received or expenses incurred because of fatal and nonfatal unintentional injuries. Stated this way, the Council's cost estimates are a measure of the economic impact of unintentional injuries and may be compared to other economic measures such as gross domestic product, per capita income, or personal consumption expenditures. (See page 109 and "lost quality of life" [page 202] for a discussion of injury costs for cost-benefit analysis.)

The general approach followed was to identify a benchmark unit cost for each component, adjust the benchmark to the current year using an appropriate inflator, estimate the number of cases to which the component applied, and compute the product. Where possible, benchmarks were obtained for each class: Motor Vehicle, Work, Home, and Public.

Wage and productivity losses include the value of wages, fringe benefits, and household production for all classes, and travel delay for the Motor Vehicle class.

Medical and work loss costs of unintentional fatal injuries are based on cost benchmarks from the CDC WISQARS Cost Model and multiplied by the Council's fatal injury estimate. Work loss includes earnings and the value of household production.

Medical and work loss costs for unintentional hospitalized injuries were computed by the Pacific Institute for Research and Evaluation (PIRE) from its costed version of the 2010 Healthcare Cost and Utilization Project (HCUP) Nationwide Inpatient Sample, using readmission rates from HCUP. Work loss includes earnings and the value of household production.

Medical and work loss costs of non-hospitalized injuries are based on costs from the WISQARS Cost Module for ED-treated-and-released injuries and multiplied by the Council's estimate of number of non-hospitalized injuries. Work loss includes earnings and the value of household production.

Cost of motor-vehicle property damage and travel delay costs were computed by PIRE from data used in Blincoe et al. (2015) and then multiplied by the Council's estimates of crash incidence (The Economic and Societal Impact of Motor Vehicle Crashes, 2010 Revised. DOT HS 812-013).

Cost per ambulance transport was benchmarked to NMES data and cost per helicopter transport was benchmarked to data in Miller et al. (1993a). The number of cases transported was based on data from Rice and MacKenzie (1989) and the National Electronic Injury Surveillance System.

Administrative expenses, include the administrative cost of private and public insurance, which represents the cost of having insurance, and police and legal costs.

The administrative cost of motor vehicle insurance was the difference between premiums earned (adjusted to remove fire, theft, and casualty premiums) and pure losses incurred, based on data from A. M. Best. Workers' compensation insurance administration was based on A. M. Best data for private carriers and regression estimates using Social Security Administration data for state funds and the self-insured. Administrative costs of public insurance (mainly Medicaid and Medicare) amount to about 4% of the medical expenses paid by public insurance, which were determined from Rice and MacKenzie (1989) and Hensler et al. (1991).

Average police costs for motor-vehicle crashes were computed by PIRE from data used in Blincoe (2015) and multiplied by the Council's estimates of the number of fatal, injury, and property damage crashes.

Travel delay costs were obtained from the Council's estimates of the number of fatal, injury, and property damage crashes and an average delay cost per crash from Miller et al. (1991).

Legal expenses include court costs, and plaintiff's and defendant's time and expenses. Hensler et al. (1991) provided data on the proportion of injured persons who hire a lawyer, file a claim, and get compensation. Kakalik and Pace (1986) provided data on costs per case

Fire losses were based on data published by the National Fire Protection Association in the *NFPA Journal.* The allocation into the classes was based on the property use for structure fires and other NFPA data for non-structure fires.

Employer uninsured costs for work injuries is an estimate of the productivity costs incurred by employers. It assumes each fatality or permanent injury resulted in four person-months of disruption, serious injuries one person-month, and minor to moderate injuries two person-days. All injuries to nonworkers were assumed to involve two days of worker productivity loss. Average hourly earnings for supervisors and nonsupervisory workers were computed and then multiplied by the incidence and hours lost per case. Property damage and production delays (except motor vehicle related) are not included in the estimates but can be substantial.

Lost quality of life is the difference between the value of a statistical fatality or statistical injury and the value of after-tax wages, fringe benefits, and household production. Because this does not represent real income not received or expenses incurred, it is not included in the total economic cost figure. If included, the resulting comprehensive costs can be used in cost-benefit analysis because the total costs then represent the maximum amount society should spend to prevent a statistical death or injury. Lost quality of life costs are benchmarked using 2010 NCHS multiple cause of death data and using the Department of Transportation's estimate of $9.1 million (2012 dollars) as the value of a statistical life.

Work deaths and injuries (page 58). The method for estimating total work-related deaths and injuries is discussed above. The breakdown of deaths by industry division for the current year is obtained from CFOI. The estimate of nonfatal medically consulted injuries by industry division is made using the Survey of Occupational Injury and Illness' estimate of total recordable injury and illness after correcting for the exclusion of self-employed, unpaid family workers, and federal government employees.

Employment. The employment estimates for 1992 to the present were changed for the 1998 edition. Estimates for these years in prior editions are not comparable. The total employment figure used by the Council represents the number of persons in the civilian labor force, aged 16 and older, who were wage or salary workers, self-employed, or unpaid family workers, plus active duty military personnel resident in the United States. The total employment estimate is a combination of three figures – total civilian employment from the Current Population Survey (CPS) as published in *Employment and Earnings,* plus the difference between total resident population and total civilian population, which represents active duty military personnel.

Employment by industry is obtained from an unpublished Bureau of Labor Statistics table titled "Employed and experience unemployed persons by detailed industry and class of worker, Annual Average [year] (based on CPS)."

Technical Appendix (cont.)

Time lost (page 62) is the product of the number of cases and the average time lost per case. Deaths average 150 workdays lost in the current year and 5,850 in future years; permanent disabilities involve 75 and 565 days lost in current and future years, respectively; temporary disabilities involve 17 days lost in the current year only. Off-the-job injuries to workers are assumed to result in similar lost time

Off-the-job (page 63) deaths and injuries are estimated by assuming that employed persons incur injuries at the same rate as the entire population.

Motor vehicle (pages 104-139). Estimates of miles traveled, registered vehicles and licensed drivers are published by the Federal Highway Administration in *Highway Statistics* and *Traffic Volume Trends*.

Selected unintentional-injury code groupings

Manner of injury	ICD-9 codes[a]	ICD-10 codes[b]	Comparability ratio[c]	OICCS v2.01[d] event codes
Unintentional injuries	E800-E869, E880-E929[e]	V01-X59, Y85-Y86	1.0305 (1.0278-1.0333)[f]	12 - 9999
Railway accident	E800-E807	V05, V15, V80.6, V81(.2-.9)	n/a	22
Motor vehicle accident	E810-E825	V02-V04, V09.0, V09.2, V12-V14, V19.0-V19.2, V19.4-V19.6, V20-V79, V80.3-V80.5, V81.0-V81.1, V82.0-V82.1, V83-V86, V87.0-V87.8, V88.0-V88.8, V89.0, V89.2	0.9754 (0.9742-0.9766)	24, 26, 27
Water transport accident	E830-E838	V90-V94	n/a	25
Air transport accident	E840-E845	V95-V97	n/a	21
Poisoning by solids and liquids	E850-58, E860-66	X40-X49	n/a	55, 59, 1224
Poisoning by gases and vapors	E867-E869			
Falls	E880-E888	W00-W19	0.8409 (0.8313-0.8505)	40, 42-45, 49
Fires and burns	E890-E899	X00-X09	0.9743 (0.9568-0.9918)	31
Drowning[g]	E910	W65-W74	0.9965 (0.9716-1.0213)	561
Choking[h]	E911-E912	W78-W80	n/a	562
Mechanical suffocation	E913	W75-W77, W81-W84	n/a	560, 563, 569
Firearms	E922	W32-W34	1.0579 (1.0331-1.0828)	1211, 1221, 1222

Source: National Safety Council.
Note: n/a means comparability ratio not calculated or does not meet standards of reliability or precision.
[a]*WHO (1977).*
[b]*WHO (1992).*
[c]*Hoyert, Arias, Smith, et al. (2001). Table III.*
[d]*BLS (2012), Occupational Injury and Illness Classification Manual, Version 2.01.*
[e]*The National Safety Council has used E800-E949 for unintentional injuries. The code group in the table omits complications and misadventures of surgical and medical care (E870-E879) and adverse effects of drugs in therapeutic use (E930-E949).*
[f]*Figures in parentheses are the 95% confidence interval for the comparability ratio.*
[g]*Excludes transport.*
[h]*Suffocation by ingestion or inhalation.*
[i]*Stuck by flying object where the source of injury was a bullet.*

Berkowitz, M., & Burton, J.F., Jr. (1987). *Permanent Disability Benefits in Workers' Compensation*. Kalamazoo, MI: W.E. Upjohn Institute for Employment Research.

Blincoe, L. J., Miller, T. R., Zaloshnja, E., & Lawrence, B. A. (2015, May). The economic and societal impact of motor vehicle crashes, 2010. (Revised) (Report No. DOT HS 812 013). Washington, DC: National Highway Traffic Safety Administration.

Bureau of Labor Statistics [BLS]. (2012). *Occupational Injury & Illness Classification Manual Version 2.01*. Downloaded from http://www.bls.gov/iif/oshoiics.htm on August 29, 2013.

Bureau of Labor Statistics [BLS]. (2014, December). *Workplace Injuries and Illnesses in 2013*. Press release USDL-14-2183.

Hensler, D.R., Marquis, M.S., Abrahamse, A.F., Berry, S.H., Ebener, P.A., Lewis, E.D., Lind, E.A., MacCoun, R.J., Manning, W.G., Rogowski, J.A., & Vaiana, M.E. (1991). *Compensation for Accidental Injuries in the United States*. Santa Monica, CA: The RAND Corporation.

Hoyert, D.L., Arias, E., Smith, B.L., Murphy, S.L., & Kochanek, K.D. (2001). Deaths: final data for 1999. *National Vital Statistics Reports, 49*(8).

Kakalik, J.S., & Pace, N. (1986). *Costs and Compensation Paid in Tort Litigation*. R-3391-ICJ. Santa Monica, CA: The RAND Corporation.

Landes, S.R., Ginsburg, K.M., Hoskin, A.F., & Miller, T.A. (1990). *Estimating Nonfatal Injuries*. Itasca, IL: Statistics Department, National Safety Council.

Miller, T., Viner, J., Rossman, S., Pindus, N., Gellert, W., Douglass, J., Dillingham, A., & Blomquist, G. (1991). *The Costs of Highway Crashes*. Springfield, VA: National Technical Information Service.

Miller, T.R., Brigham, P.A., Cohen, M.A., Douglass, J.B., Galbraith, M.S., Lestina, D.C., Nelkin, V.S., Pindus, N.M., & Smith-Regojo, P. (1993a). Estimating the costs to society of cigarette fire injuries. *Report to Congress in Response to the Fire Safe Cigarette Act of 1990*. Washington, DC: U.S. Consumer Product Safety Commission.

Miller, T.R., Pindus, N.M., Douglass, J.B., & Rossman, S.B. (1993b). *Nonfatal Injury Incidence, Costs, and Consequences: A Data Book*. Washington, DC: The Urban Institute Press.

Occupational Safety and Health Administration. (2005). *OSHA recordkeeping handbook*. OSHA 3245-01R.

Rice, D.P., & MacKenzie, E.J. (1989). *Cost of Injury in the United States: A Report to Congress*. Atlanta, GA: Centers for Disease Control and Prevention.

Adams, P.F., Heyman, K.M., Vickerie, J.L. (2009). Summary health statistics for the U.S. population: National health interview survey, 2008. *Vital and Health Statistics, Series 10, No. 243*. Hyattsville, MD: National Center of Health Statistics.

Toscano, G., & Windau, J. (1994). The changing character of fatal work injuries. *Monthly Labor Review, 117*(10), 17-28.

World Health Organization. (1977). *Manual of the International Statistical Classification of Diseases, Injuries, and Causes of Death*. Geneva, Switzerland: Author.

World Health Organization. (1992). *International Statistical Classification of Diseases and Related Health Problems – Tenth Revision*. Geneva, Switzerland: Author.

Other Sources

The following organizations may be useful for obtaining more current data or more detailed information on various subjects in *Injury Facts.*

American Association of Poison Control Centers
(703) 894-1858
www.aapcc.org, info@aapcc.org

Bureau of Labor Statistics
U.S. Department of Labor
(202) 691-5200
www.bls.gov
blsdata_staff@bls.gov

Bureau of the Census
U.S. Department of Commerce
(800) 923-8282
www.census.gov

Centers for Disease Control and Prevention
(800) 232-4636
www.cdc.gov, cdcinfo@cdc.gov

Federal Aviation Administration
U.S. Department of Transportation
(866) 835-5322
www.faa.gov

Federal Highway Administration
U.S. Department of Transportation
(202) 366-4000
www.fhwa.dot.gov
execsecretariat.fhwa@fhwa.dot.gov

Federal Motor Carrier Safety Administration
U.S. Department of Transportation
(800) 832-5660
www.fmcsa.dot.gov

Federal Railroad Administration
U.S. Department of Transportation
(202) 493-6065
www.fra.dot.gov

International Labour Organization
Phone: +41-22-799-6111
Fax: +41-22-798-8685
www.ilo.org
ilo@ilo.org

Mine Safety and Health Administration
(202) 693-9400
www.msha.gov

National Center for Health Statistics
(800) 232-4636
www.cdc.gov/nchs

National Center for Statistics and Analysis
(202) 366-4198 or (800) 934-8517
www.nhtsa.dot.gov
NCSAweb@nhtsa.dot.gov

National Climatic Data Center
(828) 271-4800
www.ncdc.noaa.gov/oa/ncdc.html
ncdc.info@noaa.gov

National Collegiate Athletic Association
(317) 917-6222
www.ncaa.org

National Council on Compensation Insurance
(566) 893-1000
www.ncci.com

National Fire Protection Association
(617) 770-3000 or (800) 344-3555
www.nfpa.org
custserv@nfpa.org

National Highway Traffic Safety Administration
U.S. Department of Transportation
www.nhtsa.gov
(800) 877-8339

National Sporting Goods Association
(800) 815-5422
www.nsga.org
info@nsga.org

Occupational Safety and Health Administration
U.S. Department of Labor
(800) 321-OSHA (6742)
www.osha.gov

Substance Abuse and Mental Health Services Administration
(877) 726-4727
www.samhsa.gov

Transportation Research Board
(202) 334-2934
http://gulliver.trb.org

U.S. Coast Guard
(800) 368-5647
www.uscgboating.org
uscginfoline@gcrm.com

U.S. Consumer Product Safety Commission
(301) 504-7923
www.cpsc.gov
clearinghouse@cpsc.gov

World Health Organization
Phone: +41-22-791-2111
www.who.int
info@who.int

Glossary

Accident is that occurrence in a sequence of events that produces unintended injury, death, or property damage. Accident refers to the event, not the result of the event (see Unintentional injury). The term "accident" has largely been replaced in the public health community with the term "incident."

Death from incident is a death that occurs within one year of the incident.

Disabling injury is an injury causing death, permanent disability, or any degree of temporary total disability beyond the day of the injury. Starting with the 2012 edition of *Injury Facts*, the definition of disabling injury was replaced by medically consulted injury for all non-fatal injury estimates.

Fatal incident is an incident that results in one or more deaths within one year.

Home is a dwelling and its premises within the property lines including single family dwellings and apartment houses, duplex dwellings, boarding and rooming houses, and seasonal cottages. Excluded from home are barracks, dormitories, and resident institutions.

Incidence rate, as defined by OSHA, is the number of occupational injuries and/or illnesses or lost workdays per 100 full-time employees (see formula on page 76).

Incident is the preferred term for "accident" in the public health community. It refers to the occurrence in a sequence of events that produces unintended injury, death, or property damage. Incident refers to the event, not the result of the event (see Unintentional injury).

Injury is physical harm or damage to the body resulting from an exchange, usually acute, of mechanical, chemical, thermal, or other environmental energy that exceeds the body's tolerance.

Medically consulted injury is an injury serious enough that a medical professional was consulted. For the motor vehicle, home and public venues, the National Safety Council uses the medically consulted injury estimates from the National Health Interview Survey. The Council uses the total recordable case estimate, using OSHA's definition, published by the Bureau of Labor Statistics (BLS) to estimate the number of workplace injuries. Because the BLS estimate excludes self-employed, unpaid family workers, and federal government employees, the Council extrapolates the BLS estimate to reflect the total worker population.

Motor vehicle is any mechanically or electrically powered device not operated on rails, upon which or by which any person or property may be transported upon a land highway. The load on a motor vehicle or trailer attached to it is considered part of the vehicle. Tractors and motorized machinery are included while self-propelled in transit or used for transportation. Non-motor vehicle is any road vehicle other than a motor vehicle, such as a bicycle or animal-drawn vehicle, except a coaster wagon, child's sled, child's tricycle, child's carriage, and similar means of transportation; persons using these latter means of transportation are considered pedestrians.

Motor vehicle incident is an unstabilized situation that includes at least one harmful event (injury or property damage) involving a motor vehicle in transport (in motion, in readiness for motion, or on a roadway but not parked in a designated parking area) that does not result from discharge of a firearm or explosive device and does not directly result from a cataclysm. [See Committee on Motor Vehicle Traffic Accident Classification (1997), *Manual on Classification of Motor Vehicle Traffic Accidents,* ANSI D16.1-1996, Itasca, IL: National Safety Council.]

Motor vehicle traffic incident is a motor vehicle incident that occurs on a trafficway – a way or place, any part of which is open to the use of the public for the purposes of vehicular traffic. A motor vehicle nontraffic incident is any motor vehicle incident that occurs entirely in any place other than a trafficway.

Nonfatal injury incident is an incident in which at least one person is injured and no injury results in death.

Occupational illness is any abnormal condition or disorder other than one resulting from an occupational injury caused by exposure to environmental factors associated with employment. It includes acute and chronic illnesses or diseases that may be caused by inhalation, absorption, ingestion, or direct contact (see also pages 73 and 79).

Occupational injury is any injury such as a cut, fracture, sprain, amputation, etc., that results from a work incident or from a single instantaneous exposure in the work environment (see also page 79).

Pedalcycle is a vehicle propelled by human power and operated solely by pedals; excludes mopeds.

Pedestrian is any person involved in a motor vehicle incident who is not in or upon a motor vehicle or non-motor vehicle. Includes persons injured while using a coaster wagon, child's tricycle, roller skates, etc. Excludes persons boarding, alighting, jumping, or falling from a motor vehicle in transport who are considered occupants of the vehicle.

Permanent disability (or permanent impairment) includes any degree of permanent nonfatal injury. It includes any injury that results in the loss or complete loss of use of any part of the body or in any permanent impairment of functions of the body or a part thereof.

Property damage incident is an incident that results in property damage but in which no person is injured.

Public incident is any incident other than motor vehicle that occurs in the public use of any premises. Includes deaths in recreation (swimming, hunting, etc.), in transportation except motor vehicle, public buildings, etc., and from widespread natural disasters even though some may have happened on home premises. Excludes incidents to people in the course of gainful employment.

Source of injury is the principal object such as tool, machine, or equipment involved in the incident and is usually the object inflicting injury or property damage. Also called agency or agent.

Temporary total disability is an injury that does not result in death or permanent disability but that renders the injured person unable to perform regular duties or activities on one or more full calendar days after the day of the injury.

Total cases include all work-related deaths and illnesses and those work-related injuries that result in loss of consciousness, restriction of work or motion, or transfer to another job, or require medical treatment other than first aid.

Unintentional injury is the preferred term for accidental injury in the public health community. It refers to the result of an incident.

Work hours are the total number of hours worked by all employees. They are usually compiled for various levels, such as an establishment, a company, or an industry. A work hour is the equivalent of one employee working one hour.

Work injuries (including occupational illnesses) are those that arise out of and in the course of gainful employment regardless of where the accident or exposure occurs. Excluded are work injuries to private household workers and injuries occurring in connection with farm chores that are classified as home injuries.

Workers are all persons gainfully employed, including owners, managers, other paid employees, the self-employed, and unpaid family workers but excluding private household workers.

Work/motor vehicle duplication includes work injuries that occur in motor vehicle incidents (see Work injuries and Motor vehicle incident).

Index

RITZ LIBRARY DUTCHESS COMM COLLEGE

7026696